Video
Communication & Production

By
Jim Stinson
Photos and graphics by the author, unless otherwise credited.

Publisher
The Goodheart-Willcox Company, Inc.
Tinley Park, Illinois

Library of Congress Card Catalog Number 00-052788
International Standard Book Number 1-56637-798-6

1 2 3 4 5 6 7 8 9 0   02   05 04 03 02 01

About the Author

After graduating from Harvard, **Jim Stinson** studied theater history at the Yale Graduate School and directing at the Yale School of Drama before transferring to the UCLA film school, where he earned the degree of Master of Fine Arts. Although he has worked on filmed commercials, TV series, and features, he has spent much of his career as a writer, producer, director, videographer, and/or editor of educational and corporate programs created in the medium of video.

Since 1993, he has been a columnist and Contributing Editor at *Videomaker* magazine. In addition to *Video Communication and Production,* his published works include four mystery novels set in Hollywood: *Double Exposure, Low Angles, Truck Shot*, and *TV Safe*, as well as the study, *Restorations of Elizabethan Public Playhouses*.

He has taught film production at Art Center College of Design, film studies at California State University, Los Angeles, and video production at La Cañada High School, La Cañada, CA. Currently, he conducts twelve video production seminars a year at *Videomaker* Expos East and West.

Library of Congress Cataloging in Publication Data
Stinson, Jim
    Video: communication and production / by Jim Stinson
        p. cm.
    Includes index.
    ISBN 1-56637-798-6
    1. Video recordings—Production and direction. I. Title.
PN1992.94 .S76 2001
384.55′8—dc21

00-052788

About this Book

Video Communication and Production fulfills the promise of its title by covering both the ways in which video communicates with viewers and the methods by which it does so. Communication is featured because production by itself has no purpose. If communication were excluded, this book would be like a carpentry manual that covered sawing, drilling, and nailing without ever explaining how to build anything.

This book treats video as a mature and independent medium, rather than merely a variant of television or a recording alternative to film. Video has become fully empowered by the digital revolution that is transforming so many aspects of twenty-first century life.

The topics in this book have been selected and organized with two groups of readers in mind: students preparing for careers in communications media and creators of personal programs who expect to make videos of professional caliber. Though the text does not pretend to include all there is to know about video, it does cover all you need to get started.

To organize this sprawling subject, ***Video Communication and Production*** is presented in six major sections:

- Chapters 1 and 2 help you start making videos immediately.
- Chapters 3 through 7 cover video communication: the concepts and principles behind the hardware and production techniques.
- Chapters 8 and 9 present the crucial process of preproduction: preparing to make successful programs.
- Chapters 10 through 14 introduce all major aspects of videography, lighting, and audio.
- Chapters 15 and 16 survey the art of directing — both the camera and the people it records.
- Chapters 17 through 20 explain the basics of postproduction in both analog/linear and digital/nonlinear modes.

This organization may be termed "semi-random-access:" On the one hand, it is possible to read only the chapters desired, in any order. On the other hand, individual chapters will generally be more useful in conjunction with the others in their sections. In most cases, larger subjects have been distributed among multiple chapters for simplicity of presentation. For this reason, expect to find occasional duplication of material, since the same concepts and techniques may apply to procedures covered in different chapters.

The author and publisher cordially solicit corrections and suggestions from readers. Please help us improve the book by e-mailing us at **www.goodheartwillcox.com**.

Finally, as you use this book, remember that video production is both a demanding discipline and a source of great satisfaction. Like pro golfers, video professionals are generally pleased to be paid for doing things that they would happily do for free. If ***Video Communication and Production*** enhances your pleasure as it increases your skills, then the book will have fulfilled its purpose.

Jim Stinson
Trinidad, California

Contents

1. About Video 9
   - About Video 10
   - Video Communication. 12
   - Video Production 14

2. Getting Started 17
   - About Video Production 18
   - Equipment Basics 18
   - Camcorder Operation. 21
   - Quality Video and Audio 23
   - The Shooting Session 27

3. Video Space 31
   - About Video Space. 32
   - Video Dimensions. 36
   - Spatial Relations. 39

4. Video Time 43
   - About Video Time. 44
   - Video Time Speed 45
   - Video Time Flow. 48
   - Video Time Direction. 50
   - Video Time Coherence 52

5. Video Composition. 55
   - About Video Composition 56
   - Organization in Composition. 56
   - Depth in Composition 60
   - Composing Video Images 62

6. Video Language 67
   - About Video Language. 68
   - Camera Angle Names 68
   - Creating Continuity. 78
   - Making Transitions 81

7. Video Sound 87
   - About Video Sound. 88
   - Delivering Information 88
   - Conveying Implications 90
   - Strengthening Continuity. 95
   - Evoking Feelings 96

8. Program Development 99
    About Program Development 100
    Defining the Program 100
    Preparing a Treatment. 104
    Creating a Storyboard. 106
    Writing a Script. 106

9. Production Planning. 109
    About Production Planning 110
    People: Crew and Cast 110
    Places: Scouting Locations 114
    Things: Equipment and Supplies. 118
    Plans: Production Logistics 120
    Budgets: Production Costs 123

10. Camera Systems. 125
    About Camera Systems 126
    Camera Functions 126
    Camera Support Systems. 129
    Camcorder Setup 132
    Lens Setup. 137

11. Camera Operation. 143
    About Camera Operation 144
    Working with Lenses. 144
    Setting Focus 155
    Exposure 159
    Operating the Camera 164

12. Lighting Design. 169
    About Lighting Design. 170
    Lighting Quality. 170
    Lighting Character 173
    Lighting Tools 175

13. Lighting Techniques 187
    About Lighting Techniques 188
    Lighting Principles. 189
    Lighting Designs. 191
    Lighting Applications 198

14. Recording Audio. 205
    About Recording Audio. 206
    Types of Audio Recording. 207
    Microphones 210
    Other Recording Equipment 214
    Audio Recording Techniques. 220

15. Directing for Content **227**

    About Directing for Content 228
    Directing for Communication 228
    Directing for Performance 235

16. Directing for Form **243**

    About Directing for Form 244
    Covering the Action 244
    Maintaining Continuity 246
    Managing Screen Direction 250
    Staging for the Screen 257
    Moving the Camera 261

17. Editing Operations **269**

    About Editing Operations 270
    The Craft of Editing 270
    Organizing 274
    Assembling 276
    Enhancing 279
    Synthesizing 281
    Archiving 283

18. Editing Principles **285**

    About Editing Principles 286
    Continuity 286
    Performance 296
    Emphasis 303
    Pace 308
    The End Result 311

19. Linear Editing **313**

    About Linear Editing 314
    Assembling a Linear Editing Setup 314
    Editing Picture and Track 320
    Transitions, Effects, and Titles 325

20. Nonlinear Editing **329**

    About Nonlinear Editing 330
    Configuring Nonlinear Projects 331
    Basic Operations 338
    Transformations 345
    Nonlinear Audio 347

Glossary **351**

Acknowledgments

Dedication: For Sue more than ever.

The following organizations supplied photographs and/or computer screen shots for the book:

Adobe

Alpenlite/Western Recreational Vehicles

Anton Bauer

Azden

Manfrotto/Bogen

Canon USA

Casablanca by MacroSystem

Cool-Lux

Corel

Gitzo/Bogen

J. L. Fisher, Inc.

Hollywood Lite

JVC Company of America

Lowel-Light Manufacturing, Inc.

Mamiya America Corporation

Microdolly Hollywood

Minnesota Public Radio

Movie Magic Budgeting/Creative Planet

NASA

Neumann

Panasonic Broadcast

PBS

Pinnacle Systems

Sennheiser

Shotmaster/The Badham Company

Sony Electronics, Inc.

Sound Forge

The Tiffen Company LLC

Videonics

Special thanks to Sue Stinson for the many photos she contributed to the book.

Many photos feature the stars of The McKinley Dramatic Arts and Vintage Tractor Society, especially, Jake Bennion, Ileana Butu, Mark Conroy, Garrett Nasalroad, Mauro V. Escobar, Jerry Ferree, Louanne Ferree, Tommie L. McAuley, Dalan Musson, Annegret Ogden, Dunbar Ogden, Jennifer Schalf, J. D. Schall, Louanne Silveira, Marge Simas, Norm Simas, Alex Stinson, Anji Stinson, Lillie Stinson, Sue Stinson, Vincent Vaughn, and Alicia Wilkinson.

The fictional town of McKinley was created from shots of people, places, and events in the Humboldt County, California, cities of Arcata, Eureka, Ferndale, Fortuna, McKinleyville, and Trinidad. The annual three-day Kinetic Sculpture Race begins in Arcata and ends, more or less, in Ferndale.

Video has become a mature and independent medium, rather than merely a variant of television or a recording alternative to film.

1 About Video

Contents

About Video
Video Communication
Video Production

Objectives

After studying this chapter, you will be able to:

❑ Explain the meaning of "Video Communication."

❑ Explain why it is important to understand the nature of the video world.

❑ List some major types of video programs.

❑ Describe the three major phases of video production.

Sue Stinson

About Video

Video is a pursuit that attracts people with a wide variety of talents, so you are almost certain to find a place in it for your particular abilities and interests. Because making videos is so interesting, you may want to pick up a camcorder right now and get started. But if you first take the time to review this chapter and the next, you will have a better idea of what video is all about, and you will be able to make better video programs from the start.

What Is Video?

Exactly what is "video?" The answer is not as obvious as it seems. Until recently, video — as we treat it in this book — did not exist. Instead, there were just two main audiovisual media: *film* and *television*.

Film was the medium used for creating most audiovisual programs, from movies to TV commercials. Film was (and is) an excellent production medium for several reasons:

- Film equipment is relatively portable, so location filming is practical.
- Film's ability to reproduce quality images in black and white or color is highly refined.
- Film picture and sound tracks are usually recorded on separate strips of film (or audio tape), so sophisticated editing is possible.

Television was the medium used for broadcasting studio programs as they happened (**"live"**), and other programs previously produced on (or copied onto) film, **Figure 1-1.**

Originally, television was not an ideal production medium for several reasons:

- Its equipment was heavy, complex, and tied down by cables to its control systems.
- Its image quality was markedly lower than that of film, and its ability to render shades of gray from black to white was limited. (Color could not be reproduced at all, except in experimental setups.)
- It could not be recorded for later editing, except by copying the live signal to film and then treating it as if it were a filmed program. These "kinescope" films degraded picture quality even further.

As the popularity of television grew over the years, equipment manufacturers gradually solved most of its problems. They miniaturized hardware until a broadcast-quality camera and its recorder could be combined in a package smaller than the size of a film camera plus its attendant sound tape recorder. This combination **camcorder** also considerably reduced the tangle of studio cables. At the same time, engineers greatly improved picture sharpness and gray scale range and developed high-quality color. They perfected videotape recording, so the television signal could be electronically copied and edited.

Today you can obtain high quality video and audio from camcorders that weigh less than three pounds, Figure 1-2.

In short, television technology eventually improved until the medium rivaled the abilities of film. Today you can produce professional quality programs on either film or videotape with comparable ease and practicality.

Figure 1-1.
Comedians Dean Martin and Jerry Lewis in a 1950s TV studio. (Gene Lester/Archive Photos)

Figure 1-2.
A consumer format digital video camcorder.

Nevertheless, the two media remain quite different in many essential respects. Though film has continued to evolve over the years, it is still essentially the same medium. By contrast, the electronic production technology that began as "television" has changed so drastically that it needs a name of its own.

That is why we now call it **video.**

Video versus Film

Some film makers think that video is less desirable than their own medium in several ways:

● Video picture clarity is comparatively coarse because its resolution is relatively low, **Figure 1-3.**

● Video color sometimes lacks a certain richness and "snap" that is hard to describe but easy to see in film. That is why many TV commercials are shot on film, even though they will be seen only on video.

● Until recently, video has offered less flexibility in sound editing. It is common for even simple films to mix as many as eight or more audio tracks. Sound editing has been more cumbersome in video.

In other ways, however, film is less desirable than video:

● Film is much more expensive to shoot and process to a final composite positive print. While small format video can cost as little as two dollars an hour, finished film costs hundreds of times as much.

● Film is less tolerant of different light levels, so it must be supplied in several grades of light sensitivity, to suit different conditions.

● Film sound is more cumbersome, since it is almost always recorded on a separate tape recorder.

● Film color balancing is time-consuming and expensive.

● Film titles and effects, such as dissolves and double exposures, cannot be added in real time and evaluated on the edited working copy. Instead, they must be created separately in the film laboratory.

● Film editing requires negative cutting, a tedious and expensive extra step. Since the original camera film is rarely used to create an edited program, a negative cutter must match it, frame-for-frame to the program's completed "work print," before viewable "release prints" can be made.

Converging Technologies

Today, however, the arguments for and against film or video are growing outdated. Whatever the alleged weaknesses of film or video, they are now becoming less important as the two media grow ever closer together. High-definition video, for example, is close to the visual quality of film; and modern film stocks have wider exposure ranges.

At the same time, visual hybrids are being created. For example, most commercials are shot on film, which is then transferred immediately to tape. The rest of the production process is pure video. In other cases, videotape work prints are made, editing is completed, and then the film negative is cut to match the tape. Finally, in many theatrical films, the special effects are created electronically and then transferred to film.

Building computerized special effects involves *digitizing* the film: scanning it frame-by-frame and converting it to a pattern of tiny dots. Since a large computer can convert a frame of film to a matrix of about 4,000 by 3,000 pixels (dots), the digitized images remain film-sharp.

Digital postproduction helps video as well as film, especially in sound editing. Since computerized editing software can handle an almost limitless number of audio channels, multilayer sound tracks are now common.

Although film and video use different production techniques, they speak the same audiovisual "language." If you master this language, you can use it to communicate in either medium or in any hybrid of both.

Figure 1-3.
At close range, the low resolution of video is obvious. (PBS)

Types of Video Production

Today, people make a wide variety of video programs ranging from five-second commercials to thirteen-hour miniseries. These are distributed by broadcast, cable, satellite TV and the Internet, and on cassettes or disks played in schools, businesses, and homes. Some videos are produced to entertain, to persuade, or to teach. Others capture a family holiday, inventory a stamp collection, or document a vacation.

Beyond the kinds of videos we think of as "programs" lie still other types, such as the specialized videography employed in areas as diverse as medicine, industry, science, and law enforcement. In fact, professional uses for video are expanding in much the same way as computer applications. It is probably safe to say that all but a few 21st Century careers will involve video in some way.

Video Talents and Jobs

If you are considering a career in video, you have a wide range of specialties to choose from.

If you like the story side of production, try writing, directing, or editing. Though these crafts involve different skills and techniques, they are really all part of the same process. If you have graphic talents, the specialties of art direction, set and costume design, and makeup are vital to sophisticated video production. You can also create postproduction video graphics and titles.

If you are intrigued by the nuts and bolts of production, then camera operation, lighting, and audio recording are skills that command respect.

If you have technical aptitude, audio and video engineering are challenging occupations. If management is your aim, video producing and production management require well-developed skills in organization, personnel, and finance.

Every type of business expertise is employed in running a video production unit or company. To function effectively, corporate managers need to know the fundamentals of video as thoroughly as their colleagues on the production side. In particular, they need to understand how the video medium communicates its message.

Not for Professionals Only

This book treats the art and craft of video on a professional level. Making video programs is usually a collaborative process carried on by personnel working in organizations — that is, by professionals.

However, you may not anticipate a career in video production. Instead, you may want to master this medium purely for personal expression, **Figure 1-4.** If so, you need not be concerned that video is discussed here in a professional context.

Figure 1-4.
Consumer camcorders offer professional features.

Like music or painting or photography or cabinetmaking, video is an art in which "amateur" practitioners can and should develop exactly the same skills that full-time professionals use to make their living in this medium.

Video Communication

You may become the best camera person on your block, the finest sound recordist, or the most talented makeup artist. But you still will not know how to make a video unless you master the art of video communication.

This book includes several chapters on video communication, covering three broad topics: the nature of the video world, the language of video expression, and the construction of video programs.

The Nature of the Video World

When you watch TV, you may think you are looking at a picture of the actual world, but you are not. The TV screen is a window that looks out on a completely different universe — a strange cosmos in which normal laws of space and time and gravity do not work at all. In the video universe:

- An actor can open a door in London and walk through it to Los Angeles.
- A car can turn a corner and jump forward a week in time.

Visual Literacy

Even if your career never involves producing video, you spend considerable time *consuming* it — several hours a day if you are a typical TV viewer. Video is the most persuasive and powerful system ever invented for delivering facts, ideas, and opinions. You may not think video affects you all that much, but it does:

- It persuades you about what to buy and how to vote.
- It explains who is important in the world and why.
- It teaches you how your community, your nation, and your planet are working — and how they *should* work if the world were an ideal place.
- It shows you what is fashionable, what is desirable, and what you are supposed to want in life.
- It models ways to love, fight, work, worship, and dream.

Video does all this with a vividness and immediacy that make you feel that you are experiencing the actual sights and sounds of the real thing.

In fact, you are *not* seeing the real thing. Instead, you are presented with a sophisticated and carefully contrived imitation of reality that the video makers want you to accept. They may present the "reality" that soap A is better then soap B. They may "prove" that political candidate X is superior to candidate Y. They may "demonstrate" that wolves are essential to sound ecology (or, alternatively, that wolves are live-stock killers that must be exterminated).

Even when they are not trying to sell you a product, a person, or an idea, makers of video programs do not present reality; rather, they offer their own versions of it. They cannot help doing this, because even the most objective program simply cannot be made without selecting and condensing reality. This essential process imposes a certain point of view on every video program, because the selection and presentation of material reflect a set of standards adopted by the program's makers.

What does that mean to you as a viewer? If you understand the techniques of video communication, you can separate the information you are watching from the methods used to organize and present it. At best, you will be able to get past the artificial reality on your screen to search for the actual reality beyond it.

At least, you will not be deceived by a medium that looks real *always* but is real *never*.

- An actor can fall ten stories onto concrete and walk away unhurt.

Except during spectacular special effects, most of the strange behavior of the video universe is quite invisible to the audience. Writers, directors, designers, and editors understand how to use the laws of the video world to fool the viewer, **Figure 1-5.** These laws are so powerful that unless you understand them, you cannot effectively tape a single scene or competently edit two shots together.

Chapters 3 and 4 explain the rules and regulations of the video universe and show how to take advantage of them to make effective programs.

The Language of Video Expression

Video communication uses a visual language — a language with rules much like those of a written language such as English or Chinese.

For example:

- An image is much like a single word.
- A shot is like a complete sentence.
- A scene is like a paragraph.
- A sequence is like a chapter.

Figure 1-5.
The outside of this door is a location.

The inside of the door is on a set.

Unlike their written languages, the video languages of England and China (and almost all other nations) are the same. Video is a powerful social force, partly because almost everyone on the planet understands the universal language of film and video.

At the basic level, video has a grammar, with the equivalents of subjects and verbs and tenses. On a more sophisticated level, video has its own rhetoric — a wealth of techniques for creating distinctive styles of expression. These techniques include the management of composition and camera movement, the creation of visual continuity, and the control of program rhythm and pace.

Like literary styles, powerful visual styles are recognizable. Just as a knowledgeable reader can tell Dickens from Hemingway, an informed viewer can identify a film by Fellini or Bergman or Scorcese.

The Construction of Video Programs

Video communication is like written communication in yet another way: it is not enough to write a grammatically correct sentence or compose a short paragraph. You must also be able to organize and develop a coherent story or essay — or even a whole book. To make a professional video program of any length, you have to design and construct it as carefully as you would a piece of professional writing.

Effective nonfiction programs, such as training films and documentaries, depend on logical subject organization, clear presentation, and energetic pacing. Fiction, music, and performance videos also demand the skills of the artist and storyteller.

The shortest videos can be as hard to construct as the longest. A 30-, 10- or even 5-second commercial must organize and present its material with rigorous economy, so that it creates its intended effect.

Video Production

Video production falls into three broad topics: preproduction, production, and post-production.

Preproduction

The preproduction phase includes everything you do before actual shooting begins. Preproduction includes scripting (or storyboarding) the video, **Figure 1-6,** as well as scouting locations, gathering cast and crew, and planning production equipment and other requirements.

Preproduction may not seem as exciting as shooting or as creative as editing, but experienced professionals know that it is a mistake to shortchange the preproduction phase. Video programs are generally made in small, disconnected pieces. Advance planning is essential to determine how these pieces should fit together, **Figure 1-7.** Also, in professional video production, time really is money, so the more thoroughly you have

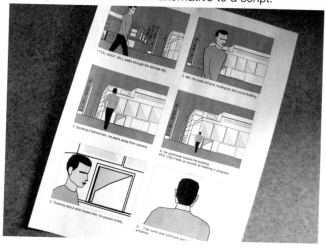

Figure 1-6.
A storyboard is a common alternative to a script.

Figure 1-7.
The storyboard is revised during preproduction.

planned your **shoot**, the faster you can complete it. In creating professional programs, the preproduction phase is often longer and more complicated than the production phase.

Production

The production phase covers the actual shooting of the material that will become the video program. In most productions, responsibility for the visual character, or "look," of the program is shared by the director, videographer, and production designer. The director also guides the performers through their roles and ensures that the program content is recorded from appropriate points of view.

The director is usually supported by a production management staff, while the videographer is assisted by a lighting director, sound recordist, and key grip. (Grips are staff members who practice many of the technical crafts associated with production.)

Working in close collaboration, the production people, technicians, and performers stage and record the video footage that will become the basis of the finished program, **Figure 1-8.**

Postproduction

At the end of the production phase, many video newcomers are essentially finished. "Shoot it and show it" might be their motto. But for more experienced video makers, the postproduction phase is just as important as production, and just as enjoyable.

When you finish shooting, you do not yet have a video program, but only a collection of footage. In postproduction you select the

shots you want to include, assemble them in order, add music and sound effects to the audio, and create titles and visual effects. Collectively, this process is called editing, **Figure 1-9.** When practiced skillfully, editing is so creatively satisfying that some video makers think of the production phase as primarily a source of raw material for postproduction.

Figure 1-9.
Most of the postproduction phase is spent editing the program. (Adobe)

The director Alfred Hitchcock said he did not find the production phase especially interesting because by the time it started, he had already finished making the entire movie in his head!

The Tip of the Iceberg

This introductory chapter has provided a very brief overview of video communication and production. The rest of this book is devoted to the details of this rich and fascinating subject.

You do not have to master every chapter, however, before you begin to shoot videos. Chapter 2 contains the essentials you need to make short, simple programs. When you have completed that chapter, you should be able to achieve satisfying results in beginning video production.

Figure 1-8.
Shooting a documentary program. (Sue Stinson)

Technical Terms

Camcorder: An appliance that both captures moving images (**cam**era) and stores them on tape (re**corder**).

Digitize: To record images and sounds as numerical data, either directly in a camcorder or in the process of importing them to a computer.

Film: An audiovisual medium that records images on transparent plastic strips by means of photosensitive chemicals.

Live: Recorded and (usually) transmitted for display continuously and in real time.

Shoot: To record film or video; also, "a shoot" is an informal term for the production phase of a film or video project.

Television: Studio-based, multicamera video that is often produced and transmitted "live."

Video: An audiovisual medium that records on magnetic tape or disk by electronic means; also, single-camera taped program creation in the manner of film production rather than studio television.

Visual literacy: The ability to evaluate the content of visual media through an understanding of the way in which it is recorded and presented.

Development of the camcorder made it possible to blend film and television techniques into a new kind of medium known as "video."

2 Getting Started

Contents

About Video Production
Equipment Basics
Camcorder Operation
Quality Video and Audio
The Shooting Session

Objectives

After studying this chapter, you will be able to:
- ❑ Operate basic video equipment.
- ❑ Videotape a simple program.
- ❑ Avoid common shooting mistakes.
- ❑ Conduct a safe and courteous shoot.

JVC

About Video Production

This chapter is designed to get you ready for successful video making as quickly as possible.

Of course, you could skip this chapter and begin right away. Many new camcorder owners unpack their hardware, drop in a tape, and start shooting immediately. But the results are often unsatisfying, because even the simplest video project demands that you know at least a few fundamental ideas and techniques.

To create a good program, you need to know how to operate the equipment, how to record good-quality video and audio, and how to tape footage that can be edited effectively. By the time you have finished this chapter, you should be able to do these things comfortably. We will begin with a quick run-through of your camcorder controls and other equipment.

Equipment Basics

Camcorders are unusual because they are both simple and complicated at the same time. On the one hand, they are so simple that small children can use them without instruction. On the other hand, they are so complicated that many owners never do figure out how to use all the buttons on their hardware.

This section assumes that you will begin videotaping with small format equipment such as mini-DV, 8mm, or VHS. If you are using industrial or broadcast cameras, you will need extra time to learn their more advanced features.

Basic Camcorder Controls

To operate a camcorder successfully, you need to understand four essential controls: power, record, zoom, and white balance.

The **power switch** turns the camcorder on and off. Many power switches include a small light to remind you whenever the unit is running. This information is important because a running camcorder uses battery power even when it is not recording.

Technically, a video camcorder includes both a camera and a videotape recorder in a single unit, while a video camera is connected by cable to a separate recorder. In practice, however, camcorders are often referred to as "cameras."

Some cameras include power-saving circuits that put the unit into "standby" or "sleep" mode when it has not been recording for a certain period. This will happen often when you are shooting, so you need to learn how to return the camera to full power. Different units are reactivated in different ways.

The **record switch** starts and stops the actual recording process. Some camcorders have two record switches, one in a convenient location on the handgrip and the other on the camera body.

Many camcorders also have a record switch on a wireless remote control.

Note that you do not have to hold down the record switch continuously while taping. Simply press it once to begin and then press it again to stop.

The **zoom control** may be a pair of buttons or a flat bar that rocks back and forth, **Figure 2-1.** In either system, you press one button (or bar end) to zoom in and fill the screen with a narrower part of the scene and the other button (or bar end) to zoom out and fill the screen with a wider part of the scene. On some camcorders you can zoom the lens at different speeds, depending on how firmly you press the zoom controls.

Figure 2-1.
Most zoom controls are rocker bars. (JVC)

The **white balance** switch matches your camcorder to the overall color quality of the light in which you are shooting. All camcorders have an "automatic" setting for white balance. For now, use this setting to let the camcorder read the incoming light color and adjust itself automatically.

In some camcorders, the white balance and many of the other controls are controlled via menus displayed in the viewfinder or on a special LCD panel.

Automatic Camera Controls

White balance is not the only control that can be set to work automatically. The camcorder can also automate lens focus and exposure control.

The **autofocus control** keeps the picture sharp and clear. (Like your eyes, the camcorder lens must be set one way to record distant objects and another way to record close ones.) On the automatic setting, your camcorder estimates the distance to the central subject in the viewfinder. Then the camcorder sets the lens for that estimated distance. For now, leave the autofocus enabled, even though this may present occasional focus problems. Later chapters discuss how and when to use autofocus to best advantage.

Throughout this book, enabled means that a function is turned on (activated) and disabled means that it is turned off (deactivated).

The **autoexposure control** regulates the amount of light admitted through the camcorder lens. Whether shooting a candle-lit birthday or a day on bright ski slopes, the camcorder must have exactly the same amount of light to form a good picture. The auto exposure system delivers that precise amount. Like autofocus, the autoexposure system can be fooled sometimes. Leave it enabled for now.

Default Settings

A **default** is an action or condition that is automatically chosen by the equipment, unless you actively select a different one. In most camcorders, the autofocus and autoexposure functions are default settings, enabled automatically when the power is turned on.

In some camcorders, the white balance does not default to the automatic setting. Instead, it remains on the setting selected before the unit was last turned off. If the light color is different when you turn it on again, you may record footage with an unpleasant color cast, **Figure 2-2**. For this reason, always check the white balance before you shoot. For now, set it to automatic.

Figure 2-2.
White balance. A—Used outdoors, the indoor white balance makes everything look blue. B—Outdoor white balance shows colors accurately.

A

B

Videotape

Videotape, of course, is the medium on which the camcorder records both picture and sound. All camera videotape is supplied in closed plastic cassettes. Later, you will learn how videotape works, but for now, you need to know just the basics of handling, loading, and running it.

Some digital camcorders record on disks or other media.

Handling tape is simple because it is well protected in its plastic armor. Store a tape in its sleeve or case when not in use, and keep it out of direct sunlight and hot car interiors. Never open the cassette's protective front flap and expose the tape inside. There is no reason to open this flap except, on rare occasions, to inspect a damaged tape. Touching the delicate tape can degrade its recording ability.

Loading videotape can be easy or difficult, depending on the design of the camcorder. Some units will accept a tape, however carelessly you insert it. Others demand that you position the cassette precisely and install it with care. No camcorder, however, will permit you to insert a tape upside-down or backward. Most cameras accept the tape with the cassette face toward you and the tape flap on the lower (or inner) edge. One caution: unlike full-size VCRs, miniaturized camcorders are somewhat delicate. You can break them by forcing a tape. If the tape does not slide in at once, make sure that it is properly oriented.

Preparing the tape

Once the tape is inside the camcorder, it must be prepared for use. If the tape is brand-new, roll it forward about 30 seconds. Do this by pressing the record button with the cap still covering the lens. This is done because the first few inches of tape will gradually stretch as the cassette is repeatedly rewound to its beginning, eventually ruining any material recorded there. By starting your recording 30 seconds in, you can avoid this problem.

If you have used some of the tape before, you must prepare it by **rolling down to raw stock.** This means previewing the tape to find the end of your previous footage, recording a few seconds of black (again, with the cap on the lens), then leaving the tape at that position, **Figure 2-3.**

To save precious battery power, it is best to use the camera's AC adapter. To record black, simply press RECORD on the VCR.

Tape preparation is more important than it may seem, because video makers usually review their footage after returning from a shoot, and they sometimes forget to roll past their final shot in preparation for their next session. Too often, valuable footage is taped over and erased by the next day's work.

Batteries

Camcorders run on battery power, though they can use household current when available. Batteries are covered in detail in Chapter 10. For now, you need to know how to charge them, handle them, and ensure an adequate supply of camera power.

Figure 2-3.
Preparing the tape. A— The existence of a picture indicates previously recorded tape. B—"Snow" or solid blue indicates a blank section. C— Black color indicates recording with the lens cap on or black color from computer.

A

B

C

Though batteries appear simple and tough, they do require care. Dropping them can split their cases. Leaving them outdoors in cold weather can reduce the amount of power they deliver. Most importantly, be careful not to short-circuit a battery by bridging its two contact terminals. This will produce high heat levels and eventually ruin the battery.

A camcorder battery can be charged in two ways: by leaving it in the camera and plugging in the camera's power/charging cord, or by attaching it directly to the camcorder's charging unit. Whichever method you choose, always charge a battery immediately after use, then unplug the unit for storage. Just prior to your next use, recharge the battery again.

Finally, never go out shooting without at least one fully-charged spare battery. Though camcorder batteries have advertised capacities of up to two hours, they seldom last that long. Older batteries, in particular, may stop working after 30 minutes or less, so a spare is indispensable.

Tripod

Another essential accessory is a camcorder tripod. Although a skilled camera operator can shoot good quality footage by hand-holding, it is difficult to obtain steady images without the support of a tripod. Shaky pictures are the most obvious signs of amateurish production.

Many beginning video makers avoid tripods because they can be clumsy and a nuisance to manage. But if you routinely use a tripod from the start, you will come to find it a natural part of the shooting process.

You can adjust the stiffness with which tripods move sideways and up and down. Locate these controls, **Figure 2-4,** on your particular unit and set them so you can move the camcorder smoothly. Be careful to set the vertical tension tightly enough to hold the camera level even when it is unattended.

Some tripods include a quick-release mechanism that makes it easier to attach and remove the camcorder. Before using one of these tripods, make sure you understand how the release mechanism works.

Now that you have located the camcorder controls and learned about tape, batteries, and tripods, you are ready to start shooting. But before you do so, use the accompanying checklist to ensure that you are ready to go.

Figure 2-4.
A typical tripod head.

Preshoot Checklist

● Battery charged and inserted in camcorder.

● Spare battery charged and ready for use.

● New videotape positioned at the end of 30 seconds of blank recording.

● Previously used videocassette rolled forward to blank tape.

● White balance control set to automatic.

● Tripod included in shooting kit.

Also make sure that the date is not visible in the viewfinder. If it is, disable the "date" function on the camcorder so that the date does not appear on the footage you will shoot.

Camcorder Operation

Camcorders are so simple to operate that anybody can obtain pictures of some sort. But if you follow just a few professional practices, you can improve your footage dramatically. The following suggestions assume that you will edit your first projects in the camera; that is, you will shoot each shot in order and make each one last as long as it will in the completed program. (Some of these tips do not apply when you are shooting footage to edit later.)

Checking the Viewfinder

All camcorder viewfinders display several types of information, **Figure 2-5.**

The problem is that many people look right through this information and pay no

Figure 2-5.
Different viewfinders display different kinds of information.

attention to it. By checking the viewfinder data before making each shot, you can avoid many common shooting problems.

Different camcorders display different types of information, but most of them will show you the following, in one form or another:

- *Battery charge:* shows roughly how much power is left in the camcorder battery. When it gets too low, change batteries, so you do not lose power in the middle of a shot.

- *Tape loaded:* shows whether or not a tape cassette is in the camcorder.

- *Tape counter:* shows how much footage has been shot. Digital camcorder displays read in hours, minutes, seconds, and frames; most analog models are less precise.

- *Record symbol:* shows whether you are actually recording or only previewing the image in the viewfinder.

- *White balance:* shows whether the camcorder is set for outdoor or indoor color, or whether the control is set to the automatic position.

- *Date:* shows whether or not a date stamp will be printed over the shot.

- *Zoom:* shows the image size, compared to the extreme wide angle setting. 2X, 3X, and 4X indicate two, three, and four times the magnification of the widest setting.

In addition to these common displays, some camcorders show other kinds of information in the viewfinder. To interpret them, consult the instruction manual for your particular model.

Checking Camera Settings

No matter how carefully you set up your camera at your base of operations, check it again when you are ready to shoot. In particular:

- Make sure the white balance switch is set to automatic.

- Verify that the autofocus and autoexposure controls are enabled. Though they default to automatic, they can be accidentally changed after the camcorder is turned on.

- Check the other camcorder controls and review the information in the viewfinder to ensure that unwanted special features, like the date stamp, have not been enabled.

- Just before making each shot, ensure that the camera has not gone into standby (sleep) mode.

Using the Tripod

Here are some tips for mounting the camera on the tripod and using the tripod effectively.

- Make sure the tripod head is level by adjusting the lengths of the legs.

- Screw the camcorder onto the head firmly enough so it does not wobble, but not tight enough to make it difficult to remove.

- If the tripod has a center column, do not raise it. This will make the unit less stable.

- Point one leg at the subject to be videotaped. Doing this will let you stand close behind the camera, in the space between the other two legs.

- When you pan the camera (pivot it from side to side), stand facing the center of the move, **Figure 2-6.** To make the shot, twist your upper body to frame the start of the shot, then follow the camera, twisting your body the opposite way until you frame the end of the shot. By doing this, you will avoid tangling yourself in the tripod.

Hand-holding the Camera

Because a tripod will sometimes be impractical, here are some tips for making steady hand-held shots:

- Whenever possible, brace yourself on something. Lean your elbows on a wall or table. Prop yourself up with a tree, light pole, or wall.

- To shoot a low angle, sit with the camera firmly in your lap, swing the viewfinder or viewing screen up and look down into it to make the shot.

Figure 2-6.
Start a pan with your feet aimed at the center of the pan and twist your body as you rotate the camera.

 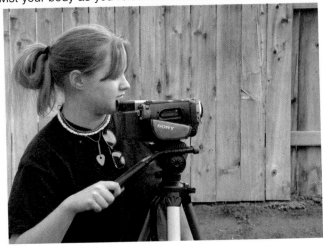

- Do not walk while shooting if you can avoid it.
- Unless the shot is quite long, take a deep breath and let half of it out before starting, then hold your breath as you shoot.
- Use the widest-angle lens setting. The wider the angle, the less obvious any camera shake will be.

Avoiding Camera Problems

The do's and don'ts of good camera work are covered more completely in later chapters. At this stage, just remember four tips:

- Avoid swinging the camera around to center one subject, and then another, and then another. Instead, get a good-looking picture of each subject and shoot it as a separate shot.
- Do not make shots too brief for the viewer to look at. Three to five seconds is generally a good minimum length for this kind of project.
- Do not pose subjects against the sky, white walls, or other backgrounds that are lighter than their faces. This will deceive the auto exposure system and result in poorly-lit pictures.
- Avoid zooming while shooting. If you want to change from a wider to a closer view, for example, shoot each angle as a separate shot.

As you will see later on, professional video makers rarely use the zoom except in studios or when covering live activities like sports.

If you follow these four tips, your footage will look technically competent, but it still may not be very pleasing. To record good-looking video and clearly audible sound, you need to remember just a few more basic ideas.

Quality Video and Audio

Your program will be judged on how it looks and sounds, so here are some tips for improving both video and audio quality.

Good Quality Video

You can make better-looking images by using four key ideas: head room, look room, lead room, and the rule of thirds.

Allowing proper *head room* means positioning subjects at a pleasing distance from the top of the picture. When videotaping people, most beginners center the subjects' heads in the frame because that is how we look at people with our own eyes. The problem is that the results look awkward on a video screen, **Figure 2-7**. For better composition, place the subject's eyes in the top third of the frame, except in wide shots.

Look room is similar to head room. When watching people, we tend to center them left-to-right as well as top-to-bottom, **Figure 2-8**. As you can see, this appears pleasing only when the subject is looking straight at the camera. If the subject is looking to one side, the composition seems constricted on that side. The remedy is to shift the subject away from the direction of the look.

Lead room is look room with the subject moving, **Figure 2-9**. If you center moving subjects left-to-right, they seem about to run into the edge of the picture. By positioning subjects away from the frame edge toward which they are moving, you achieve more satisfying results.

Figure 2-7.
Head room. A— Centering the eyes in the frame results in too much head room. B—Try to keep the eyes in the upper third of the frame.

A

B

Figure 2-8.
Look room. A— Looking forward, the subject may be centered in the frame. B— When looking to one side, a centered subject crowds the frame edge. C— Allow somewhat more space on the side toward which the subject is looking.

A

B

C

The ***rule of thirds*** offers the simplest way to achieve good pictorial composition. People tend to center subjects in their pictures. A tree is photographed dividing the frame vertically. The horizon is placed so it divides the image horizontally. The resulting picture looks balanced and rather dull. You might call this kind of composition "the rule of halves" because the frame is divided in half on both axes.

If you imagine a tic-tac-toe grid in front of your picture, you can divide the image into thirds instead of halves, **Figure 2-10.** The resulting compositions will be much more interesting.

An "axis" is the same in video as in graphed algebra equations. The X axis is horizontal (left-to-right) and the Y axis is vertical (top-to-bottom).

Figure 2-9.
Lead room. A— Do not allow a moving subject to crowd the frame edge. B— Allow extra room ahead of a moving subject.

A

B

Figure 2-10.
Rule of thirds. A— Centered compositions may look stiff. B— This composition is organized on a grid of thirds. (Corel)

A

B

Good Quality Audio

For your first video projects, you will probably use the camcorder's built-in microphone. Here are three simple tips for recording better-sounding audio.

Stay close to the subject

Place the camera, with its microphone (mike), as close as possible to the subject. The farther away the microphone is, the more it picks up interfering background noise. Instead of setting the lens at full telephoto and shooting from, say, twenty feet away, set it at wide angle to obtain a similar composition from a five-foot distance, **Figure 2-11.**

Minimize background noise

Set up your shoot so that the camcorder is aimed away from major noise sources. Do not place subjects in front of a busy street because the mike will be pointed directly at the traffic noise behind them. Instead, position your subjects so that the camcorder mike points away from the traffic.

Direct silently

Do not give verbal instructions from the camera position while shooting. Camcorder mikes pick up sounds to the sides as well as in front. You can ruin sound takes because your own voice is mixed with the production sound.

Figure 2-11.
Moving the camcorder/microphone closer to the subject captures better quality sound.

Camera Angles

When people begin making videos, they often set up shots that look very similar. The three frames shown simply document a person walking. Because the person is nearly the same size in every shot and the camera is in nearly the same position, the resulting shots are not very interesting.

As you can see, the sequence is more interesting when the shots are more varied.

Too-similar shots make uninteresting video.

Varying subject size and camera position makes more interesting shots.

The Shooting Session

Speaking of directing, we need to mention a few things about guiding both the performers in front of the camcorder and the crew behind it.

Directing the shoot

On more advanced video projects, you will be shooting to obtain raw footage for later editing. On beginning projects, however, you will probably be editing in the camera to create a finished video in the process of shooting it.

To edit in the camera successfully, you need to observe a few simple rules:

● Record every shot in the order in which it will appear in the finished program.

● If you are taping continuous action, such as somebody walking, try to leave the

Notice that the shots vary in both size and camera position. Changing only the image size makes the camera appear to jump toward or away from the subject.

On the other hand, changing only the camera position produces shots that are too similar.

Only subject size changes.

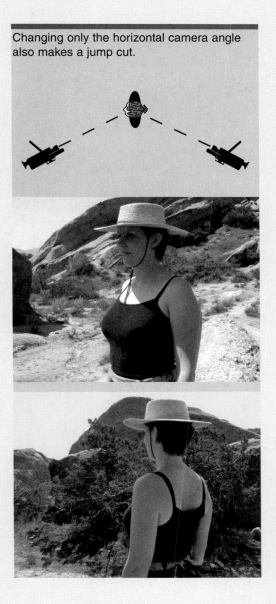

Changing only the horizontal camera angle also makes a jump cut.

screen empty between shots. For example, let people walk off-screen at the end of one shot and then show them walking again at the start of the next shot. See **Figure 2-12.**

The rule works as well in reverse: show people walking at the end of the outgoing shot; then have them walk into an empty screen at the start of the incoming shot. By doing this, you will not have to match the actions in the two shots.

- Try to make each shot look different from the preceding one. Varied images will make your video much more interesting to watch. (See the sidebar *Camera Angles* for tips on varying image look.)

Finally, it is worth repeating that the crew should keep quiet during each shot, because the camcorder mike will pick up all the sounds of the crew as well as those of the cast.

Managing the Shooting Session

Shooting video can sometimes become such an intense activity that perfectly responsible people get carried away. A few reminders about video security, safety, and courtesy may help avoid this problem.

Security refers to the care of your expensive and somewhat delicate video equipment. To keep your hardware safe:

- Designate one person to take responsibility for the camcorder and tripod at all times. That person is never to leave the immediate area of the equipment.

- If you are hand-holding the camcorder, never set it down on anything except its tripod. It is easy to grab a camera from a table or a sidewalk and run. It is much harder and more conspicuous to snatch both camera and tripod. Also, the tripod makes the camera more visible, so it is

Figure 2-12.
The first two shots (A and B) make a jump cut. Allowing the subject to leave the frame (C and D) hides the mismatched action.

A

B

C

D

CORRECTING COMMON MISTAKES

Symptom	Cause	Cure
Viewfinder blank	Power not on Battery dead Camera on standby	Turn on power Replace battery Reactivate camera
Camera won't record	No tape inserted VCR mode enabled	Insert tape Enable camcorder mode
Colors too blue or too orange	White balance set incorrectly	Switch white balance to automatic setting
Date appears on screen	Date function enabled	Disable date function
Shaky pictures	Hand-held camera	Use tripod
Too much head room	Subject head centered in frame	Place subject's eyes in top 1/3 of frame

less likely to be bumped or knocked to the ground.

● Detach the camcorder from the tripod when transporting them. If the camcorder has a handle, never use it to lift both camera and tripod together. The handle is not strong enough to carry the weight of both pieces.

● Always protect the camcorder from the weather. Keep it out of hot sun except when actually shooting. Do not allow it to get wet, particularly the delicate glass of the zoom lens.

Security for cast and crew is important. Many video projects involve action sequences such as fights and car chases. To keep everyone safe:

● Do not ask people to perform feats for the camera that they would not normally attempt. Professional stunt people are highly trained, very experienced, and well paid for taking risks. Your cast and crew are not.

● Do not put the crew at risk, (say, by hanging out over balconies or climbing on high roofs) in pursuit of interesting camera angles.

● Remember that the videographer is concentrating intently on the viewfinder. It is easy for that person to run into objects or stumble on stairs. An assistant should guide the videographer during moving shots.

Finally, practice simple courtesy. You have a right to shoot outdoors in public places as long as you observe the rules of both law and good manners. Do not shoot inside (in stores or offices, for example) without permission. Though passers-by may walk through the background of your shots, do not use them as actual subjects without their permission. Some people feel uncomfortable or irritated when suddenly confronted with a camcorder. Respect their right to privacy.

Getting Started

By following the suggestions in this chapter, you can make simple but satisfying videos. Soon, however, you will want to undertake more ambitious projects and create programs of fully professional caliber. To do this, you will use the more sophisticated production techniques covered in the rest of this book. All of these techniques have essentially the same purpose: to communicate effectively with viewers in the medium of video. For this reason, Chapters 3 through 7 cover the principles of video communication.

Key Terms

Autoexposure: The camera system that delivers the correct amount of illumination to the recording mechanism, regardless of the light level of the shooting environment.

Autofocus: The camera system that ensures that the subject in the image appears clear and sharp.

Camcorder: An appliance that both captures moving images (**cam**era) and stores them on tape (re**corder**).

Default: A setting that is selected automatically unless the user changes it manually.

Head room: The distance between the top of a subject's head and the upper edge of the frame.

Lead room: The distance between the subject and the edge of the frame toward which it is moving.

Look room: The distance between the subject and the edge of the frame toward which it is looking.

Pan: To pivot the camcorder horizontally on its support.

Roll to raw stock: To advance a video-tape through previously recorded sections to blank tape, in preparation for additional recording.

Rule of thirds: An aid to composition in the form of an imaginary tic-tac-toe grid superimposed on the image. Important picture components are aligned with the lines and intersections of the grid.

White balance: A camera system that neutralizes the color tints of different light sources, such as sunshine and halogen lamps.

Zoom: To magnify or reduce the size of a subject by changing the focal length of the lens while recording.

Many camcorders use image stabilization techniques to steady hand-held shots (Canon).

3 Video Space

Contents

About Video Space
The Frame
Video Dimensions
Spatial Relations

Objectives

After studying this chapter, you will be able to:

❏ Use the video frame to control what viewers see.

❏ Compose images and action for the two-dimensional screen.

❏ Create the illusion of depth in the image.

❏ Exploit the elements of scale, distance, position, and relationship.

About Video Space

This chapter explains the very different laws that govern space in the video universe and shows how you can turn these odd-seeming laws to your advantage in communicating information and feelings to your audience.

Though we use the term "video" here, as usual, the rules of the film universe are identical. It was the pioneer film makers, of course, who discovered these rules to begin with.

When viewers watch video they unconsciously think they are looking through a sort of window at the events on the other side. In real life, both sides of a window belong to the same world and observe the same laws of space and time. For this reason, viewers assume the same about the world on the other side of the screen "window."

However, the screen is not a window and it has no "other side." Video images are not *behind* the screen but *on* it, and that creates two fundamental differences from the real world.

First, video information is limited by the borders of the image, **Figure 3-1**. By opening a real-world window and leaning through it, you can see more of the scene outside. But no matter how close you get to a screen, you can never see anything beyond its borders, and of course you cannot thrust your head through it.

Second, the screen itself is flat, or nearly so, which means it has only two dimensions instead of three. There is no true depth in a movie image. No matter how dramatically that spaceship seems to zoom away from you, it is

not actually moving farther back from the screen surface, but merely growing smaller on it.

In short, space (and time as well) work very differently in the special world on the screen. It is these crucial differences that make video possible. If you master the laws of video space, you will be able to use some of the major tools of video communication.

The Laws Of Video Space

This chapter discusses the four laws of video space. Here are those laws in summary form:

- What is outside the frame does not exist, unless that existence is implied.
- Height and breadth are determined solely by the frame and depth is only an illusion.
- Size, position, distance, relationship, and movement are not fixed.
- Direction is determined solely by the frame.

The Frame

The frame is not just a passive border around the picture. It is a powerful video communication tool. First, the frame defines and controls what the viewer sees. Even the most honest videos show only selections from reality, and those selections are made by including them within the frame. Second, screen composition and movement are defined by reference to the frame around the image.

In video, the word *frame* has a two completely different meanings, **Figure 3-2**: 1) the border around the screen and 2) a single film or video picture, as in "Video is displayed at 30 *frames* per second."

Figure 3-1.
Screen proportions (aspect ratios). A—The traditional video frame, proportioned 4 to 3 (1.33 to1). B—The wide screen video frame, proportioned 16 to 9 (1.78 to 1). (Sue Stinson)

A   B

Figure 3-2.
A "frame" is both the border around the screen and a single video image in a series.

The Frame Controls Content

The first law of video space is perhaps the most important: *what is outside the frame does not exist* in the video world, no matter how real it is in the actual world. This is the law that makes media production possible. The sound stage or location may be packed with people, cameras, lights, and sound equipment, but because the camera operators exclude these extraneous elements from the frame, they are completely invisible to the audience. And because the audience cannot see it, it does not exist for them.

Video makers use the frame to alter reality in countless ways. Here are a few examples:

● By having a small number of spectators sit close together and framing off the many empty seats around them, you can make an audience seem bigger than it really is. Since all the empty seats are outside the frame, they do not exist.

Note that to frame off something is to exclude it completely from the image, while to frame something is not only to include it but to feature it. The command, "Frame off that tree" means keep it out of the picture, while "Frame that tree" means make it the center of interest in the picture.

● By framing off the many well-kept homes in a neighborhood and framing only the few run-down houses, you can make a prosperous area look like a slum. In the video world, the attractive homes outside the frame do not exist.

● By showing the skyscraper tops behind your actor but framing off her feet and the flat roof on which she is standing, you can make her seem dangerously close to the edge of the building. On the screen, the roof outside the frame does not exist.

Using the frame to include and exclude information from a shot is perhaps the most universally exploited technique in video communication.

Although real world elements outside the frame do not exist in the video world, the converse is also true: elements that do *not* exist in the real world *can* exist in the video world if the video maker implies that they lie somewhere outside the frame.

For example, suppose viewers see three shots: a rodeo from a spectator's point of view, the spectator herself, and another shot of the rodeo. Crowd noises and the announcer on the public address system fill the sound track across all three shots, **Figure 3-3.** Imagine, too, that the director has sent other people walking in front of the spectator.

Figure 3-3.

AUDIO: Rodeo background sounds

AUDIO: Rodeo sounds continue.

AUDIO: Rodeo sounds continue.

The Power Of The Frame

The frame that bounds the video world is a versatile tool. The frame can conceal production.

The frame isolates the subjects from the production around them. (Lowel Light)

The frame can alter reality.

Though the subject seems to be high in the air, he is actually standing on firm ground.

The frame can create a visual composition.

The frame isolates a composition within the random elements of the scene. (Corel)

The frame can define movement.

Against a featureless background, the car's movement is in relation to the frame.

In fact, the spectator never was at a rodeo, as you can see from the wider view of her in **Figure 3-4**. The passing extras and the sound effects laid under her closeup *imply* that the rest of the scene extends far beyond what viewers can see on the screen. Because the frame prevents them from seeing the reality of the desert background, they believe that the spectator is at a rodeo.

Figure 3-4.
The "spectator" as actually videotaped.

To include this ability to suggest things that are not really there, we must amend our law of video space to add this idea: what is outside the frame does not exist, *unless that existence is implied*. By exploiting this law, video makers use the frame to determine what information viewers receive and how they interpret it.

The Frame Determines Composition and Movement

Video makers also use the frame to control how information is presented. The frame is the viewers' only fixed reference (though they are almost never consciously aware of it). They depend on the frame to locate and organize the parts of the pictures they are watching, and to judge the speed with which things move. That is, viewers use the frame to perceive composition and movement.

Composition is the organization of the elements (parts) of a picture. These elements are arranged in relation to one another. More importantly, they are also arranged by their relationship to the frame that surrounds them. Without the defining border supplied

by the frame, composition would be difficult or even impossible. (Composition is covered more fully in Chapter 5.)

Movement refers to motion on the screen, and viewers perceive that motion by two sets of clues:

● How rapidly the background (such as scenery flying past a car window) changes in relation to the subject in the foreground.

● How quickly the subject moves in relation to the frame.

Since this discussion concerns the frame, we are more interested in that second clue to movement: motion in relation to the frame.

Think of the video images you have seen of satellites in orbit, as recorded from a space shuttle. They do not move on the screen at all, but seem to float in space as quietly as a boat on a pond, **Figure 3-5**. In truth, of course, those satellites are whirling along their orbits at thousands of miles per hour. But since the cameras recording them are moving at exactly the same speed, the images of the satellites do not move *in relation to the frame*.

Now think of the spaceships that zoom across movie and TV screens at warp speeds, spanning whole galaxies in minutes. In reality, these spaceships are often miniature models that do not move at all. They are fixed in place, and the illusion of rapid motion is created by moving the camera past them, **Figure 3-6.** Making the camera fly past the stationary ship models causes them to move violently *in relation to the frame*.

Figure 3-5.
A fast-moving satellite does not move in the frame. (NASA)

Figure 3-6.
Making a spaceship move. A—Plan of the shooting setup: the spaceship remains fixed, while the camera moves right to left. B, C —On screen, the spaceship seems to enter the frame from the left and leave it on the right.

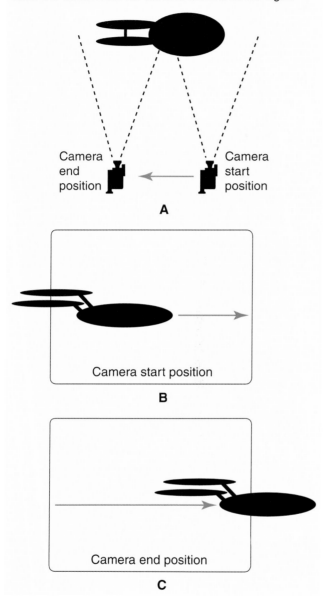

Today's spaceships are usually computer animations rather than models; but for big-screen science fiction movies, the large scale and fine details of models are still sometimes preferred.

In the actual world, the satellite in space is traveling at thousands of miles per hour, while the model spaceship is not moving at all. But in the video world, the exact opposite is true: the satellite is not changing position with respect to the frame, while the model is.

It is fair to say that the frame around the screen world is the video maker's most powerful single tool. It determines what does or does not exist in that world, how objects in that world relate to one another, and how things move in that world. Every decision made by the director, the videographer, the lighting director, the production designer, and even the sound recordist, is determined first and foremost by the characteristics of the frame.

Video Dimensions

While the frame around the screen forms the boundaries of the video world, it is the screen itself that displays that world as a strange, flat universe in which space acts differently from real-world space. In the video world, the dimension called "height" is not always vertical and the dimension called "breadth" is not always horizontal. The dimension called "depth" does not even exist. What viewers perceive as that third dimension is merely an illusion.

This brings us to the second law of the video world: *Height and breadth are determined solely by the frame and depth is only an illusion.*

If you understand how this second law operates, you can make it do all kinds of tricks. So, let us see how video height and breadth differ from those dimensions in the actual world.

Horizontal and Vertical

In the real world (at least on Earth), height and breadth are defined by gravity: height is the dimension parallel to the direction in which things fall; breadth is the dimension at right angles to that direction. Newton's apple always falls in a vertical path to the horizontal ground because the orientations of height and breadth are unchangeable, **Figure 3-7.**

Figure 3-7.
In the real world, horizontal and vertical are defined by gravity.

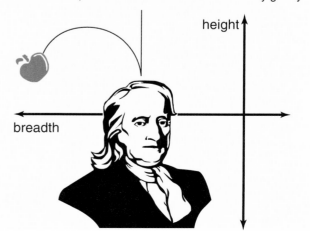

In the video world, however, height and breadth are not defined by gravity but by the frame around the image. Height is the dimension parallel to the sides of the frame. Breadth is the dimension parallel to the top and bottom.

The difference is important, because it means video height and breadth are determined entirely by the video maker. By tilting the camera sideways, you can make "vertical" and "horizontal" whatever directions you choose.

Naming Screen Dimensions

In technical discussions of screen-world space, the dimensions are sometimes given the names of the axes of a mathematical graph because such a graph, like a video screen, occupies a two-dimensional space.

The horizontal dimension is called the "X axis" and the vertical dimension is called the "Y axis." The apparent third dimension, at right angles to both the others, is called the "Z axis." It is indicated by a dashed line because in video, depth is only an illusion.

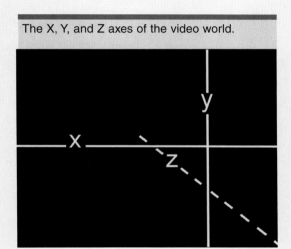

The X, Y, and Z axes of the video world.

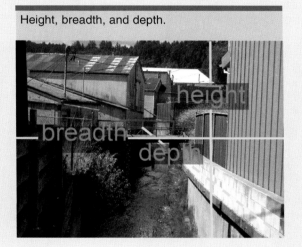

Height, breadth, and depth.

Artists working in animation have long used a different system. In calling for the animation camera to move up, down, left, or right on a drawing they use compass directions: North, South, East, and West.

Though all three sets of names have advantages, this book uses the familiar terms, *height, breadth, and depth.*

In classic animation, the screen axes are called North/South and East/West.

Playing Tricks With Video Space

Since height and breadth are not fixed in the video world, you can play all kinds of tricks with them. For example, by turning the camera 90 degrees, you can reverse the two dimensions. In this example, an actor standing on a walkway appears to be scaling a vertical concrete wall.

In the next example, the actor appears to be able to do pushups with just one finger. (In a moment, he will remove his finger from the "floor" and float in midair!) Note how the cup affixed to the wall helps sell the gag that the wall is actually a floor. (In movie jargon, a *gag* is any trick or stunt, and to *sell* an illusion is to include information that makes it more believable.)

The subject appears to be scaling a wall, but the camcorder is actually turned sideways.

Because the camcorder is turned 90 degrees, the subject seems to be floating above a concrete floor.

The Illusion of Depth

Though screen height and breadth are different from their real-world counterparts, they do exist in some form, at least, because the screen itself has height and breadth. However, the flat screen surface has no depth, and so the image on it cannot have depth either. In video, depth is purely an illusion.

In both the real and video worlds, the farther away objects are, the smaller they appear. But though the appearance is the same in both worlds, the realities are exact opposites. In the actual world, receding objects really do get farther away but they only seem to shrink in size. In the video world, receding objects only seem to get farther away (they remain on the surface of the screen) but they really do shrink in size, **Figure 3-8.**

Figure 3-8.
Though the spaceship seems to have traveled away from the viewer, its image has simply shrunk on the screen surface.

  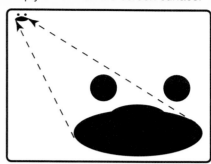

The lack of true depth in the video world is both an advantage and a disadvantage. On the one hand, since depth is just a trick, video makers can manipulate it like any other illusion. On the other hand, since the screen is really flat, you must use a variety of compositional tricks to create the illusion of depth upon it.

Spatial Relations

The second law of the video world leads directly to the third law: *size, position, distance, relationship, and movement are not fixed.* Video space is completely fluid and is controlled by the video maker. In the actual world objects keep the same size and position; but in video space nothing is fixed. You can use this fact to your advantage.

Size, Position, and Distance

In the actual world, an inch is always an inch and a meter is always a meter. That means the size of an object is always the same. The object's position also remains the same (at least until it actually moves). Finally, the distance between objects stays the same too. None of this is true in the video world. For example,

● Two actors may escape from a full-size automobile just before it explodes, but the car that actually blows up is only a foot-long model. An object's size can be altered as long as it looks unchanged to the viewer.

● An actor standing a foot away from a wall in long shot may be *"cheated"* several feet farther from it for a closeup (to allow more room for camera and lights). Though the actor's position has changed, the shift is not visible to the audience.

● Two aircraft that actually pass each other a safe distance apart seem, on screen, to be a hair's breadth from colliding, **Figure 3-9.** The trick is done with a telephoto lens, which greatly reduces the apparent distance between the two objects.

As these examples suggest, movie makers routinely change the space in the screen world to fit the needs of the moment. Changes in size, position, and distance are all forms of changes in scale. In the video world, the apparent length of an inch or a meter or a mile can vary tremendously from one shot to another.

Relationships among Objects

You can control more than just the scale of screen world space. You can also control the relationships among different objects.

Figure 3-9.
As photographed by a telephoto lens, the planes nearly collide. In reality, they are a safe distance apart. (Corel)

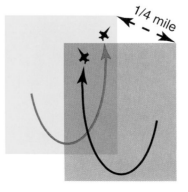

Controlling spatial relationships usually means putting things together in the screen world that are far apart in the real world. This is so common in movie making that professionals take the process for granted. Typically, spatial relationships are altered by editing two or more separate shots together into what seems like a continuous action. For example:

● On screen, a character walks down a street, turns a corner, and continues up a side street. In the actual world, the main street is a location and the side street is a construction on the studio lot.

● On screen, a character climbs six flights of stairs. In actual shooting, a single flight was used repeatedly, with different floor number signs and camera angles.

● On screen, two characters carry on a conversation. In actuality, each actor was photographed separately in similar-looking sets, playing the scene with a crew member. In postproduction, the editor replaced the crew members with the absent actors.

● On screen, a character crosses a courtyard in fifteen steps. The real-world location is 50 steps wide and obstructed by a large fountain, but the director and editor have condensed the space by means of clever camera setups and editing, **Figure 3-10.**

A setup is a single camera position.

In short, screen-world relationships between unconnected places and people can be created by recording them separately and editing the different shots together.

Figure 3-10.
Controlling spatial relationships. A— The audience sees the actor start to cross the courtyard. B— The audience sees the actor complete the cross. C— The whole courtyard, showing the central portion omitted from the two shots.

A

B

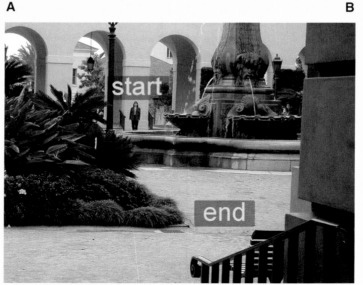

C

Direction of Movement

In addition to controlling the relationships between screen-world places, video makers can control the way in which on-screen people get to those places. That is, they also control direction in the video world. To state this fact in the form of the fourth law of video space, *direction is determined solely by the frame.*

In the real world we express directions in compass terms: North, South, East, West, and those directions are fixed. If the street on which you live runs north and south, it *always* runs north and south. In the screen world, by contrast, compass directions are quite meaningless. Instead, direction is perceived with reference to the borders of the screen. For instance, successive shots may show an actor walking south, east, and then north; but as long as she is oriented in approximately the same way *on the screen*, the audience perceives her to be continuing in the same direction, **Figure 3-11.**

Directions in the video world are subject to certain conventions. For instance, a plane traveling from England to the U.S. is usually shown moving from screen right to screen left, **Figure 3-12.** That is because conventional maps show North America on the left side of the Atlantic Ocean and Europe on the right.

If the plane flying west were photographed from the north side, it would move from screen left to screen right instead. Though the resulting video would be a perfectly accurate record of the plane's movement in the actual world, it might confuse audiences watching it on the screen.

Back to the Frame

In discussing direction on the screen, we come full circle to the idea of the frame — the powerful border that lets video makers dictate what is in the screen world, where it is located, how big it is, and how it relates to other things in that world.

Figure 3-11.
In the real world (A), the subject walks south, turns east, then turns north. On the screen, however (B and C), she always walks left to right.

A

B

C

Figure 3-12.
Conventional maps show the U.S. on the left and Europe on the right. Flying from Europe to the U.S., a plane is conventionally shown heading screen left. (Corel)

(Corel)

At first, the laws governing screen-world space may seem like abstract theories, and in a way, they are. But remember that professional video makers understand these fundamental rules of screen-world operations and use them constantly in practical ways to make their programs.

Key Terms

Cheat: To move a subject from its original place (to facilitate another shot) in a way that is undetectable to the viewer.

Composition: The purposeful arrangement of the parts of an image.

Frame: The four edges that make up the border of the screen. Also, a single video image.

To frame: To feature a subject in a composition.

To frame off: To exclude an object completely from the screen.

Gag: Any effect, trick, or stunt in a movie.

Screen direction: The orientation of on-screen movement with respect to the left and right edges of the frame.

Sell: To add details to increase the believability of a screen illusion.

Setup: A single camera position, usually including lights and microphone placements as well.

The videographer and the harbor are actually two shots composited together.

4 Video Time

Contents

About Video Time
Video Time Speed
Video Time Flow
Video Time Direction
Video Time Coherence

Objectives

After studying this chapter, you will be able to:

❏ Explain the differences between actual time and video time.

❏ Describe the characteristics of video time.

❏ Exploit the characteristics of video time in making programs.

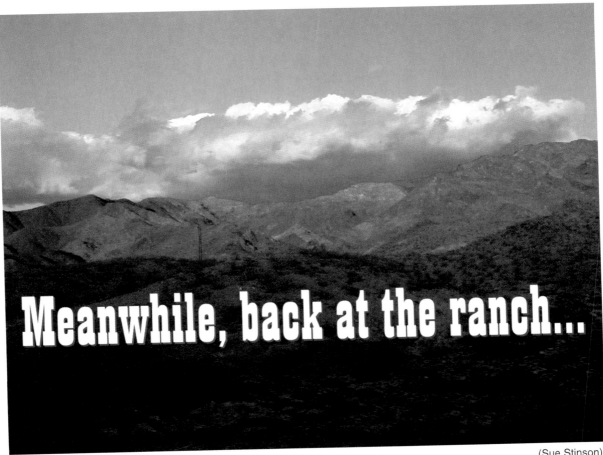

(Sue Stinson)

About Video Time

This chapter examines the nature of video time, just as Chapter 3 explores video space. Like video space, video time is quite different from real-world time, and operates by its own set of rules. If you master these rules, you can alter video time in your programs, by cutting, pasting, stretching, squeezing, and otherwise manipulating it to suit your own purposes. You can time-travel backward, forward, and sideways —or operate in multiple time flows at once. In short, you can control video time with an ease and power that any science fiction writer might envy.

Space and time are as closely connected in the video world as they are in the real one, but we are considering them separately to simplify the discussion.

Not only *can* you control video time, you *must* control it. Otherwise, you could not possibly fit the actions of your program into the brief time allotted to it. And if you did present a program in real-world time —say, a two-hour hike that actually lasted two hours on screen— your audience would be profoundly bored long before your literal video ended. A wise observer once noted that movies are life with the boring parts cut out. You remove those boring parts by managing video time.

The film 2001 A Space Odyssey begins in the prehuman past and concludes in the 21st century, a real-world time period of perhaps a million years

To manage video time you have to understand the laws by which it operates. An easy way to do that is by comparing the nature of video time with the laws of actual time, as we perceive it in the real world.

The Nature of Real-World Time

The most important characteristic of real-world time is its constancy. Time always behaves in exactly the same way with respect to its speed, flow, direction, and coherence.

We are talking about time as humans experience it. How time may be viewed by philosophers or scientists lies outside our subject area.

Speed

Time always passes at exactly the same speed. A second is always one second long and a year (as the calendar counts it) always lasts one year — no more, no less. Despite our subjective feelings that time sometimes drags and sometimes flies, it actually proceeds at a rigidly fixed pace, **Figure 4-1**.

Figure 4-1.
Real-world time always flows at the same rate.

Flow

That pace is never interrupted, because real-world time is always continuous. Though we may sometimes feel that time seems to stop, it actually rolls along without even the briefest pause.

Direction

Real time flows one way only: the future becomes the present and the present becomes the past, like a river that never passes the same spot twice. In the actual world we can revisit the past only in memory.

Coherence

In our world time affects everything identically, so everything moves together. Here, time is *not* like a river, in which some water drops flow along faster than others. In the world as we perceive it, everything is always at exactly the same "point in time."

At any one moment, people in different parts of the world may be at different hours of the day or even days of the week; but in the flow of time, all of us are always at exactly the same point.

Video Time Speed

You can control the speed at which time passes in your program, expanding an eye blink or compressing a hundred-yard stroll so that each event fills exactly the same amount of screen time.

Screen time is the length of real-world time in which a video program (or a designated piece of it) is actually displayed on-screen.

There are two ways to change time speed: you can either alter the *actual* speed within individual shots or else alter the *apparent* speed of the action in editing different shots together. The two methods of varying time speed have markedly different effects on the viewer.

Altering speed within a shot

Altering speed within a shot is achieved by recording or playing the shot at a slower or faster rate than normal. The result is an obvious change in the speed of time on the screen. For example:

- In slow motion, the lovers float lazily toward each other across a flowery field; the whirring wings of a hummingbird seem to flap as deliberately as a buzzard's, **Figure 4-2.**
- In fast motion, the clowns skitter around the screen like doodlebugs; the flower's night-long opening unfolds in two brief seconds.

As these examples suggest, different degrees of slow or fast motion serve different purposes.

Moderate slow motion imparts a dreamlike effect. The feeling may be pleasant or romantic, as with the loping lovers; it may be nightmarish, as when a victim falls sedately toward certain death —and slowly falls and falls and falls. The mood may be nostalgic, as when a former football star recalls the 80-yard touchdown run that was the highlight of his career.

More pronounced slow motion has a different effect: it allows us to see otherwise invisible actions. It can divide a horseshoe pitch into many separate parts for analysis or reveal the complex movement of the hummingbird's wings. In its most extreme form, slow motion lets us watch as a bullet explodes a lightbulb.

With fast motion, the differences are similar, though of course the effect is the opposite. Moderate fast motion alters the mood, usually making an ordinary action look funny. Silent comedy chases were often filmed in moderate fast motion, to heighten the comic effect.

More pronounced fast motion condenses action to make its overall shape or pattern easier to see. It can show us a sky full of small clouds boiling up into a full-fledged thunderhead right before our eyes. Very fast motion goes further by shortening actions that are so long we cannot normally see them at all, like the passage of the moon across the sky, **Figure 4-3,** or the blooming of a flower. In its most extreme form, fast motion can compress whole months into a few seconds, as when the audience sees an office building go from vacant lot to finished structure in what seems like a single shot.

Figure 4-2.
Slow motion can make a hummingbird's wings visible. (Sue Stinson)

Figure 4-3.
Very fast motion can condense hours into seconds. (Sue Stinson)

Popular editing software includes stop-motion commands that allow you to create time lapse photography by automatically selecting, say, one frame for every minute of source footage, speeding up the motion by 1800 percent.

In short, slow motion expands the screen time during which an action happens and fast motion contracts it. In both cases the effect is obvious to the audience. When you watch a swinging baseball bat float majestically across the screen or the moon spring up in the sky, you realize that time has been stretched or condensed and you know that the appearance of the action is not realistic.

Filmed model shots such as toy-size trains exploding are generally recorded in slow motion to make the action look more realistic, while car chases are often shot in mild fast motion to increase the apparent speed.

Slow and fast motion are used extensively in educational video programs, where their ability to present actions for analysis is valuable. In fiction programs, however, the movie makers want you to believe that the story is real. Since slow or fast motion shots remind you that you are watching a video or film, these effects are used sparingly in fiction programs. Fiction and nonfiction programs alike rely mainly on a second method of controlling video time. This method is *editing*.

Altering speed in editing

Slow and fast motion techniques are always visible because they vary time speed within each shot. In controlling time through *editing*, however, the action within every shot unrolls at a perfectly normal, realistic pace. It is *between* shots that editors expand or condense the passage of time. Because the manipulations occur between shots instead of within them, they are usually invisible to the viewer. Editors control video time speed in two ways: they slow time down by *overlapping* action and speed it up by *omitting* action. **Overlapping and Omitting.** To slow an action down, editors show parts of it more than once. For example, suppose you want to dramatize the feelings of a character who is wearily descending a flight of stairs. To do this, the director first covers the action from above, and then again, from below, **Figure 4-4.**

Suppose that the staircase has 15 steps. To extend the time required to descend it, the editor shows the actor walking down steps 1 through 10 from the rear, and then cuts to the front angle. Here is the trick: even though the first shot ends on step 10, the second shot starts back up on step 5. Because the shots have such different points of view, the audience does not notice the overlap and the editor has extended the action by five steps.

To speed an action up, editors use the opposite technique: they cut out repetitive or otherwise uninteresting action, **Figure 4-5.** Imagine the same staircase scene, only this time the character is jogging briskly down the steps. To enhance the impetuous feeling of the scene, the director uses exactly the same camera placements as before; but this time the editor ends the first shot with the actor on step 5 and starts the second shot on step 10. This shortens the time required to descend the stairs and, as before, the audience does not notice that the character has mysteriously skipped steps 5 through 9.

In both speeding the action up and slowing it down, the key is invisibility. The editor is able to compress or expand video time by adjusting it *between shots*, where the audience cannot see what is happening.

Altering Video Time To Edit Performance

Editors routinely adjust video time in order to fine-tune the performances of actors. To see how this works, imagine a romantic comedy in which a young woman is taking her boyfriend home to meet her parents, who believe she is marrying a wealthy man. In successive shots she says, "Don't forget, you're worth 50 million dollars," and he replies, "I'm not worth 50 dollars."

In the first version, his line follows hers immediately. In the second version, the editor begins the boyfriend's shot about 1.5 seconds before he speaks. Though the actor is simply looking at his partner, the added time makes him appear to be thinking about the hazards of this lie.

Figure 4-4.
Overlapping action through the use of a reverse angle.

Shot One

step 1

step 10

Shot Two

step 5

step 15

Overlapping Action

WOMAN: "Don't forget, you're worth 50 million dollars."

MAN: "I'm not worth *50* dollars."

WOMAN: "Don't forget, you're worth 50 million dollars."

(No dialog)

MAN: "I'm not worth *50* dollars."

Figure 4-5.
Omitting action through the use of reverse angles.

Omitting Action

Video Time Flow

Omitting or overlapping action changes not only the speed of video time, but its flow as well. Real-world time flows continuously, without so much as a moment repeated or cut. But as we have seen, time flow in the very different world of video is constantly interrupted to control its speed. We adjust video time flow for other purposes too. To see how this works, we need to consider the three main forms of video time progression: *serial*, *parallel*, and *disjointed*.

Serial Time Flow

Up to this point, we have been discussing time flow in *serial* form: a stream of events moving forward in a single sequence. For example, a character first showers, then gets dressed, then eats breakfast, then leaves for work. This serial flow of actions is the most common depiction of time in video because that is how we perceive time in real life.

Single-stream time flow can be compressed to an amazing degree. A story can span three or four generations in two hours. A documentary video may cover hundreds of years of history. Despite its many advantages, however, a strictly serial time flow is limiting because you can show only one set of related actions. When you want to show two or more sequences of events at a time, you need to establish multiple streams of video time, flowing *parallel* to one another.

Parallel Time Flow

In the video world we often see two or more sequences of action that are happening at the same time. To use a melo-dramatic cliché as an example, we might see the hero hanging from a railing around the roof of a building while the heroine races up an endless stairwell to rescue him, **Figure 4-6.**

Figure 4-6.
Two sequences take place simultaneously: the hero hangs from the railing, as the heroine races to save him.

The editor switches back and forth among these parallel sequences in what is called ***cross cutting.***

Cross cutting is so widespread in movie story telling that the silent movie title, "Meanwhile, back at the ranch..." has become a common phrase.

The audience never notices that in watching the movie, they are seeing the same moments of time twice-over (though in two different locations).

Here, video time is flowing in just two parallel streams; but skillful directors and editors can keep three, four, or even more parallel time-streams going at once.

The record for parallel cutting may be held by the film, *The Longest Day*, which follows several people at once through the D-day invasion of Normandy in World War II.

Disjointed Time Flow

If serial and parallel time flow are alternate methods of presenting sequences on the screen, *disjointed* time flow describes the way those sequences are usually recorded in production. Most programs are shot out of chronological order and then reorganized into proper sequence during the editing process.

To save time and money, a production will typically shoot all the scenes that take place at one location (or on one set) at the same time, regardless of their positions in the edited program.

For example, imagine that we see the parents of a naive young woman putting her on a train for the big city. Four years later, in story time, they return to the same station to welcome back their now successful and sophisticated daughter. Typically, those scenes will be shot back-to-back in real-world time, often on the same day, to avoid the expense of a second trip back to the station location.

On the other hand, many sequences that seem continuous on the screen are shot in separate pieces days, weeks, or even months apart. The most common example involves moving from exteriors to interiors and back. Often, the outside of the door is a real door on location and the inside is part of a set, **Figure 4-7.** Though the actor's passage from outside to inside seems continuous in screen time, the two shots of that passage were made at very different points in real time.

In fact, *every* seemingly continuous video sequence is actually built from individual shots made at different points in real-world time. For example, a dialogue sequence that plays for two minutes on the screen may take a whole production day to shoot. (This is not true of multi-camera TV programs like comedies and talk shows, in which all of the camera angles are recorded simultaneously by multiple cameras.) Different points in real-world time can even be combined in single video shots, as when actors play multiple roles via double exposure or are matted into backgrounds photographed at other times.

Figure 4-7.
The two sides of a movie door are often not the same door. A—Exterior. B—Interior in a studio.

A

B

As long ago as 1921, in *The Playhouse*, Buster Keaton populated an entire theater with copies of himself, at one point playing nine different actors in the same shot!

But whether video time is manipulated to adjust pacing, to show parallel actions simultaneously, or to combine multiple real-world moments into single video time sequences, its flow is routinely stopped, started, and moved around in a way that is impossible in the actual world.

Video Time Direction

In the real world we perceive time as moving always in one direction, from future to past. Or perhaps we think of ourselves as moving *forward*, so that the future is always becoming the present as the present becomes the past. Though events in the video world usually move in the same way, the rules of this different universe also allow us to reverse time direction and to jump forward and backward in time. The simplest way to reverse video time is by playing a recording backward, either for comedy or to achieve a special effect. We have all seen shots that show things like pie fragments leaving an actor's face and reassembling themselves into a complete pie, or milk rising like a small water spout to re-enter a milk bottle. Like fast motion, reverse motion within a shot often has a comic effect.

Time Running Backward

Reverse-motion can also be used to simulate actions that would otherwise be impossible, **Figure 4-8**. For example, imagine two actors making an impossible leap from the ground to a wall six feet high. To accomplish this feat, they are recorded jumping *backward* from the top of the wall to the ground. The editor then reverses the shot.

Like slow and fast motion, reverse motion shots tend to be used sparingly because when they are noticeable; they look obviously unnatural and contrived.

Flashing Backward (and Forward)

Though audiences do not really believe that time itself can run backward, they readily accept the idea that the video program can jump backward in time and then resume its forward direction. A time jump like this is called a ***flashback***. The flashback is such an old and familiar technique that two examples of it will illustrate it sufficiently.

Figure 4-8.
A—The actors approach the wall and crouch to jump. B—They leap upward. C—They appear to jump to the top of the wall and... D—land there.

In shot C as originally recorded, they jump *backward* off the top of the wall... and drop toward the ground. The original ending of shot C is discarded.

- At a high school class' 25th reunion, the now-sedate participants remember the crazy stunts they pulled as teenagers; and, as each story unfolds, we jump back 25 years to watch it happen.

- As she takes the oath of office, the new governor thinks of her long climb to get to this moment; and we begin reliving that struggle with her.

In the first example, we jump back to the past in order to *contrast it* with the present. In the second, we explore the past in order to *explain* the present.

In both cases, the movie makers flash us backward in time — a leap that is impossible in the actual world.

It is not a flashback when a character in a program actually travels through time (as people often do in science fiction stories). In a flashback, it is the story, rather than the character, that changes position in time.

Of course, we can also flash *forward*, jumping into the future for a look, before returning to the main narrative in the present. In this case, time changes direction not when we make the leap, but when we jump backward again to return to the present.

Video Time Coherence

Video makers manage time in one additional way. They pull moments in time apart by splitting their video and audio components and mixing them with those of other moments. A common application of this technique is ***voice-over narration***. When a boy on the screen delivers newspapers from his bicycle as an adult voice on the sound track says, "Little did I know what would happen on that Spring day so long ago...," the picture is unfolding at one point in time, while the sound is at a point years later.

Split Edits

An equally useful time-splitting technique is called, appropriately, a ***split edit***: a transition from one shot to another in which the video and audio portions do not change simultaneously. Split edits take two forms: *video* changes first or *audio* changes first.

To illustrate both forms, imagine a young woman planning a trip. In the first scene, she estimates her driving time and in the second, she tries to fix her broken-down car.

Video leads. When video changes first, the old audio continues offscreen, over the new video, **Figure 4-9**.

Audio leads. When audio changes first, the sound from the new scene begins over the preceding video, **Figure 4-10**.

Whichever way the edit is split, the time of one element is overlapped with the time of the other.

About Time

It is evident that video time behaves very differently from actual time because nothing about it is fixed: not its speed, flow, direction, or coherence. The skillful video maker uses the changeability of video time, manipulating it to condense the action, unfold the narrative, and create special effects.

Figure 4-9.
WOMAN: I can get there in an hour.

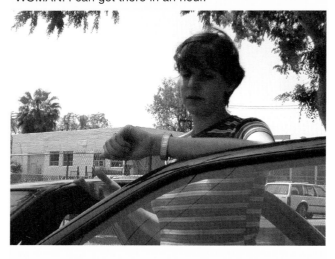

WOMAN (offscreen) I've got time to spare!

Figure 4-10.
WOMAN: I can get there in an hour. I've got time to spare! SOUND EFFECTS: Clanking of tools

WOMAN: SOUND EFFECTS: Clanking of tools continues.

Our discussion of time has been, necessarily, somewhat abstract and theoretical. In actual production most video makers deal with space and time instinctively, and so can you. However, by taking the trouble to understand the very different laws that rule time in the video world, you will be able to use them to greater advantage in your own programs.

Now that we have considered video time in this chapter and video space in Chapter 3, we are ready to look at video and audio: the two components of every program. Chapters 5 and 6 concern communicating with video images: through composition in Chapter 5 and through video grammar in Chapter 6. Communicating with audio is discussed in Chapter 7.

Technical Terms

Cross cutting: (also, "intercutting"), showing two actions at once by alternating back and forth between them.It can also be used to show three or even more parallel actions.

Flashback: A sequence that takes place earlier in the story than the sequence that precedes it.

Screen time: The length of real-world time during which a sequence is displayed on the screen (in contrast to the length of video world time that apparently passes during that sequence).

Split edit: An edit in which the audio and video of the new shot do not begin simultaneously. When "video leads," the sound from the preceding shot continues over the visual of the new shot. When "audio leads," the sound from the new shot begins over the end of the preceding visual.

Overlapping or omitting action can adjust video time.

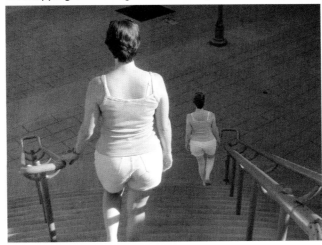

SPACE, TIME, AND PERSUASION

This chapter and Chapter 3 explain how video makers manipulate video space and time and why they do it. They do it to change reality to suit their purposes.

What are those purposes? Some are unavoidable, such as condensing time and space to cut out the boring parts. Some are constructive, such as focusing viewers on the essentials of a subject and presenting it coherently. Some are harmless and dramatically useful, such as turning two different doors into one or adjusting the pace of an actor's performance.

However, one very common purpose is not always so innocent: some videos falsify reality to encourage viewers to buy a product, vote for a candidate, or support a social agenda. That is, they seek to persuade viewers by distorting the truth.

Of course, false or misleading rhetoric is not new. People have used it for many centuries in speeches and writings. The problem with video is that the persuasive powers of the medium are inherently greater than any found in other forms of communication. This means that viewers are more likely to believe the manipulated "reality" in video than to accept false facts and arguments in the older media of speech and writing.

Though Bazin's essay is concerned with the medium of film, his ideas are equally applicable to video; and though his reasoning is extensive and subtle, it is based on a simple idea. Bazin suggests that photographs compel belief because they appear to prove the existence of their subjects.

His argument is something like this: the original photos that most people see are snapshots made with simple cameras and without manipulation by the photographer. Therefore, if something appears in a snapshot, it "must" be real, or, at least, it must have been real when that photo was taken. After all, you cannot take a snapshot of something that does not exist; so when you look at a photo of someone on a ferry boat with the Statue of Liberty behind her, you see apparent evidence of three things. At the instant when that photograph was snapped:

● The person existed.
● The statue existed.
● The person stood in front of the statue.

This belief in the literal truth of photographs has been reinforced by over 150 years of photography, most of it news pictures, portraits, and snapshots — all records of actual people and places. Consequently, an unconscious assumption has

A snapshot seems to prove that the person was at the Statue of Liberty.	But the subject…	was matted into the original image

What is it about video that makes it so compelling, so good at selling false realities? There are several answers, but perhaps the central one was articulated by the French critic Andre Bazin in an essay called "The Ontology of the Photographic Image." (Ontology is the formal study of existence, of being.) The essay was translated and published in *What is Cinema?* University of California Press, 1967.

developed that moving photographs too (cinema and video) do not lie, just as mathematical figures do not lie.

But remember the old cliché: "Figures don't lie, but liars figure." You could say with equal truth, "Photographs don't lie but liars photograph."

5 Video Composition

Contents

About Video Composition
Organization in Composition
Emphasis in Composition
Depth in Composition
Composing Video Images

Objectives

After studying this chapter, you will be able to:

❑ List the key principles of video composition.
❑ Explain how contrast is used for emphasis.
❑ Describe techniques for creating depth in compositions.

(Sue Stinson)

About Video Composition

The word ***composition*** (literally, "putting together") has many different, though related, meanings. In video, composition is the purposeful arrangement of the components of a visual image. These components, often called pictorial elements, may be objects such as people, buildings, or trees. They may also be abstract elements such as lines, shapes, degrees of brightness, or colors.

What is the purpose of composition? One easy answer is that it somehow renders a picture more "pleasing" or more "artistic." But that reply makes composition seem rather unimportant: nice to have, but not absolutely necessary. In fact, however, composition is absolutely essential in video because it helps images communicate with viewers more quickly, efficiently, and powerfully. Composition does this by:

- Organizing pictorial elements so that viewers can quickly sort them out and identify them.
- Adding emphasis to direct attention to the most important elements on the screen.
- Creating an illusory third dimension in a two-dimensional picture.

Overall, composition is such a powerful communication tool that every video maker needs to master its fundamentals. So let us see how composition affects visual organization, emphasis, and depth.

Organization in Composition

Composition organizes the elements within an image, to help viewers decode it.

Decoding an image means assigning meaning to the elements in it and identifying a relationship among them.

For example, the first image in **Figure 5-1** shows a number of small tools. Dropped in a disorganized heap, they are hard to identify. In the second image, the individual tools are easy to spot because they have been arranged in a composition. Viewers need composition to help them decode pictures, because they are unable to organize screen images as easily as they organize visual information from the real world.

Simplicity, Order, and Balance

In organizing the pictorial elements in images, composition follows the key principles of simplicity, order, and balance, **Figure 5-2**.

Figure 5-1.
Composition helps viewers "read" the image.
A—Disorganized. B—Organized

A

B

Simplicity means eliminating unnecessary objects from the image, so that the viewer has fewer things to identify. Notice that the first picture is already easier to decode, merely because the number of tools in it has been reduced.

Order means arranging objects in the image. In the center photo, the tools are even easier to recognize because they have been lined up neatly.

Balance means distributing the objects in a way that gives about equal visual "weight" to each section of the image. Also, notice that arranging the large hammer so it balances the group of smaller tools makes it stand out in the composition.

Emphasis in Composition

Organization helps viewers make sense of the elements in an image, but by itself, it does not confer special importance on any

Figure 5-2.
Principles of composition

Simplicity   **Order**   **Balance**

Composition and the Frame

We have noted that the **frame** around the image forms the border of the video world. At the same time, the frame acts as the most powerful component of visual composition. In fact, it is the frame that makes composition possible. A composition is the visual organization of a defined area and that definition is provided by the frame.

To see how this works, look at Photo A. Though the edges of this picture do form a frame of sorts, the image as a whole lacks an overall sense of composition. However, as you can see from Photos B, C, and D, we can create several different compositions, according to how we place frames around different components of the original picture.

Different compositions within a frame. A—Frame that is poorly composed. B—Composition 1. C—Composition 2. D—Composition 3. (Corel)

A

B

C

D

In addition to defining an area, the frame tells you what is **horizontal** (parallel to the horizon) and what is **vertical** (perpendicular to the horizon). In both the following images, the person is positioned upright. In the second one, however, she seems to be tilted sideways. In fact, it is the frame and not the person that has been tilted in the second shot. But because we derive our sense of vertical and horizontal from the frame, the picture continues to appear level, while the person within it seems tilted.

A portrait with a level horizon.

A portrait with an off-level horizon.

of them. That is the function of emphasis. **Emphasis** is any technique that attracts the viewer's attention to one part of a composition. Techniques of emphasis include position, relationship, significance, and contrast.

Position

You can emphasize a compositional element by the way in which you position it within the frame. In any composition, the upper left quadrant attracts the eye first, because that is where we automatically look to start reading a new page of text.

Obviously, not everyone begins reading at the upper left. Readers of Chinese or Hebrew, for example, begin the page at other points.

Psychological experiments have confirmed that in a composition, the upper left quadrant is most attractive, the upper right is next, the lower left is third, and the lower right is the least attractive. See **Figure 5-3.**

Figure 5-3.
In Western cultures, the upper-left quadrant is the most powerful part of the image.

Relationship

You can emphasize an element by placing it in relationship to other elements in the composition. These other components lead the eye to the center of interest. You can see this in **Figure 5-4**. Since the elements of video images are usually moving, a good director can exploit their ever-changing relationships.

Significance

Some compositional elements attract attention simply because they mean something to the audience. For instance, when you

Figure 5-4.
Leading lines, such as the diagonal lines of this stairway, lead the viewer's eye to the center of interest. (Sue Stinson)

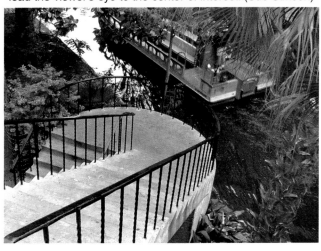

look at a photo of a celebrity, **Figure 5-5,** your eye goes immediately to the famous person because you recognize the face. It means something to you. Significance in a composition is widely used in Hollywood movies because the highly recognizable stars automatically attract viewers' attention.

Figure 5-5.
Actress Marilyn Monroe entertaining troops in Korea during the 1950s. (Archive Photos)

Emphasis through Contrast

Contrast is the technique of emphasizing one element in a picture by making it look different from the other elements. An element can be contrasted by adjusting its traits — traits that include size, shape, brightness, color, and focus.

In videography, the word *contrast* is also used in the more technical sense of difference in luminance (*brightness*) between the lightest and darkest picture elements.

Contrasting size

The bigger something is, the more it calls attention to itself, **Figure 5-6.** It is simple to make one object appear bigger than other objects of a similar size: just place it closer to the camera. Not surprisingly, important action is typically staged in the foreground, where the actors are largest.

Contrasting shape

The rectangle in **Figure 5-7** attracts attention because its shape contrasts with the circles around it.

Contrasting brightness

Light elements attract the eye more than dark ones, **Figure 5-8.** Much of the craft of video lighting involves emphasizing important elements through careful control of brightness.

Contrasting color

Perhaps the simplest form of contrast is color. The viewer's eye is attracted to elements colored differently from the prevailing hues of the overall image. In **Figure 5-9,** the red circle stands out.

Contrasting focus

Focus refers to the visual sharpness (clarity) of a pictorial element. Sharp, well-detailed elements attract viewers' attention away from soft, out-of-focus elements. Because video

Figure 5-6.
Using contrast in size to emphasize one element in a picture.

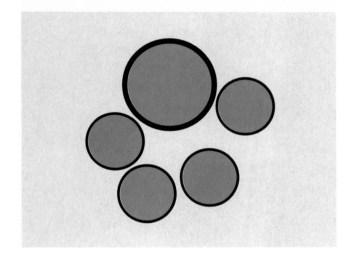

Figure 5-7.
Using contrast in shape to emphasize one element in a picture.

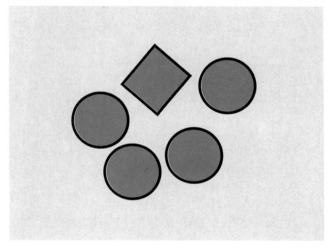

Figure 5-8.
Using contrast in brightness to emphasize one element in a picture.

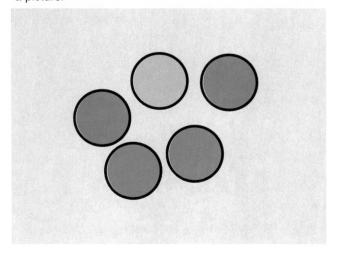

Figure 5-9.
Using contrast in color to emphasize one element in a picture.

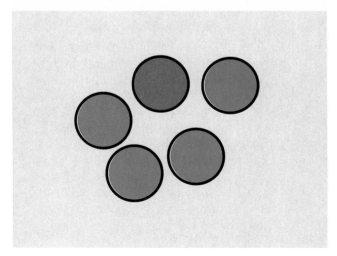

images are rarely equally crisp throughout their depth, videographers set the focus on the elements they want to emphasize. Although the pink and yellow flowers in the background of **Figure 5-10** are bright and colorful, they have been de-emphasized by throwing them out of focus. Sometimes you will see the focus change in the middle of a shot, to shift attention from one element to another.

Figure 5-10.
Using contrast in focus to emphasize one element in a picture. (Sue Stinson)

Great painters like Renoir often achieved the effect of selective focus by painting important picture elements in fine detail and leaving less important ones sketchy and less distinct.

Depth in Composition

As we noted in Chapter 3, the video world has only two true dimensions: height and breadth. On the essentially flat monitor screen, what appears to be depth is only an illusion. Since most video programs are intended to mirror the actual world, depth-enhancing techniques play an important role in pictorial composition. Collectively, these are called perspective.

Perspective

Perspective is a group of techniques used to suggest the presence of depth on a two-dimensional surface — a surface such as a painting, a photograph, or a video screen. Over many centuries, artists have evolved several ways to represent three dimensions on two-dimensional surfaces. These effects will appear in your compositions

whether or not you employ them intentionally. But if you purposely apply them, you can greatly enhance the sense of depth in your images. Perspective techniques include *size, overlap, convergence, vertical position, sharpness,* and *color intensity*.

Size

In the actual world, the closer an object is, the larger it appears, **Figure 5-11.** So in a two-dimensional image, apparent size is a powerful clue to distance.

Figure 5-11.
Using apparent size as a perspective technique.

Overlap

In the actual world, one object will mask part of another if it is in front of it. So in two-dimensional compositions, an object that overlaps another is perceived to be closer, **Figure 5-12.**

Figure 5-12.
Using overlap as a perspective technique.

Figure 5-14.
Using vertical position as a perspective technique.

Convergence

In the actual world, parallel lines such as railroad tracks or the edges of roads seem to gradually come together as they recede into the distance. In two-dimensional compositions, converging lines convey a powerful sense of depth, **Figure 5-13.**

Vertical position

In the actual world, the farther away objects are, the higher they usually appear in the field of view. In **Figure 5-14,** notice that the subjects in the background are higher on the screen than the foreground objects. Also, the fence lines and horse heads gradually rise up the picture plane as they recede.

Sharpness

The farther away objects are, the more indistinct they appear, for two reasons. First,

their fine details are smaller and harder to distinguish. Second, distant objects are softened by the amount of air between them and the viewer. Because the effect is created by air, this is often called **atmospheric perspective.** This type of perspective is evident in a picture of foothills with mountains behind them, **Figure 5-15.** Each ridge appears softer and less distinct than the one in front of it.

Color intensity

The same atmosphere that softens the appearance of objects also reduces the intensity of their colors. The farther away something is, the paler or more pastel its colors appear. In **Figure 5-16,** the orange color of the runner's shirt is much more intense in the closer view at right than in the long shot at left.

Figure 5-13.
Using converging lines as a perspective technique.
(Sue Stinson)

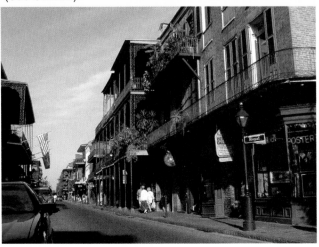

Figure 5-15.
Using decreasing sharpness as a perspective technique.

Figure 5-16.
Using color intensity as a perspective technique.

Using Perspective in Composition

In most compositions, you want to enhance the illusion of depth. You can do this by framing naturally-occurring perspective effects, especially converging lines and subject size, **Figure 5-17**.

In seeking perspective effects, you consciously exploit the principles of perspective to increase the feeling of depth.

You should also try to reinforce natural perspective by staging action in depth, **Figure 5-18.** The shot at left is visually flat and uninteresting. The one at right adds depth by moving the camera around to show the strong convergence of the lines of the building. By staging the action in depth in the actual world, the director has increased the illusion of a third dimension in the screen world.

Composing Video Images

After everything has been analyzed and explained, composition is still more an art than a set of technical procedures. There are, however, some simple techniques that you can use to dramatically improve the compositions you create.

Direct the Viewer's Eyes

Make sure that the most important subject in each shot is the most visually prominent. Look through the camera viewfinder and verify that your eye goes naturally toward the center of interest, **Figure 5-19**. Remember that the viewer has only a brief time to receive a video image and make sense of it. So as you frame each shot, verify that its visual message is clear.

Figure 5-17.
Emphasizing depth by using converging lines... and by subject size.

Figure 5-18.
Staging action in depth reinforces natural perspective.

Figure 5-19.
Receding lines direct the viewer's eye to the most important subject.

Figure 5-20.
This photo uses several forms of perspective. How many can you identify?

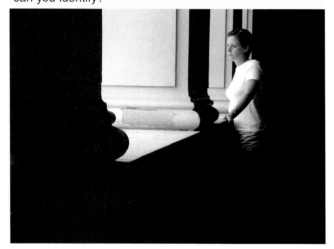

Enhance Apparent Depth

We have emphasized that video displays a two-dimensional world pretending to be three-dimensional. As you create pictorial compositions, you usually wish to sustain the illusion of that third dimension. When framing each shot, check to see that it conveys a feeling of depth. Use the forms of perspective discussed previously to enhance that feeling, **Figure 5-20.**

Use Asymmetrical Balance

Generally speaking, compositions are more pleasing when the various elements seem to balance one another — that is, they appear to have the same visual "weight." But when visual elements are balanced symmetrically, the result is often static and dull. The trick is to organize pictorial elements so that their characteristics are different and their positions are not evenly opposed. To see the difference between symmetrical and asymmetrical compositions, study **Figure 5-21.**

The elements in the first image divide the frame into neat quarters. The resulting composition is perfectly balanced, but not very interesting. In the second picture, the elements have been rearranged to create a less balanced composition. The **asymmetrical balance** of this version is more interesting.

Composition Guidelines

Pleasing compositions are often created by deploying pictorial elements to create asymmetrical arrangements. An way to create such compositions is by using the so-called "rule of thirds."

The rule of thirds

To do this, mentally fill the camera viewfinder with a tic-tac-toe grid that divides the space into three equal vertical and horizontal sections. Then create compositions in which the important pictorial elements line up with the grid.

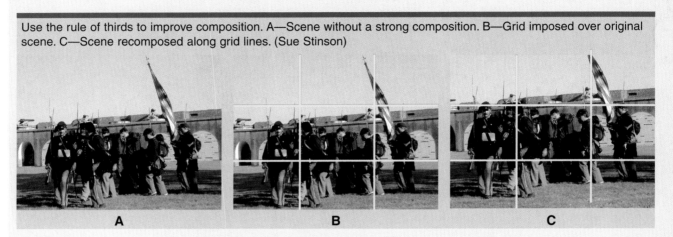

Use the rule of thirds to improve composition. A—Scene without a strong composition. B—Grid imposed over original scene. C—Scene recomposed along grid lines. (Sue Stinson)

The rule of thirds can be applied to most kinds of subjects. Note that compositions need not use every grid line or intersection.

Three compositions based on the rule of thirds. (Sue Stinson)

Breaking the rule of thirds

The rule of thirds is only a general guideline. Often you will want to organize your compositions in other ways, as the four following figures demonstrate.

(Sue Stinson)

(Sue Stinson)

(Sue Stinson)

Composing on the Picture Plane

Finally, instead of enhancing the sense of depth in a composition, you may wish to suppress it. Often called "composing on the picture plane" (screen), this approach can yield effective compositions, as you can see from the following figures.

(Sue Stinson)

Figure 5-21.
A—Symmetrical balance is static. B—Asymmetrical balance can make a more interesting composition. (Sue Stinson)

A

B

Trust Yourself

Finally and most importantly, trust your taste and instincts to guide you to good compositions. Creating pictorial composition is like driving a car. When you are just learning, you have to remember every part of a complicated process; but before you know it, driving has become so instinctive that you do it without conscious thought. The same thing happens as you make video programs. You gradually internalize the principles of composition until you can use them naturally and instinctively.

From Image to Program

This chapter on composition has focused on the design of individual images. A video program consists of many thousands of these single frames, organized into shots, scenes, and sequences. Chapter 6, *Video Language,* presents the principles behind this organization.

Technical Terms

***Brightness*:** The position of a pictorial element on a scale from black to white.

***Composition*:** The purposeful arrangement of elements in an image.

***Contrast*:** The difference between one pictorial element and others; also, the ratio of the brightest part of an image to the darkest.

***Decoding*:** Identifying and understanding the elements in a composition.

***Emphasis*:** The process of calling attention to a pictorial element.

***Focus*:** Photographically, that part of the image (measured from near to far) that appears sharp and clear; also, generally, the object of a viewer's attention.

***Leading lines*:** Lines on the picture plane that emphasize an element by pointing to it.

***Leading the eye*:** Using compositional techniques to direct the viewer's attention.

***Perspective*:** The simulation of depth in a two-dimensional image.

6 Video Language

Contents

About Video Language
Camera Angle Names
Creating Continuity
Making Transitions

Objectives

After studying this chapter, you will be able to:
- ❑ Explain the concept of camera angles.
- ❑ Name the principal types of camera angles.
- ❑ Vary shot types effectively.
- ❑ Create continuity of action.
- ❑ Select and use scene transitions.

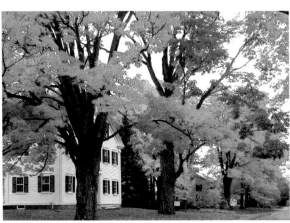

(Sue Stinson)

About Video Language

No matter how seamless videos may appear, they are really long assemblies of individual pieces, placed one after another in strings as long as one thousand units or more. These individual pieces are called shots.

A *shot* is a single, uninterrupted visual recording, a length of tape during which the camera has operated continuously. Of course, shots are not just strung together in random order. On the contrary, they are organized according to a set of rules. Collectively, these rules may be called the language of video.

A "take" is one attempt to record a shot. Slating (labeling) a single recording as 37A3 would translate to "Scene 37, shot A, take 3."

Video Language Terms

Though the analogy between video and a language like English is not perfect, it does provide a useful comparison. For example:

A *frame* is like a unit of sound (a "phoneme"), an essential building block that is usually too brief to deliver meaning by itself.

An *image* (a more or less static segment of a shot that is perceived as a picture) is like a word.

A *shot* (a continuously recorded stream of evolving images) is like a sentence. It is the shortest assemblage that conveys a complete piece of information.

A *scene* is like a paragraph. Composed of several shots (visual sentences), it conveys meaning about a single topic.

Though the terms shot and scene have separate meanings in this book, they are sometimes used interchangeably.

A *sequence* is like a chapter. It assembles a number of scenes into a longer action that is also devoted to a single (though larger) part of the narrative. The analogy between video and verbal language could be carried still further. In dramatic programs for TV, a major assembly of video sequences is called an act (just like an act in a stage play) and a complete video program could be compared to a book.

Studying Video Language

Mastering the formal language of video can be quite intriguing. Individual shots are like the building blocks in a fascinating con-struction set that is very rewarding to experiment with. This chapter presents the basic rules for using that video construction set. Since we cannot discuss video components without identifying them, our construction guide begins with the naming of camera angles.

Camera Angle Names

A *camera angle* is a distinctive, identifiable way of framing subjects from a particular position at a particular image size. Most camera angles have specific names because they are relatively standardized setups that are used again and again. This is not because video directors lack originality but because a century of film and video production has developed a certain number of angles that convey information effectively and look attractive to viewers.

Technically, a shot is a single piece of video recording, an angle is a particular view of the subject, and a setup is a distinct camera position. In actual video production, however, these words are sometimes used inter-changeably.

Usually, angles are named for one of several different sets of characteristics: subject distance, horizontal camera position, vertical camera position, lens perspective, shot purpose, and shot population.

Angle names are not standardized, so the labels used in the following discussion are only typical. For more on angle name variations, see the sidebar, What's in a name?

Figure 6-1.
A "worm's-eye" angle of a subject.

Subject Distance

The most common angle names describe the apparent distance between the camera and a standing adult human, as you can see from **Figures 6-2 through 6-11**. (These names can be confusing because, strictly speaking, they *actually* refer to the subject size in relation to the frame.) These angles are:

Extreme long shot: The figure is tiny and indistinct in a very large area.

Long shot: The figure is small in the frame (half the frame height or less) and slightly indistinct.

Medium long shot: The standing human is distinct and somewhat closer, but with considerable head and foot room.

Full shot: The standing figure fills the screen from top to bottom, often with just a small amount of head and foot room.

Three-quarter shot: The shot shows the subject from about the knees to the top of the head.

Medium shot: The shot shows the subject from the belt line to the top of the head.

Medium closeup: The shot shows the subject from about the solar plexus to the top of the head.

Closeup: The shot shows the subject from the shoulders to the top of the head.

Big closeup: The shot shows the subject from below the chin to the forehead or hairline.

Extreme closeup: The shot shows the subject from the base of the nose to the eyebrows.

Figure 6-3.
Long shot.

Figure 6-4.
Medium long shot.

Figure 6-2.
Extreme long shot.

Figure 6-5.
Full shot.

Figure 6-6.
Three-quarter shot.

Figure 6-7.
Medium shot.

Figure 6-8.
Medium closeup.

Figure 6-9.
Closeup.

Figure 6-10.
Big closeup.

Figure 6-11.
Extreme closeup.

Figure 6-12.
A head shot is always called a closeup.

Although these names all use a standing human for reference, they are also employed with both smaller and larger objects. For example, though a horse's head is obviously larger than a human's, a shot framing it would still be called a closeup, **Figure 6-12.**

Horizontal Angle

After subject distance, the most frequently used angle names are based on horizontal camera positions. In the angles named according to subject distance, as shown in Figures 6-2 through 6-11, we always see the person from the front; but the camera can view its subject from other directions as well, and the more common horizontal positions have specific names. These are shown in **Figures 6-13 through 6-17**.

Front angle: The camera faces the front of the subject.

Three-quarter angle: The camera is placed between 15 and 45 degrees around toward one side of the subject.

Profile angle: The camera is at a right angle to the original front shot.

Three-quarter rear angle: The camera is another 45 degrees around, so that the subject is now facing away.

Rear angle: The camera is directly opposite its front position and fully behind the subject.

Taken together, horizontal camera angle and subject distance provide the most typical shot descriptions; for example, "three-quarter closeup." However, an equally important component of every angle is the camera's height.

Figure 6-13.
Front angle.

Figure 6-14.
Three-quarter angle.

Figure 6-15.
Profile angle.

Figure 6-16.
Three-quarter rear angle.

Figure 6-17.
Rear angle.

What's in a Name?

If you consult various books on videography and cinematography, you will discover that there is no standard set of angle definitions — let alone the shot names that describe them. The reasons for this are simple. First, movie production developed independently in the United States, Canada, the United Kingdom, Australia, and New Zealand, and each country evolved its own terminology. Second, video, which began as broadcast television, developed its own vocabulary. It borrowed some terms from the film medium and invented others of its own. To illustrate this confusing situation, the table at right lists just some of the alternative names for common shot lengths. (The terms used in this book are in **bold** type.)

Of these alternative names, the most common variants are *extreme wide shot*, *wide shot*, and *medium wide shot* instead of extreme long shot, long shot, and medium long shot.

Notice that the same terms are sometimes applied to different image sizes. For instance, some sources label a medium closeup as a closeup and a tight closeup as an extreme closeup. One British source also includes something called a "mid shot," reaching from the mid-hip level to the top of the head.

The cutoff levels of all these shots are based on two very different theories. One theory advises videographers to avoid cutting subjects at body joints because the results look unattractive. The opposite theory (endorsed by this book) says that joints and other natural bending places like the waist are appropriate levels for framing off the subject.

While you are reading this book, you need to understand its shot definitions and terminology. Then, as you actually make videos, you will pick up the terms used in your particular production environment.

Camera Height

Shots may also be labeled by the vertical angle from which the camera views the action. The easiest way to describe standard camera heights is by pretending that the camera is at the end of a clock hand and pointed at the center of the dial, as you can see from **Figure 6-18.**

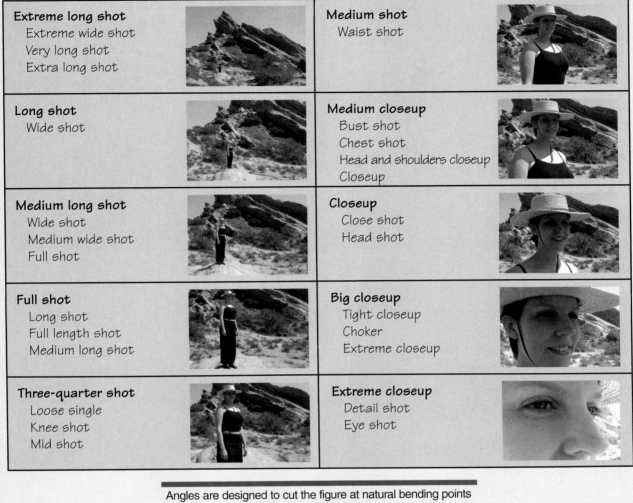

Extreme long shot Extreme wide shot Very long shot Extra long shot	**Medium shot** Waist shot
Long shot Wide shot	**Medium closeup** Bust shot Chest shot Head and shoulders closeup Closeup
Medium long shot Wide shot Medium wide shot Full shot	**Closeup** Close shot Head shot
Full shot Long shot Full length shot Medium long shot	**Big closeup** Tight closeup Choker Extreme closeup
Three-quarter shot Loose single Knee shot Mid shot	**Extreme closeup** Detail shot Eye shot

Angles are designed to cut the figure at natural bending points

Using the clock for reference, here are some common camera height names:

Bird's-eye angle: An extremely high camera position (around 1 o'clock) that simulates the view from a plane or high building, **Figure 6-19.**

High angle: A shot in which the camera is evidently higher than the eye level of a human subject (between 1:30 and 2:30), **Figure 6-20.**

Neutral angle: A shot in which the camera is more or less at the subject's eye level (3:00), **Figure 6-21.**

Low angle: A shot in which the camera is evidently below eye level (between 3:30 and 4:30), **Figure 6-22.**

Worm's-eye angle: An extremely low camera position, looking dramatically upward (5:00), **Figure 6-23.**

Figure 6-18.
Vertical angle shot names.

birdseye

high

neutral

low

wormseye

1 2 3 4 5

Figure 6-19.
Bird's-eye angle.

Figure 6-20.
High angle.

Figure 6-21.
Neutral angle.

Figure 6-22.
Low angle.

Figure 6-23.
Worm's-eye angle.

The height of an angle names the position of the camera, not the subject. For instance, the position of a dog may be very close to the ground, but in taping the pet from a standing position, you are shooting downward from a high angle.

Lens Perspective

Another type of shot name is based on the appearance created by a particular camera lens. Directors will often call for a shot by the type of lens to be used when they want a stylized rendering of perspective. See **Figures 6-24** and **6-25.**

Wide-angle: A wide-angle lens exaggerates apparent depth and dramatizes movement toward and away from the camera. Directors often employ a wide-angle shot in taping a chase, a fight, or some other sequence full of dynamic action

Normal: A normal-angle lens renders perspective approximately the way human vision perceives it, neither increasing nor reducing the apparent depth.

Telephoto: A telephoto lens compresses apparent depth and de-emphasizes movement toward and away from the camera. Telephoto lenses are used to dramatize congestion and to intensify composition on the two-dimensional screen.

Strictly speaking, the opposite of a "wide-angle" lens ought to be called a "narrow-angle" lens. But in real-world production work, the term "telephoto" is used instead.

Figure 6-25.
Scene viewed through a telephoto lens.

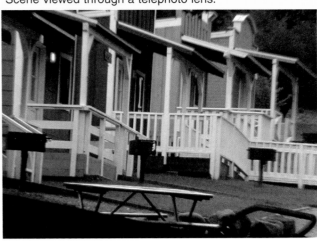

Shot Purpose

In addition to camera position, camera height, and lens type, shots are often named for the purpose they serve in the program. Here are some common examples**:**

Master shot: The purpose of a master shot, **Figure 6-26,** is to record all or most of a scene in a full shot or even longer, capturing the action from beginning to end. After the master has been taped, matching closer shots of the same action are made to replace parts of the master in the final edited version. Today, shooting complete master shots is often considered old-fashioned.

Establishing shot: The purpose of an establishing shot is to orient viewers to the general scene and the performers in it. Though beginning a sequence with an establishing shot is also considered old-fashioned, it is often helpful to introduce one early in a sequence.

Figure 6-24.
Scene viewed through a wide-angle lens.

Figure 6-26.
A master shot records a scene from beginning to end.

Since an establishing shot shows all the important parts and players in a scene, it is sometimes the beginning section of a master shot.

Reverse shot: The purpose of a reverse angle is to show the action from a point of view nearly opposite that of the main camera position, **Figure 6-27.** The position is *nearly,* but not fully, the opposite point of view because the camera usually stays on the same side of an imaginary action line to preserve screen direction.

Over-the-shoulder shot: The purpose of an over-the-shoulder shot, **Figure 6-28,** is to include part of one performer in the foreground while focusing on another performer. In addition to controlling emphasis, an over-the-shoulder shot enhances the feeling of depth.

Cutaway shot: The purpose of a cutaway shot is to show the audience something outside the principal action, or to reveal something from an on-screen person's point of view. For example, if we see several angles of a man mowing his lawn and then a shot of a dog lying in the uncut grass, the dog is a cutaway shot, **Figure 6-29.**

Insert shot: The purpose of an insert is to show a small detail of the action, often from the point of view of a person on the screen. The middle frame in **Figure 6-30** is an insert because it shows the steering wheel from the driver's point of view. Because an insert often serves the same functions as a cutaway, it is sometimes called a "cut-in."

Figure 6-28.
An over-the-shoulder shot.

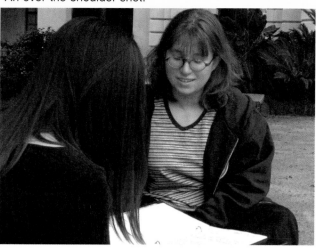

POV shot: The purpose of a POV (point-of-view) shot is to show the audience what someone on the screen is seeing. The insert shown in Figure 6-30 is from the driver's POV.

Glance-object shot. Often, the cutaway, insert, and POV shots are used with other angles to make pairs of shots that some critics call "glance-object," **Figure 6-31.** This term means just what its name implies. In the first (glance) shot, a performer looks at something off screen. In the second (object) shot, we see the person, place, or object the performer was looking at.

Shot Population

Finally, shots may be labeled according to how many performers are in them:

Single: A shot showing one person.

Two-shot: A shot showing two people.

Figure 6-27.
Reverse shot. Left, the original angle. Right, the reverse angle.

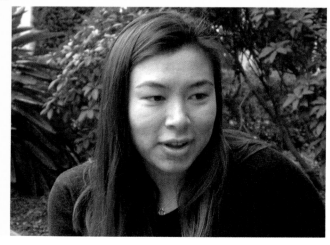

Figure 6-29.
The third frame in this sequence is a cutaway shot.

Figure 6-30.
The middle frame in this sequence is an insert.

Figure 6-31.
A—The subject checks his watch. B—He then looks offscreen at ... C—the "object" of his glance.

| A | B | C |

Three-shot: A shot showing three people. See **Figure 6-32**.

By custom, a one-person angle is not called a "one-shot," but simply a "single."

Note that these terms number only the principal performers. For example, a shot of two people having dinner with other restaurant diners in the background could still be called a two-shot.

Shot Name Confusions

Shot names can be confusing at first, for several reasons. Many shot names are synonymous with the camera angles from which they are made ("low angle") — but others are not ("reverse"). Shots are often given multiple names. For instance, a director might call for a "neutral over-the-shoulder two-shot," or a "high-angle POV closeup." Shots may be identified by different names.

Figure 6-32.
A single, a two-shot, and a three-shot.

For example, if you have just made an "over-the-shoulder two-shot," asking for a "reverse" indicates that you want *another* over-the-shoulder two-shot, from the opposite point of view. Finally, shots often have different names in different countries (U.S., U.K.), in different media (video, film), in different production centers (New York, Hollywood), or and even in different studios in the same area.

In practice, however, you will soon pick up the shot names favored in the environment where you work.

To add to the confusion of names, some people use "scene" interchangeably with "shot." In this book, a scene is a short, single piece of action, usually conveyed through a number of consecutive shots.

Creating Continuity

If the "words" in the language of video are shots, then video "sentences" are scenes made of several successive shots, **Figure 6-33.** Why break the action of a scene into separate shots? Why not simply record everything from start to finish in one continuous piece of video? The most important reason is to show each individual part of the action from the best possible position. This would be impossible to do if the camera were limited to one continuous take. Separate shots also enhance the interest of the material by providing visual variety.

In most video programs, you wish to conceal the fact that you are constantly changing camera angles. Every time viewers notice a new angle they are briefly distracted from the program content; so the goal is to make the action appear to happen in a single, continuous flow. The process of doing this is called *continuity*. In creating video continuity, you stage each shot so that it can be combined unobtrusively with the shots that precede and follow it. The key requirement for doing this is *matching action*. In matching action, you make the incoming shot appear to begin at precisely the point where the outgoing shot ends.

Of course, the action is never truly continuous (unless you are editing shots from two cameras recording simultaneously). In fact, apparently uninterrupted action is an illusion created by a collaboration between the director and the editor.

The continuity described here is the classic Hollywood style that has become the worldwide standard for commercial production.

Varying Shots

It might seem that the best way to conceal a change in shots would be to make the new angle as much as possible like the old one, as in **Figure 6-34.** But as you can see, the opposite is true. Instead of two shots that cut together invisibly, the result looks like a single shot with a piece chopped out of its middle. This is called a *jump cut,* because the subject seems to jump abruptly on the screen.

Editors use the term "cut together" to describe how successfully one shot follows another.

To make a smooth edit, the technique is to match the action closely, while decisively changing the camera angle. See **Figure 6-35.**

Generally, this means changing at least two of the angle's three major characteristics: camera position, camera height, and subject size. Unlike Figure 6-34, both **Figure 6-36** and **Figure 6-37** *do* change one trait out of three. However, altering only a single trait still results in an undesirable jump cut that calls attention to the edit. To achieve a smooth edit, a new camera setup should change *two* angle traits, most often the image size plus either the camera position or height.

Figure 6-33.
On screen, what appears to be continuous action is actually constructed of multiple shots.

A setup is a completely new camera location, including the lighting and the microphone position.

Examples of effective old/new angle combinations are shown in **Figure 6-38** and **Figure 6-39.**

Figure 6-34.
A too-similar angle makes an obvious cut.

Figure 6-35.
A change in angle conceals the cut.

Figure 6-36.
Changing only the vertical angle creates a jump cut.

Figure 6-37.
Changing only the image size also creates a jump cut.

Figure 6-38.
Changing to a new image size and horizontal angle.

Figure 6-39.
Changing to a new image size and vertical angle.

Matching Action

While the angle should change decisively from one shot to the next, the *action* should be closely matched, to make the second shot seem to begin exactly where the first shot ends. There are two basic ways to match action. The first is to have the performer repeat part of the action from the first shot in the second shot. In **Figure 6-40,** for example, the subject pours milk into a mixing bowl, repeating this action in each of two shots. In the establishing shot, she raises the milk carton over the bowl. In the second shot, she pours the milk. In the third shot, the subject tilts the carton upright and sets it down. If the edits are made correctly, the three different shots will appear to display a single continuous action.

A second (and easier) way to synchronize action is by concealing the match point.

A match point in two shots that record the same action is any point at which the editor can cut from one shot to the other, continuing the action without an apparent break.

In **Figure 6-41**, the performer exits the frame, leaving the shot empty. The next shot starts with an empty frame, and then the performer enters. Though the shots may have been made in completely different locations, the action appears continuous. The performer does not have to both exit the first shot and enter the second one. Typically, an actor will leave the first shot and then be shown again as the second shot begins — or vice versa.

Making Transitions

Up to this point, we have discussed the language of video at the level of "sentences" (shots) and "paragraphs" (scenes). Now we need to add a few rules for making transitions between "chapters." In video language, a chapter is a sequence: (a program component assembled from several related scenes.) The conventions for transitions from one sequence to another were established long ago and were strictly observed in classic Hollywood movies. Today, however, these rules are broken as often as they are observed.

Classic Hollywood Transitions

With few exceptions, traditional movies have marked transitions with two effects, fades and dissolves.

Silent films also used an effect called an iris out, in which a black screen gradually revealed an image in an ever-expanding circle. An iris in reversed the effect.

Figure 6-40.
The subject begins pouring …   finishes pouring …   and sets the carton down.

Figure 6-41.
In the first shot, the subject leaves an empty frame, then enters an empty frame in the second shot.

Video Program Components

We have identified shots, scenes, sequences, and acts as components of a video **program**; and we have established that a shot is a single, uninterrupted recording. But what do the other terms mean? To obtain a feel for these different program components, imagine a dramatic hour-long TV show about a daring museum robbery.

Program

The program includes the entire story: planning the robbery, committing the deed, fleeing with the loot, and finally being captured and jailed.

Act

Typically around 10-15 minutes in length, an act is devoted to each of the four main parts of the story outlined above. In Act Two, for example, we see the entire museum robbery, from approach to escape. An act contains several — even many — separate sequences.

Sequence

A sequence is a major component of an act and has its own beginning, middle, and end. One sequence in the museum robbery act might be breaking in through the roof. First the robbers cut a hole in the roof, then they anchor a climbing rope to a chimney and drop the rope through the hole. Two men climb down the rope while a third robber remains on the roof as lookout. Notice that this sequence is composed of several different actions, each of which is a scene.

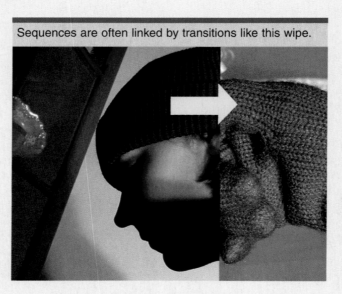

Sequences are often linked by transitions like this wipe.

Scene

In the sequence of breaking in through the roof, one scene shows the anchoring of the climbing rope. This scene is built up from several individual shots.

Shot

A shot is a single uninterrupted recording. The rope-anchoring scene might require three separate shots. In a medium shot, a robber loops the rope around the chimney. In a closeup insert, he ties a knot in the rope. In a full shot, he tosses the other end of the rope out of frame. The camera pans to follow the rope, revealing a second robber dropping its end through the roof hole. (Remember: a "take" is not a program component, but only a single attempt to record a shot.)

Image

The last shot in the rope-tying scene contains two distinct pictures: first, the man throwing the rope and then, the second man lowering it down the hole. Since the shot includes two quite different pieces of visual information, we may say that it contains two images. A long moving shot may consist of a great many identifiably individual images.

Frame

For completeness, we should include the still picture called the frame. Each second of video consists of 30 frames (in the North American NTSC format). However, a frame is too brief to be used as a distinct video component, except in very special cases.

A *fade-in,* **Figure 6-42,** begins with a black screen, which lightens gradually until the image reaches full brightness. A *fade-out* is the exact opposite. Fades mark the beginnings and endings of major program segments. For example, most commercial TV programs fade-out before each commercial break and then resume by fading in again.

A *dissolve* (often called a "mix" in video) is an effect in which one image is gradually replaced by another, **Figure 6-43.** A dissolve, in fact, is a fade-in superimposed over a fade-out. A dissolve is used instead of a fade to indicate a shorter break in the action or a less decisive transition in the story.

A *wipe* is an effect in which a line moves steadily across the screen, progressively replacing the old image ahead of it with the new one behind it, **Figure 6-44.** Though a wipe may move along any axis, it is typically a vertical line that progresses from left to right. After falling out of fashion for some years, wipes are once again quite popular.

Modern Transitions

Today's audiences are so well-trained to follow story continuity that fades and dissolves are used less often, though fades almost always begin and end a program. Instead, editors use straight cuts or, sometimes, digital video effects.

Today, fades and dissolves are also created digitally.

A *digital video effect (DVE)* is any computer-generated transition from one shot to another, **Figures 6-45** and **6-46.** Modern switchers offer many different types, including:

- *Flips,* in which the screen appears to revolve, as if to show its other side.
- *Fly-ins,* in which the incoming picture swoops to the center of the screen, growing from a tiny dot until it fills the frame completely.
- *Rotations,* in which geometric forms with the outgoing shot on one face revolve to reveal the incoming shot on another face.

Figure 6-42.
A fade-in and a fade-out are exact opposites. (Sue Stinson)

Figure 6-43.
A dissolve gradually replaces one image with another.

Figure 6-44.
A wipe is a traditional form of transition. (Sue Stinson)

Figure 6-45.
A digital rotation. (Sue Stinson)

Figure 6-46.
A digital page return. (Sue Stinson)

In addition, there are hundreds of other DVEs available — far more than an editor might ever use.

In this respect, DVEs are like the thousands of type faces available for word processing and desktop publishing. Typically, people settle on a few favorites, reserving the others for occasional use in special situations.

Digital video effects defy the main rule of editing, that transitions should be unobtrusive. On the contrary, DVEs purposely emphasize transitions by dramatizing them. Used judiciously, these arresting visuals add excitement and punch to a program. If they are overused, however, they soon grow tiresome and annoying.

DVEs are lavishly employed in TV commercials and music videos, however. Commercials are very brief, sometimes as short as 5 seconds. They need to get viewers' attention quickly, and DVEs are effective attention-grabbers. Because commercials are so short, their rapid-fire effects don't last long enough to wear viewers out.

As for music videos, these programs often use the music as an excuse to explore the possibilities of the video medium. This means that they don't always play by the rules of video grammar. At their best, music videos and other experimental programs may be compared to poems. Just as poets take "poetic license" with the rules of verbal language, so video artists sometimes use camera angles, editing continuity, and transition effects without regard to the normal rules of the video medium.

Playing by the Rules

You can disregard the rules of video language when you make a program like a music video, or, for that matter, when you make any other type of video. Nevertheless, you need to learn and practice the language of video until you are thoroughly at home with it. Remember that even the most experimental art is grounded in a mastery of classical technique.

Though the artist Picasso usually created "unrealistic" images, he was a master draftsman who could execute highly realistic works when he chose to do so.

Video Language in Action

This simple sequence demonstrates the wide variety of shot names commonly used in making videos. To include every name would require three times as many images.

Establishing shot

Two-shot

Over-the-shoulder shot

Reverse

Insert

Profile shot

Medium closeup

Single

High-angle

Glance

Object (cutaway)

Big closeup

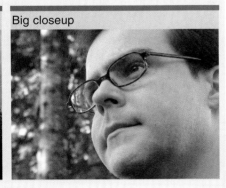

Technical Terms

Act: A major section (usually between 10 and 45 minutes) of a longer program.

Camera angle: The position from which a shot is taken, described by horizontal angle, vertical angle, and subject distance.

Continuity: The organization of video material into a coherent presentation.

Cut together: A term with two meanings: 1) to follow one shot with another; 2) to select edit points on outgoing and incoming shots so that an edit is not apparent.

Digital video effect (DVE): Informally, any digitally-created transitional device other than a fade or dissolve. (Technically, fades and dissolves are usually digital, too).

Dissolve: A fade-in that coincides with a fade-out, so that the incoming shot gradually replaces the outgoing shot. Typically used as a transition between sequences that are fairly closely related.

Fade-in: A transition in which the image begins as pure black and gradually lightens to full brightness. Used to signal the start of a major section such as an act or an entire program.

Fade-out: A transition in which the image begins at full brightness and gradually darkens to pure black. Used to signal the end of a major section such as an act or an entire program.

Frame: A single still picture, 30 of which make a second of NTSC video. (Also, the border around the image.)

Image: A single unit of visual information. An image may last for many frames, until the subject, the camera, or both, create a new image by moving. Most shots contain several identifiable images.

Jump cut: An edit in which the incoming shot is too similar visually to the outgoing shot.

Match point: The places, in two shots, where they can be cut together to make the action appear continuous.

Point of view (POV): A vantage point from which the camera records a shot. Unlike a camera *angle*, a point of view is not described by subject distance ("closeup," etc.) and unlike a *setup*, a point of view is not concerned with production equipment.

Program: Any complete video presentation, from a five-second commercial to a movie two or more hours long.

Scene: A short segment of program content, usually made up of several related shots.

Sequence: A longer segment of program content, usually consisting of several related scenes.

Setup: An arrangement of production equipment (typically camera, microphone, and lighting) placed to record shots from a certain point of view.

Shot: A single continuous recording. In editing, shot A may be interrupted by shot B before resuming. When this happens, the second part of the original shot A may be considered a new shot.

Telephoto: A lens or a setting on a zoom lens that magnifies subjects and minimizes apparent depth by filling the frame with a narrow angle of view.

Wide-angle: A lens or a setting on a zoom lens that minimizes subjects and magnifies apparent depth by filling the frame with a wide angle of view.

Wipe: A transition between sequences in which a line moves across the screen, progressively covering the outgoing shot before it with the incoming shot behind it.

7 Video Sound

Contents

About Video Sound
Delivering Information
Conveying Implications
Strengthening Continuity
Evoking Feelings

Objectives

After studying this chapter, you will be able to:

❑ List the most important functions of audio (sound tracks).

❑ Explain the major contributions that sound makes to video programs.

❑ Listen analytically to video sound tracks.

❑ Describe the component parts of a typical composite sound track.

❑ Discuss the principal roles of music in video programs.

(Corel)

About Video Sound

Sound is vitally important in the medium of video. It communicates so powerfully that you can create successful programs of audio without video (which, of course, is called *radio*), but not video without audio. Even so-called silent films were not truly soundless. Because stories unfolding in absolute silence conveyed an eerie feeling, even the smallest silent movie theaters showed their programs with musical accompaniment.

And yet, sound is often undervalued in video production. In amateur programs especially, the finished audio track may be nothing more than whatever the camcorder's microphone happened to pick up.

Sound is what you record and hear, while audio is the audible half of a program (as opposed to "video"). In practice, the terms sound and audio are often used interchangeably.

Quality audio depends on both a mastery of the technical processes and an understanding of how sound contributes to the effect of a video program. The technical processes are covered in later chapters on sound recording and editing. In this chapter we focus on how to use sound as a tool to communicate information and stir emotion. Along the way, we will explain the principal components of a typical sound track, consider the role of music in video, and look briefly at the history of audio recording. We will begin with sound's most important role: *delivering information*.

Delivering Information

The biggest task that sound performs is delivering information, most often through dialogue spoken by on-screen performers or the words of an unseen narrator. The audio track also provides information through sound effects. As we will see, these humble noises laid down by sound editors form a remarkably eloquent (and economical) method of communicating.

To "lay down a track" means to record one or more audio components. To "lay in" an individual piece of audio means to add it to an audio track in postproduction.

Dialogue

Video is essentially a visual medium, but part of good scriptwriting lies in knowing when it is more efficient to tell something than to show it. Since reading lengthy on-screen titles is tiresome, "telling" typically involves some form of audible speech, usually *dialogue*, which is the on-screen conversation between characters, **Figure 7-1.**

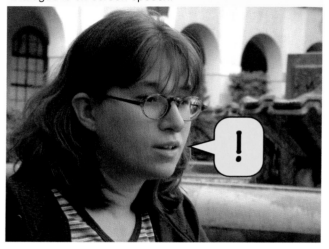

Figure 7-1.
Dialogue is on-screen speech.

Though "dialogue" properly refers to conversations between two or more performers, it is commonly used to label all on-screen speech.

Dialogue often delivers information explicitly. "I'm going to the zoo" tells us, in a straightforward way, where the speaker is headed. Dialogue may also contain implicit information. "I'm going back to the zoo," also tells us that the speaker has come from the zoo, while, "I'm going to the zoo again" indicates that the speaker has been there at some time in the past. If a second character says, "You're not going to the zoo again?" we learn three things: that the first character is going to the zoo, that he or she has been there often, and that the second character disapproves of these repeated visits. This dialogue has delivered three pieces of information in seven words and two seconds, working far more economically than visuals could in this case.

In a well-directed story video, dialogue also provides information about emotions and character. If "You're not going to the zoo again?" is said with fond amusement, it conveys certain things about the speaker's feelings. But if the line is delivered with weary resignation instead, or perhaps in a resentful whine, the speaker's feelings appear quite different.

Dialogue is also important in many nonfiction videos, where it often takes the form of interviews. Some interviews are presented as conversations between two people on-screen. (This approach is common in news and discussion programs.) In other cases, the interview is conducted and edited so that the interviewer is invisible and the questions are unheard, **Figure 7-2.** The interviewee seems to be speaking only to the viewer.

Figure 7-2.
In the contemporary interview style, only the subject appears on screen. (Corel)

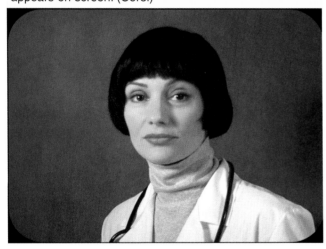

Narration

Often, a person being interviewed begins on screen, but after a few moments the visual component of the interview is replaced by footage that illustrates what the person is talking about, while his or her voice continues on the sound track. This is called *voiceover* (usually abbreviated "V.O." in scripts).

The terms "offscreen," "off camera," and "V.O." are essentially interchangeable.

Voiceover interviews are widely used in documentary programs, where they may alternate with fully scripted narration. Spoken by professional voiceover actors, narration is by far the most efficient way of delivering verbal information. A good script

can pack a great deal into a short space, as you can see by the brief excerpt shown in **Figure 7-3.**

Figure 7-3.
An excerpt from a script.

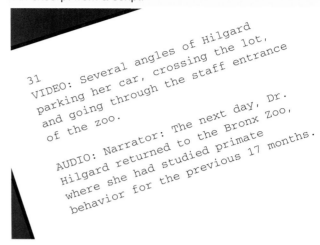

31
VIDEO: Several angles of Hilgard parking her car, crossing the lot, and going through the staff entrance of the zoo.

AUDIO: Narrator: The next day, Dr. Hilgard returned to the Bronx Zoo, where she had studied primate behavior for the previous 17 months.

If you take a moment to study the narrator's sentence, you will discover that just 22 words deliver ten pieces of information:

1. The subject is female.
2. Her name is Hilgard.
3. She has a doctorate.
4. She went to a zoo.
5. It was the Bronx Zoo.
6. She had been there previously.
7. She had studied there.
8. Her study was in primate behavior.
9. Her study lasted 17 months.
10. The study period was quite recent.

The visuals, on the other hand, are essentially meaningless filler included to occupy the screen while the narration is spoken.

Another reason for narration's power lies in the skill of the professional narrator. Using pace, inflection, and emphasis, a narrator organizes and highlights text in the process of speaking it. This makes the narration easier to understand and more interesting to listen to. If you have ever winced at the sound of an amateur reading a text in a droning monotone, you will appreciate the complex techniques involved in speaking narration with professional skill.

Sound Effects

Sound effects are the noises that come from the world on the screen. Some are recorded with the video and consist of the actual sounds produced by the on-screen action. Many others are laid in by the sound editor in postproduction, **Figure 7-4.**

Figure 7-4.
Waveform displayed by a digital sound editing program. (Sound Forge)

Typically, the sound effects synchronized with on-screen action are designed to heighten the sense of reality. To see how this works, try muting your TV sound during a sequence of vigorous action such as a car chase or a fight. Notice how the on-screen activities suddenly grow remote and uninvolving.

Although sound effects are typically used to heighten the realism of visual action, they can also deliver information independently of the video. For example, imagine a car chase during which our hero's brakes suddenly fail. The director communicates this information with an insert, a close shot of a foot repeatedly punching a brake pedal. The problem with this is that the foot movement looks no different from that of heavy braking, so the shot does not convey the essential information that the car's brakes have failed.

To supply this information, the sound editor lays in repeated sound effects of the pedal clanking on the floorboard of the car. It is that sound, not the picture, that tells the audience the brakes are useless, **Figure 7-5.**

Conveying Implications

Although sound is often used to supplement the video, its most important informational role is to tell you about things that are not on screen —things that exist only by implication. Remember the first law of video space: what is outside the frame does not exist, *unless that existence is implied.* If you provide the audience with evidence that something they cannot see is nonetheless there, they will believe it.

Sound Implies Existence

By far the easiest way to imply the presence of things off screen is through sound. In **Figure 7-6,** for example, a mother says goodbye to her daughter and watches her ride away.

But what, exactly, is the daughter riding in or on? We can't tell from the visuals because her transportation remains outside the frame.

Now suppose we add sound effects to the sequence, as **Figure 7-7.**

Figure 7-5.
By itself, the video communicates only "braking." With an added sound effect, it communicates "brakes failed!"

Figure 7-6.
The mother and daughter embrace ...   the daughter leaves the frame...   and her mother watches her ride away.

Figure 7-7.
SFX: A bus horn honks impatiently.
DAUGHTER: G'bye, Momma
MOTHER: Honey, you take care, y'hear? ...   SFX: the hiss of bus doors opening ...   SFX: ...and then closing; followed by the diesel rumble of a bus engine, fading in the distance.

In video scripts, "SFX" is the standard abbreviation for "sound effect."

With only a honk, a hiss, and an engine roar, we have constructed a complete bus, **Figure 7-8,** and added it to the scene; a bus whose existence is only implied, and implied exclusively by sounds.

Figure 7-8.
A phantom bus has been created entirely by sound effects. (Sue Stinson)

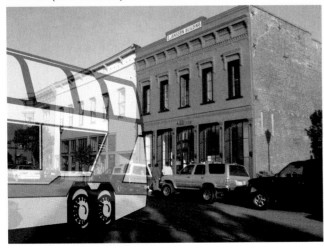

We could change the woman's transportation just by substituting different effects:

● A brass bell chimes over an idling speedboat motor. The motor revs up and then gradually fades, leaving the sound of gulls and water lapping around a pier.
● A conductor calls, "*Booooard!*" and we hear the first slow chuffs of a big steam locomotive. The puffing grows louder and faster, then diminishes in the distance, with the wail of a whistle.
● The motor of a single-engine plane idles smoothly. After a moment, the door chunks shut, the engine revs, and the sound moves farther away as the plane starts to taxi down the runway.

By using sound effects alone, we could supply the daughter with four completely different modes of transportation.

Sound Implies Locale

With the bus and the airplane we can only assume that the scene is set on a road or an airstrip. In the case of the train, however, the conductor's call supplies the train station for us. In the same way, the gulls and lapping water inform us that we are on a boat dock.

The Perception of Sound

Sound does not really exist in nature. What we think of as "a sound" is actually a disturbance of the air, moving in a pattern of waves. These waves apply rapidly shifting air pressures to our ears, which create nerve impulses, which our brains organize and interpret as "sound."

Sound in the actual world

Human hearing is marvelously acute and subtle, because our brains are skilled at organizing, processing, and interpreting the audio babble that continuously assaults our ears. We can regulate overall volume, adjusting our tolerance for loudness to suit the environment. For instance, imagine driving at 65 miles per hour with the car radio playing. When you slow to 30 mph, the radio suddenly sounds uncomfortably loud, even though the volume has not increased. The noisy radio did not seem too loud at 65 mph, because your brain can adjust for the higher overall sound levels of high-speed driving.

We can also listen selectively, processing some parts of the overall sound but ignoring others. For example, most people quickly filter out the drone of an air conditioner until they don't notice it at all. On the other hand, parents can often hear the faint cries of a baby two rooms away, even through the sound of a TV program. With the air conditioning, they suppress and ignore the sound; but with the baby, they isolate and recognize the sound, despite the competition from other noise. Even though people *hear* everything, they *listen* selectively.

The listener hears the TV sound and the baby's cry, but filters out the air conditioner noise.

Sound from video programs

Unfortunately, we do not seem able to listen to an audio track as selectively as we listen to real-world sound. This creates both a problem and an opportunity for video makers. The problem is that the sound editor must do the job that our brains do with real-world sound: regulate volume and filter out unwanted sounds, while isolating and emphasizing wanted ones. The opportunity lies in the brain's ability to recognize and process many sounds at once. This allows editors to build audio programs out of many layers of audio. In complex, big-budget productions, individual sound track elements can number in the dozens.

Until recently, complex audio was uncommon in video programs because the hardware required to play back, synchronize, and mix audio tracks on videotape was very expensive. The alternative of **mixing** a few tracks at a time and then remixing the subassemblies resulted in loss of audio quality. (Larger studios could build up multiple tracks on one- or two-inch audiotape.) With the establishment of digital recording, however, these difficulties have disappeared, and videotape-based audio can now match the sophistication of audio for film.

You can easily think of the locations that are established by sounds like the crackle and roar of a forest fire, the hiss of rain and rattle of thunder, or the deafening roar of a steel mill, **Figure 7-9**. We could multiply examples but the point is clear: sound is psychologically powerful in evoking a sense of place.

Figure 7-9.
The sounds of a steel mill are as overwhelming as its images. (Corel)

Sound Implies Relationships

Sound is very useful in bringing together and unifying program components that were originally shot separately. For example, look carefully at the sound elements supporting the visuals in **Figure 7-10**.

The exterior shots of the truck were probably made on location with stunt doubles doing the driving. The interiors with Bob and Bill were shot separately, with their pickup towed safely behind a camera truck. To meld these different times and places into a single sequence, the sound editors used three common techniques:

● They laid some of the actors' dialogue in as offscreen voiceovers accompanying the exteriors.

● They continued the car sound effects over shots of the auto's interior.

● They varied the volume, perspective, and quality of the dialogue and sound effects from shot to shot to match the different viewpoints of the audience.

The combination of audio styling and matched-action cutting reinforces the illusion of a single, continuous sequence.

Figure 7-10.
BOB: Yer goin' too fast, Bill!
SFX: (muted) engine roar.

BOB: (O.S., faint).That's a field!
SFX: (loud) engine, gravel, continue.

BILL: (O.S., faint) Not fast enough!
SFX: (loud) engine roar, gravel spraying.

BOB: (muffled by windshield) Now ya done it!
SFX: (loud) engine, springs creaking, rocks hitting metal.

BILL: (muffled by window) Hey, there's a shortcut.
SFX: (loud) engine continues.

BOB: (O.S., faint) We're stuck
SFX: (loud, close) engine, hiss of broken radiator.

Layers of Sound

The audio part of a video program is usually built up from several different sound tracks. These individual components can vary considerably in both their level of reality and their function in the overall sound track.

Levels of reality

Some sounds are absolutely authentic, some are completely artificial, and some fall in between these two extremes. Listed in order of reality, we find:

- *Live sound.* This audio is recorded simultaneously with the video and is often called the **production track**. Live sound includes spoken dialogue, the noises created by the action, and the ambient sounds of the shooting location.

- *Sweetened sound.* This is live audio that has been processed in postproduction to improve its quality. In some cases, a process called **equalization** strengthens certain sound frequencies (pitches) while relatively weakening others. Often, extra live sound is added to conceal the audio differences between different shots.

- *Foley sound.* This is a track of sound effects recorded live in a special studio while the video is displayed, so that Foley technicians can synchronize the sounds they are creating with the program in real time. For example, a Foley studio may have several sections of floor covered variously with gravel, asphalt, concrete, or tile, for use in recording footstep sound effects synchronized with the footfalls of on-screen actors walking on similar material.

A Foley setup for recording footsteps on different surfaces.

- *Library sound.* This is audio that is not created specifically for a particular program, but is stored on compact disks for use where needed. Some sound libraries contain thousands of different effects. General background sounds such as waves or forest noises or city traffic are often recorded on audiotape cartridges or digital "loops."

- *Synthesized sound.* This is digital audio that is created on a computer instead of being recorded acoustically.

Audio functions

Audio tracks can also be classified by their functions. Here are some of the most common uses for sound:

- *Production sound.* As noted, this is sound that is recorded with the video.

- *Presence.* Often called room tone, presence is recorded at a shooting location while the cast and crew remain perfectly still. The result is a recording of the location's ongoing background sounds, whether birds, distant traffic, air conditioners, or anything else. Presence is used to fill gaps in the production track left when unwanted sounds are cut out.

- *Background sound.* This is an ongoing sound effect like the chatter of diners and the tinkle of china and silver in a restaurant. When the background track is mixed with the live production tracks, shot-to-shot changes in sound quality are smoothed over. Like presence, background sound smoothes out differences in the production track. But it is also intended to supply sound that was not present during production recording.

- *Sound effects.* Sound effects (often abbreviated "SFX".) are specific sounds such as walking, gunfire, or car engines that are added in postproduction, whether from Foley recording or from a sound effects library.

Thousands of sound effects are available on CD-ROM disks.

No	Effect	Disk	Track	Time
			72	00:0
		21	73	00:
		21	74	00
2115	Gunshot: heavy caliber	21	73	
6405	Gunshot: light caliber	21	76	
0213	Gunshot: shotgun blast	21	53	
0799	Gunshot: semi-automatic	12	56	
1944	Gunshots: multiple	12	07	
4363	Machine Gun: short bursts	17	08	
	Machine gun: sustained fire	17		

- *Dialogue replacement.* This is a process by which actors rerecord dialogue in a studio, synchronizing it to the lip movements of performers as played back on a monitor or screen. The procedure is still called "looping" because in predigital days it was accomplished by splicing the film containing a few lines of dialogue into an endless, head-to-tail loop, which could be projected continuously.

- *Music.* Music is added to the sound track to enhance continuity and communicate feeling. Music composed for a specific program may be timed right down to the frame. Library music (precomposed and stored selections) may be selected by length, or else faded in, faded out, or both, in order to time it to the picture. Digital music loops contain embedded information that allows them to be adjusted precisely to fit any length required.

Strengthening Continuity

Sound is a great smoother of rough connections. In the example of Bill and Bob, Figure 7-10, those connections are between shots in a sequence. Sound is also used to tie separate sequences together through a technique called a split edit.

Splits edits are also discussed in Chapter 4, Video Time.

The Split Edit

A **split edit** is a transition from one shot to another in which video and audio do not change simultaneously. Either the incoming video is accompanied by a few extra seconds of the outgoing audio or, conversely, the incoming audio is laid over the last part of the outgoing video. Split edits are usually, though not always, used during transitions between two sequences. To see how split edits work, we return to Bob and Bill.

Since the next four trios of pictures are identical, pay close attention to their captions, which demonstrate the different options for split edits.

Straight cut version

For reference, **Figure 7-11** shows a **straight cut** (without a split edit). Notice that, in the middle shot, Bill's picture and sound conclude together. In this straight cut version, the joke is plain but heavy-handed.

Split edit, video leading

In **Figure 7-12**, the video changes to the new sequence ahead of the audio. We cut to Bob sitting in the darkness (last shot) as Bill's line from the preceding scene is completed in voiceover. Placing the old line over the new shot adds an ironic comment.

Split edit, audio leading

Figure 7-13 shows the opposite form of split edit. In this version, we hear the obvious sounds of night creatures as Bill completes his line in the middle shot. Instead of conveying a sense of irony, like Figure 7-12, this opposite approach allows the audience to anticipate the joke.

Two-way split edit

Figure 7-14 shows the audio split both forward and backward. The sound effects for the incoming (night) sequence begin offscreen

Figure 7-11.
BOB: (O.S., faint) We're stuck!
SFX: (loud, close) Engine, hiss of broken radiator.

BILL: Aw, simmer down. Someone'll come along any minute.

SFX: Night frog/cricket sounds: ribbet, ribbet, ribbet.

Figure 7-12.
BOB: (O.S., faint) We're stuck.
SFX: (loud, close) Engine, hiss of broken radiator.

BILL: Aw, simmer down.

BILL: (O.S) Someone'll come along any minute.
SFX: Night frog/cricket sounds: ribbet, ribbet, ribbet.

Figure 7-13.
BOB: (O.S., faint) We're stuck.
SFX: (loud, close) Engine, hiss of broken radiator.

BILL: Aw, simmer down.
SFX: Night frog/cricket sounds: ribbet, ribbet, ribbet.
BILL: Someone'll come along any minute.

SFX: night sounds continue.

over the outgoing (day) sequence, then the day-sequence dialogue continues, offscreen, over the start of the night sequence.

Which version is best? It depends on the dramatic needs of the program.

Figure 7-14.
BOB: (O.S., faint) We're stuck.
SFX: (loud, close) Engine, hiss of broken radiator.

BILL: Aw, simmer down.
SFX: Night frog/cricket sounds: ribbet, ribbet, ribbet.

BILL: (O.S.) Someone'll come along any minute.
SFX: night sounds continue

Evoking Feelings

In addition to performing all its other tasks, sound is very useful for conveying and enhancing feelings, both momentary responses and overall moods. Music is the most powerful mood setter, as we will see, but sound effects and background noises can also stimulate viewers' emotions.

Sound and Mood

Certain background sounds are useful for setting the overall mood or tone of a video sequence. For example:

- Gentle surf and steady rain both sound peaceful and soothing.
- Howling wind sends a message of desolate emptiness.
- Steady mechanical vibration imparts a mood of tenseness. (That is why the Death Star megaship in the original *Star Wars* film is always accompanied by an ominous, almost subsonic rumble.)
- The sounds of busy city streets convey feelings of energy.
- Jet engine background sounds deliver a feeling of power, **Figure 7-15**.

Figure 7-15.
Jet engine sound effects convey a sense of power. (Corel)

● The crackling of logs in an open fire suggests cozy safety.

These sound effects are mood setting, partly because they are more or less continuous, running in the background of the audio track.

Sound and Emotional Response

Other sounds can evoke more specific emotional responses. This is often because they are associated with particular actions or objects. For instance:

● Echoing footsteps on concrete create suspense.

● The crackle of crunching bones and the pulpy thud of smashed flesh can arouse disgust and even pain.

● The metallic click when a rifle hammer is cocked can provoke a sense of dread.

● The chuckling sound of pouring champagne says warmth and romance.

● Fireworks explosions, **Figure 7-16,** can signal triumph.

Figure 7-16.
Triumphant fireworks are enhanced by sound explosions.

When any sound is weirdly distorted it can impart a feeling of disorientation and even insanity. Listed on the printed page, these evocative sounds may seem like clichés; but when editors lay them skillfully to appropriate visuals, they can be remarkably effective.

Unrealistic Sounds

Some sound effects are frankly unrealistic, especially in comic programs. For example, as a running character skids around a corner, we hear the sound effect of squealing tires and when he rushes past the camera he is accompanied by an engine roar.

Unrealistic effects can also be used in serious programs. For instance, in a fine nature documentary titled *The Year of the Jaguar*, we hear the ominous rattle of a shell or bamboo wind chime whenever a jaguar spots some off-screen prey. Note the care with which this effect was selected. The sharp tinkling of a glass wind chime would sound out of place in this Central American rain forest. But the

more organic sound of shells or bamboo is acceptable, even though it is equally unrealistic.

Perhaps the most unrealistic effects of all are the sounds made by the spaceships in many science fiction programs. We all know that sound cannot exist in the vacuum of space, but we accept it anyway, as an evocation of the power of these mighty vessels.

The Role of Music

The most powerful sound tool for evoking emotion is music, and music has been an integral part of movies since their very beginning. Joy, sorrow, excitement, dread, and almost every other human feeling have been summoned in music. Building upon the innovations of opera composers, the creators of film and video music have evolved a wide variety of techniques for supporting and enhancing the visual track, **Figure 7-17.** Though music's emotional effect is evident in fiction programs, it is equally important in other types of videos.

Commercials and promotional videos rely heavily on emotions to sell their ideas or products. Even documentary and training programs utilize music to set an overall tone, create transitions between program sections, and supply a sense of closure at the end. Like production sound, sound effects, and background sound, music is treated by sound editors as a separate audio component to be blended with the other sound elements to create a final composite sound track.

Communicating with Sound

As you can see, sound is a powerful resource in creating effective video programs. It can deliver abstract information far more efficiently than visuals could. It can suggest places, things, and even people that don't appear on screen. Sound helps bind the many separate shots that make up the visuals into a

Figure 7-17.
Library music compositions are offered in several versions.

Track	Title	Time	Description
16	Corporate Energy: Main	03:30	Pulsing, powerful
17	Corporate Energy: Main	03:30	Brass and percussio
18	Corporate Energy: Short Ver.	00:60	String underscore.
19	Corporate Energy: Short Ver.	00:30	Brass and percussi
20	Corporate Energy: Finale	00:05	Brass climax.
21	Progress & Profits: Theme	03:00	Driving, confident
22	Progress & Profits: Theme	03:00	Strings only
23	Progress & Profits: Short Ver.	60:00	Full orchestra
24	Progress & Profits: Short Ver.	30:00	Full orchestra
25	Progress & Profits: Opening	00:20	Long version, w
26	Progress & Profits: Opening	00:05	Short version, :
	Wrapup	00:20	Big finish, with

single, flowing whole. Sound has the power to arouse all kinds of emotions in viewers. And now, digital editing offers the ability to weave subtle audio textures, creating composite tracks as rich and complex as the sound in any theatrical film.

Technical Terms

Audio: Collectively, the sound components of an audiovisual program.

Dialogue: Speech by performers on-screen.

Equalization: The adjustment of the volume levels of various sound frequencies to balance the overall mixture of sounds.

Mixing: The blending together of separate audio tracks, either in a computer or through a sound mixing board.

Production track: The "live" sound recorded with the video.

Sound: The noises recorded as audio.

Sound effects: Specific noises added to a sound track.

Split edit: A cut in which audio and video do not change together. When "audio leads," the sound with the incoming video is heard over the end of the outgoing video; when "video leads," the sound with the outgoing video continues over the incoming video.

Straight cut: An edit in which audio and video change simultaneously; also, an edit that does not include an effect such as a fade or dissolve.

Voiceover: Narration or dialogue recorded independently and then paired with related video.

The History of Video Sound

Radio

The first medium to use audio was radio, and radio (of course) was sound only. It was here in this "theater of the mind" that sound technicians invented ways to suggest places and events through sound effects. Background noises such as theater audiences or rushing rivers were recorded on phonograph records.

Sound effects teams provided "live" sounds, operating miniature doors, "walking" shoes across different surfaces, and firing blank shots in real time, while the story unfolded. Once sound movies arrived, these live sound effects operations became the Foley recording studios of movies.

Sound effects technician Tom Keith rehearses for the Prairie Home Companion radio program. (Minnesota Public Radio photo by Frederic Petters)

Sound films

At first, movie audio was necessarily simple: a live production track "sweetened" with some effects and underscored with music.

After World War II, movie sound advanced with the introduction of magnetic recording on both tape and film. (Previously, sound had been recorded optically by photographing the changing light outputs of photoelectric cells.) Magnetic recording offered improved quality, flexibility, and economy, so that the sound track elements used to make a composite audio track could multiply from fewer than a dozen to as many as fifty or more.

Magnetic recording brought another benefit, too: it allowed sound technicians to lay down control tracks that made it easier to synchronize sound tracks with one another (and with the picture) without a mechanical connection. As the techniques of film and video gradually merged, film sound engineers began using the time code method, in which the length of a recording is measured in hours, minutes, seconds, and frames, and the time "address" of every single frame is recorded with it.

Television

In the early days of TV, music and background effects were usually prerecorded on audiotape, but individual sound effects were often produced in real time. The arrival of videotape permitted more sophisticated sound editing and the development of time code made it practical to lay in individual synchronized sound effects.

Video sound today

Video sound came of age with the development of computer-based editing, in which audio components are digitized and all editing is performed on the computer. Digital sound editing allows almost instant access to all sound components, and the computer can handle dozens of tracks at once. As a result, the possibilities for creating video sound tracks are almost limitless.

8 Program Development

Contents

About Program Development
Defining The Program
Preparing a Treatment
Creating a Storyboard
Writing a Script

Objectives

After studying this chapter, you will be able to:

❑ Discuss a video program in terms of its subject, objectives, audience, delivery system, production scale, content scope, length, and concept.

❑ Select appropriate formats for developing the program.

❑ Write a simple treatment for a short video program.

❑ Develop a storyboard illustrating a program sequence.

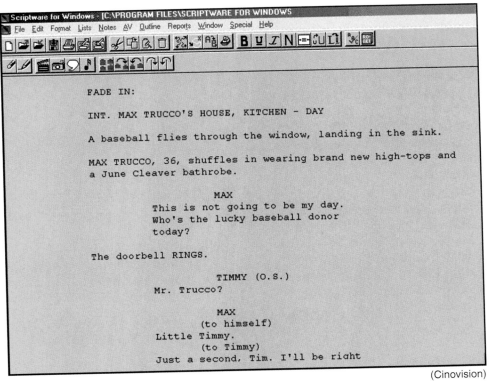

(Cinovision)

About Program Development

In Hollywood, a movie being prepared for production is said to be "in development." Why not just say that it is being "scripted" or simply "written"? The reason is that no matter how important a script may be, it is only an end product in a much larger creative process: the process of program development.

This chapter covers the fundamentals of this vital process. We will start with a common-sense approach to defining the video program you wish to produce. Then we will look at various ways to create a design for your program, a design intended to guide you and your colleagues through production and postproduction.

If you propose to shoot a short simple video, you may be tempted to skip the development process. If, for example, you are making a music video about a garage rock band, you may feel that all you have to do is tape the band playing a song and then edit the results. But this approach is almost guaranteed to produce a less-than-satisfactory program. Even as simple a program as that garage band video can benefit from the process of development.

Defining the Program

You begin the development process by defining the program. The first step is to describe exactly the video that you want to make. This may sound obvious, but far too many programs suffer because they were poorly defined to begin with. By developing a detailed blueprint of your program, you provide the information you need to plan, shoot, and edit your video.

To illustrate the steps in defining a program we will use a promotional video for a fictional product. Imagine that you have been hired by Acme Power Tools, Inc., to produce a short program that explains their new cordless electric drill, the Sidewinder. Acme will distribute your video to hardware and building supply stores.

At first, the approach appears obvious: simply show what the Acme Sidewinder drill can do. But there is much more than that to defining this program. To draw a detailed blueprint, we need to specify the program's *subject, objectives, audience, delivery system,* and *length*.

Subject

The first step is to identify the subject matter, and the easiest way to do this is by assigning your program a temporary working title that announces its topic. *Our Camping Trip, Ed and Darlene Get Married, Warehouse Operations, The Lions Club in Our Community* — each of these titles summarizes the content of a proposed video.

For your finished program, you may replace the literal working title with a more imaginative alternative.

Later, you will further limit and refine your subject; but even at this first step, your title may suggest that your topic is too unfocused. For instance, the title Warehouse Operations may tip you off that your topic is too broad for a single training program. To reduce it to manageable size, you might select one important part of warehouse operations and plan a program titled *How to Drive a Forklift*.

In the case of Acme Power Tools, Inc., your imaginary client, the subject/title is obvious: *The Sidewinder Cordless Drill,* **Figure 8-1.**

Figure 8-1.
The Sidewinder cordless drill.

Objectives

The next step is to identify the client's objectives: what does Acme want this program to achieve? The obvious answer is to make customers buy Sidewinder drills. But that is only a start. Some potential buyers may not even think that cordless drills are very useful. Others may understand that such drills are worth considering, but they are leaning toward drills made by Acme's competitors. These facts suggest that two obvious objectives for your program are to persuade customers that

● a cordless drill is a tool worth buying, and

● the Acme Sidewinder is the best cordless drill to buy.

Notice that these objectives are clear, specific, and simple; and they are phrased in terms of their effect on viewers. An objective like, "to demonstrate cordless drills" merely seeks to present information. By contrast, "to persuade customers that a cordless drill is worth buying," is an improvement because the objective in this form intends to actively move the viewer.

Even a personal video benefits from at least one clear objective. For instance, the objective for a child's birthday party video might be to communicate the love and care that went into creating the event.

Finally, these objectives are few in number and they fit together logically. To see why limiting objectives is important, imagine that Acme Power Tools initially wants two additional objectives: to increase customer interest in do-it-yourself projects in general, and to develop positive feelings toward the company. But you realize that general "do-it-yourselfing" would make the subject too

broad to cover properly, and that the Acme public image is not directly relevant to product usefulness. So you convince your client to limit the program's objectives to those that specifically sell the Sidewinder drill.

Audience

Now, to whom do you want to sell the drill? Different audiences will watch your video with different interests, different prejudices, different amounts and types of information. To communicate effectively, you must identify your target audience and address your video directly to it. To see how this works, imagine that you are preparing two programs: *How to Choose a Retirement Community*, an informational video for older people, and *Power on the Water*, a commercial aimed at speedboat buyers. See **Figure 8-2.** The senior audience will probably appreciate a straightforward, low-pressure presentation of their retirement options. The potential boat buyers will respond to dynamic, exciting shots of action on the water, backed by pulsing music and the howl of big engines.

Imagine what would happen if you delivered a loud and frantic video to the mature viewers and a steady, systematic presentation to the boat racers. Both groups would reject your message. To succeed, your video must be carefully tailored for its target audience.

To return to the Sidewinder cordless drill, pretend that in discussing the program with the Acme marketing department, you discover at least four different groups of potential viewers:

Figure 8-2.
Retirement community vs. power boating. (Corel)

● *Buyers for hardware and building supply chains.* These people will decide whether to offer the Sidewinder for sale, and if so, how to promote it against drills made by Acme's competitors.

● *Potential customers.* These people will decide whether they want to buy a cordless drill, and if so, whether the Acme Sidewinder is their best choice.

● *Female customers.* Unlike some males, these potential buyers are not dependably attracted to tools merely because they are intriguing adult toys. Instead, they want to know what the Sidewinder drill will do, how easily it will do it, and why doing this will be useful to them, **Figure 8-3.**

Figure 8-3.
Female customers want to know how well the product works.

● *Canadian customers.* Some of these viewers speak French rather than English.

Once you have identified your potential audience, you can make some informed decisions. First, you know that Acme wants to sell its drills in Canada, so you will need to plan for a second sound track in French. Secondly, store buyers have interests that are quite different from those of customers, so you eliminate them as primary targets. Next, you realize that it would be impractical to provide a separate program for female viewers, but you decide to address their interests and concerns as you aim your program at potential customers of both genders.

So, by comparing Acme's objectives to groups of possible viewers, you have decided that your primary audience consists of potential drill buyers of both genders in all of

North America. As you continue developing your program, you will try to speak directly to this target audience.

Delivery System

The next question is, how and where will this audience see your video? The answer will determine many things about your program. Acme has asked for what is called a "point-of-sale" video, a program to be shown in stores to customers who are ready to decide right then and there whether to buy a Sidewinder drill. That situation requires a particular method of displaying your program, a particular **delivery system.** It probably involves a small video monitor placed on a high stand or in a special Acme display kiosk in an aisle in a retail store, with customers strolling past it as they shop, **Figure 8-4.**

Figure 8-4.
A point-of-sale display.

This delivery system imposes certain requirements on your program:
● It must be vivid enough to make passing shoppers stop and watch it.

● It must be visually simple, so that people can see it clearly on a small screen that may be several feet away.

● It must not depend too heavily on its sound track, since the audio may be degraded or even lost in the noise of the store.

● It must be nonlinear in its organization, so that customers need not watch it from the beginning in order to understand its essential message.

● Above all, it must be short — brief enough so that customers (who did not come to the store to watch TV) will remain for its whole message.

In contrast to a point-of-sale program, a training video designed to teach people how to use the Sidewinder might be watched by an employee in a quiet room or by a do-it-yourselfer in the comfort of a home den. With those very different delivery systems, these restrictions would not apply. Whatever form it may take, your program's delivery system (the situation in which it will be shown) should have a strong influence on its approach and style.

Program Length

The next step is to determine your video's length. Program running time may be governed by one or more of several factors:

● *Standard time units*. In broadcast and cable TV, for example, programs and commercials alike are always produced in standardized lengths, **Figure 8-5**.

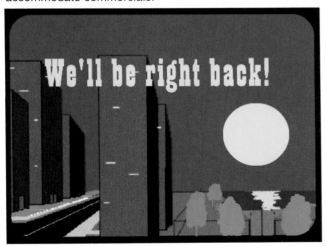

Figure 8-5.
TV program segments are standard lengths, to accommodate commercials.

● *Resources*. As a rule, the longer a video runs, the more it costs to produce; so your program's length may be affected by the size of your budget.

● *Audience tolerance*. The length of the audience's attention span depends on the type of program you are making. Viewers might enjoy a movie for two hours or more. An infomercial about a line of products might hold them for 30 minutes at most. Training videos are hard to sustain for longer than 10 or 15 minutes, and commercials are too intense to hold up much longer than 60 seconds.

● *Subject matter*. Within the program types that are not standardized in length, the actual duration of a video may depend on the extensiveness of its content.

Superficially, subject matter might seem to be the first determiner of length, rather than the last. It would appear logical to allow a video to run as long as it takes to cover the chosen content with appropriate thoroughness. This is often how publishers set the lengths of nonfiction books such as this one. A book may have, say, 300 pages, or 600 or 1,200, depending on the extent of its subject. But a book is a random-access document. You can dip into it anywhere you please, read it at your own pace, pick it up and put it down when you feel like it. The length of a book is not critically important because the reader controls how much of it to absorb at any one time.

The video viewer, by contrast, cannot control the speed at which information is delivered, and most programs are designed to be watched continuously, at a single sitting. For these reasons, the lengths of video programs are influenced less by their subjects than by the other factors discussed previously.

Of course, if your intended delivery system is a computer-based interactive video or Web site, you will want to design it for random rather than linear access.

Considering how these factors influence your Acme Sidewinder video, you realize that busy shoppers are not going to stand in front of a TV screen for even five minutes. On the other hand, you cannot demonstrate the major benefits of the new drill in a 30-second commercial. With this in mind, you set a program length of about three minutes.

Selecting a Concept

When you have specified the objectives, the audience, the delivery system, and the length of your program, you have developed a nearly complete profile of your intended video. With these determining factors firmly in mind, you are *almost* ready to start developing your program. But you still need to come up with a program concept. A **concept** is an organizing principle, an idea that gives shape and meaning to your video. It determines what you include and how you treat it. You could say that the concept guides your approach to your subject or your perspective on it or simply your "angle," **Figure 8-6.** However you describe it, the concept of your video program enables you to make a coherent statement that your audience can understand and respond to. These program organizers are simple to demonstrate by examples, so the sidebar *Sample Program Concepts* suggests plausible concepts for various types of personal and professional videos.

Figure 8-6.
The subhead of this news story reveals the concept: *David Slays Goliath.*

McKinley Beats Fillmore High
Underdogs Rally to Defeat League Champs

Sparked by quaterback Charley Folsome, the McKinley Presidents rallied in the third quarter to power home two touchdowns that opened a lead Fillmore was never able to close. When the ground attack pursued in the first half failed against the bigger Fillmore line, Folsome took to the air, completing three passes to teammates Bruce Petit, Mickey Fleschner, and Norm Simas.

Booster Club Donates Scoreboard

At a ceremony during the pep rally before Saturday's game, McKinley Boosters Club President Amanda Wang turned on the new all-digital

In the case of the Sidewinder cordless drill, a possible concept is hidden in the already-selected objectives and audience. Acme Power Tools, Inc., wants to communicate the message that their drill is the best choice and they want to appeal to female buyers as well as male. Considering these two desires together, you develop a concept: *Get your own Sidewinder so your husband can have his back.*

With the concept in place, the whole program suggests itself: a group of brief scenes in which a husband keeps asking for his Sidewinder and his wife keeps promising to give it back as soon as she's finished with it. In each scene, she uses the drill in a different type of project, demonstrating its simplicity and versatility as she does so.

Preparing a Treatment

If you are planning a short, personal video, you can probably start production as soon as you have settled on the content,

length, and above all, concept. Most professional videos, by contrast, require that your informal design be transcribed onto paper as a script, a storyboard, or a treatment, **Figure 8-7.**

Figure 8-7.
A treatment is an outline in narrative form.

The Sidewinder: Part Two, Scene Three ... at the kitchen table, the wife is repairing a toy for her admiring daughter. First she drills a pilot hole for screw. DISSOLVE TO seating a repair screw with a drill bit. DISSOLVE TO smoothing the repair edges with a sanding drum. DISSOLVE TO buffing the repaired joint with the sheepskin pad. Daughter is increasingly impressed and happy throughout. As we hear the off-screen voice of the husband say, "Honey, I can't find my Sidewinder again!" wife and daughter exchange conspiratorial looks. Then daughter takes the toy and runs out while the wife drops the drill out of sight into her lap. Husband enters and registers humorously on wife's guilty expression.

Uses for Program Treatments

The simplest transcription is called a ***treatment:*** a few paragraphs that explain the program's concept, its subject, its order of content presentation, and its style. A treatment serves two purposes: it allows you to see and evaluate the organization of your video, and it communicates your plan to others. By committing your ideas to paper, you can determine whether they are appropriate to your program and whether they flow smoothly and logically. By examining your treatment you can spot problems and opportunities that might otherwise be overlooked.

A treatment is also useful in communicating your vision to other people, especially the colleagues who will help you produce your program and the clients who will pay for it. Without a treatment's overview of the program, your crew can only make one blind shot after another, without knowing how they should fit together and what they should achieve. As for the clients, few if any will underwrite your production without a clear idea of the program you propose to deliver.

Many clients demand a full script rather than just a summary treatment.

Sample Program Concepts

To provide a clear idea of what program concepts are and how they can guide the video maker's approach to developing programs, here are six examples: three personal programs and three professional ones.

Personal Programs

Program type: *Vacation video*
Subject/working title: "Lake Omigosh Vacation".
Concept: Triumphing over rain.
Summary: Video focuses on comic results of trying to camp out during two solid weeks of bad weather.

Program type: *Holiday*
Subject/working title: "Easter Egg Hunt."
Concept: The great Easter egg deception.
Summary: Before letting the kids find the eggs, the parents repeatedly hide them in spots where the children have already looked.

Program type: *Family oral history*
Subject/working title: "Grandfather Reminisces."
Concept: Family connections survive despite long times and great distances.
Summary: Questions and Grandfather's answers focus on family continuity across three continents and two hundred years.

Professional programs

Program type: *Training video*
Subject/working title: "Using Your Multiline Business Phone."
Concept: Conquering fear of buttons.
Summary: Humorous acknowledgment that business phones can be complex and frustrating

Grandfather reminisces.

evolves into the idea that a little study clears up the confusion.

Program type: *Community service promotional*
Subject/working title: "The McKinley Boosters"
Concept: Communities depend on volunteers.
Summary: The Boosters Club preserves and beautifies the town of McKinley.

Program type: *Wedding video*
Subject/working title: "The Anders/Goldstone Wedding."
Concept: As the glass flies apart, two lives come together.
Summary: Starting with a slow-motion shot of a goblet shattering under a cloth, the video moves from this symbol to documenting a traditional Jewish wedding.

Levels of Treatment

Video program treatments have no fixed style or length. They can be a one-sentence statement of concept and content or a multi-paragraph synopsis. They can be an outline so detailed that it identifies every separate content component. Whatever their level of detail, program treatments attempt to convey the effect of finished videos. Here are samples of program treatments developed to three different levels of detail. Each is for the Sidewinder drill program.

A skeletal treatment

This treatment covers all three parts of the Sidewinder video, in the briefest possible form:

The Sidewinder Drill

Part One: a succession of quick scenes shows the many jobs performed by the drill. Part Two: several vignettes in which a husband is frustrated because his wife is always using his Sidewinder drill. Part Three: After he presents her with her own Sidewinder, the two of them collaborate happily on a construction project.

A summary treatment

This excerpt from a summary-level treatment covers just one-third (Part Two) of the skeletal treatment in greater detail:

The Sidewinder, Part Two

Scene One: Husband asks where his Sidewinder is as we see wife using it to repair kitchen cabinet hinge. Scene two: As wife assembles picnic table bench in backyard, husband appears and again asks where his Sidewinder is. Scene Three: Wife is repairing child's toy at kitchen table when she hears husband asking where drill is. As he appears in kitchen doorway, she hides drill in lap.

A detailed treatment

This excerpt from a detailed treatment covers only Part Two, Scene Three, as summarized in the previous version.

The Sidewinder: Part Two, Scene Three

Seated at the kitchen table, the wife is repairing a toy for her admiring daughter. First she drills a pilot hole for screw. DISSOLVE TO seating a repair screw with a drill bit. DISSOLVE TO smoothing the repair edges with a sanding drum. DISSOLVE TO buffing the repaired joint with the sheepskin pad. Daughter is increasingly impressed and happy throughout. As we hear the off-screen voice of the husband say, "Honey, I can't find my Sidewinder again!," wife and daughter exchange conspiratorial looks. Then daughter takes the toy and runs out while the wife drops the drill out of sight into her lap. Husband enters and registers humorously on wife's guilty expression.

The amount of detail in your own treatments will depend on how minutely you need to previsualize your program and how completely you want to communicate it to clients and colleagues.

Creating a Storyboard

The old saying claims that one picture is worth a thousand words, and this is often true in developing video programs. In graphic-based program design, a succession of pictures resembling a comic book sketches all the important moments in the program. This script in picture form is called a **storyboard.**

Storyboards got their name from the bulletin boards on which the drawings of scenes for animated cartoons are pinned for inspection and editing.

Storyboard Uses

Storyboards have two main uses: to help others visualize the look of the eventual program and to preplan complex sequences shot-by-shot.

Visualization

Storyboards are particularly valuable for communicating content to clients and crew, because they present concrete images instead of the abstract words that describe them. Some people have less talent than others for thinking graphically. The problem is that they are often unaware of their inability to visualize, and so they indicate understanding of written descriptions when they really can't imagine them. The result can be serious miscommunication. A storyboard presents the images in previsualized form, along with captions containing dialogue, sound effects, and descriptions of the action.

Shot planning

Where complex visual sequences are involved, storyboarding can help you as well as others. By planning all camera shots in advance, you can see how well they will edit together and how clearly they will communicate their content. Many directors make extensive use of storyboards in their productions, especially in laying out highly complex action sequences. Storyboarding is also useful for working out consistent screen direction in complex physical sequence like fights and chases.

Writing a Script

Another way to lay out a detailed production design is by writing a full **script.** A script describes every sequence in your program, including both video and audio components. A script is especially useful if the program contains dialogue to be memorized and spoken by actors and/or voiceover text to be read by an offscreen narrator. Scripts are also a common alternative to storyboards for

A Storyboard Sequence

Here is a storyboard sequence as an advertising agency might create it for the Sidewinder Drill program.

1. SFX: drill.

2. SFX: drill continues

3. SFX: drilling stops. **DISSOLVE TO:**

4. SFX: Slower sound of power screwdriver. **DISSOLVE TO:**

5. SFX: Abrasive sound of sanding. **DISSOLVE TO:**

6. SFX: Sanding continues. **DISSOLVE TO:**

7. SFX: Softer whine of sheepskin pad. Then, **HUSBAND** (OS): "Honey, I can't find my Sidewinder again!"

8. SFX: Drill noise stops.

9.

10. SFX: daughter's chair scraping back.

11. SFX: girl's footsteps.

12. HUSBAND (OS but closer): "Seems like every time I need that drill..."

13. HUSBAND: "It disappears."

14.

15. HUSBAND (meaningfully) "Doesn't it? "

presenting programs to clients. They are especially valuable for planning and budgeting production, since they include every element of the program in a compact narrative form.

The Scripting Process

Writing a script can follow any system — or no system at all. In commercial and industrial production, however, the process of creating a script often breaks down into five stages:

1. Producer and client agree upon the program's content and concept.
2. A detailed content outline is written. This is often critiqued by the client and then revised by the writer.
3. A first draft script is written. This is the initial attempt to lay out a complete production script. Usually the client reviews this draft and orders revisions.
4. A revised draft of the script incorporates the client's changes.
5. The revised script draft is reviewed by the client and further changes are ordered. If all is going well, these changes do not require a complete third draft, but only a refinement of the second one.

Which Method Is Best?

Professional video makers employ all the forms of program development that we have covered, sometimes mixing and matching them as needed. For example, a program may be documented completely in script form, which is supplemented by storyboards of action sequences or other activities that demand precise visual preplanning. When you make fairly short, simple programs it is usually enough to write down your concept, develop a narrative treatment that covers the major components of your video, and perhaps storyboard critical sequences for camera angles and continuity. As your productions grow in scope and complexity, you will probably move up to fully scripted programs, with or without more extensive storyboarding. Whatever form or forms you choose, the result is the blueprint from which you construct your video.

Technical Terms

Concept: The organizing principle behind an effective program. Often called an angle, perspective, or slant.

Delivery System: The method (such as website, TV monitor, or kiosk) by which a program will be presented, and situation (alone at a desk, in a training room, in a crowded store) in which it will be watched.

Script: A full written documentation of a program that is formatted like a play. It includes scenes, dialogue, narration, stage directions, and effects.

Storyboard: Program documentation in graphic panels, like a comic book, with or without dialogue, narration, stage directions, and effects.

Treatment: A written summary of a program, formatted as narrative prose, that may be as short as one paragraph or as long as a scene-by-scene description.

A Nonfiction Script Format for Word Processing

The traditional nonfiction script layout consists of two vertical columns with the visuals on one side of the page and the dialogue, narration, and other audio on the other side. The problem is that this side-by-side layout can be inconvenient to use in a word processing program. For this reason, nonfiction scripts like the following excerpt are now often formatted over-and-under instead of side-by-side.

```
25.
VIDEO Insert: sanding the repair.
AUDIO SFX: Sanding sound.

26.
VIDEO Admiring daughter, as before.
AUDIO SFX: Sanding continues.

                          DISSOLVE TO:

27.
VIDEO Insert: Buffing the repair.
AUDIO Husband (OS): Honey, I can't find my
      Sidewinder again!
      SFX (under) Buffing sound.
```

9 Production Planning

Contents

About Production Planning

People: Crew and Cast

Places: Scouting Locations

Things: Equipment and Supplies

Plans: Production Logistics

Budgets: Production Costs

Objectives

After studying this chapter, you will be able to:

❑ Determine production requirements for a small-scale video production.

❑ Assemble people, equipment, and other resources for the production.

❑ Develop a production schedule.

❑ Calculate costs and budget the production.

(Shotmaster storyboard software, The Badham Company)

About Production Planning

When the content of your proposed video is well developed, you are ready for **production planning** — the process that will organize and manage the complexities of shooting. Planning is critically important for two reasons: time and money. For example, you may have permission to shoot in a key location for only eight hours (time). Or, you may be renting equipment or paying crew and talent by the day (money). In professional video production the phrase, "time is money" is literally true because nearly everything (and everyone) is paid for by the week, day, or hour.

Thorough production planning can make the difference between a smooth, successful shoot and a disaster. To show you how to plan effectively, this chapter will take you through the process of preparing to produce a simple video.

The Big Moment

The importance of production planning becomes obvious if you think of an actual video shoot as similar to a theatrical performance. With a stage play, many people spend weeks conducting rehearsals, building sets, sewing costumes, and publicizing the show. All this lengthy preparation is for the two or three hours of the play's actual performance. During that critical period there should be no major mistakes, because all that preproduction effort has paid off in a show that works.

Though even a simple video may take longer than two or three hours to shoot, its production phase is much like a theatrical performance: a short, intense period when all the planning and preparation are rewarded. That planning involves:

- *People*: the cast and crew of the production.

- *Places*: the locations and/or sets where shooting will take place.

- *Things*: the equipment used to shoot the program, the props and costumes in it, and miscellaneous items like talent and location releases, **Figure 9-1.**

- *Plans*: the scheduling and other organizational processes that ensure a smooth shoot.

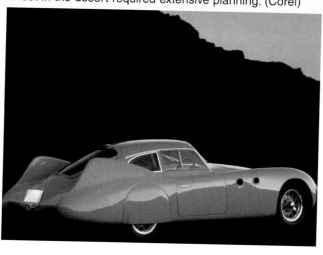

Figure 9-1.
Finding, renting, and scheduling this vintage car for a sunset shoot in the desert required extensive planning. (Corel)

- *Budgets:* the predicted production costs.

The rest of this chapter examines each of these planning topics, in turn.

People: Crew and Cast

In most professional video productions, the personnel involved demand the largest organizational effort and consume the majority of the budget. Some of these people appear in the production. Other equally important personnel work behind the camera.

The people who appear in video programs, whether actors, narrators, interviewees, or others, are often collectively called the talent.

If you make personal or small- scale professional programs, finding and recruiting people can be difficult because most amateurs lack the technical skills that video production demands and most producers lack the money to pay professional-level salaries. Here are some ideas for solving these problems when gathering people for low-budget videos.

Finding Production People

Even the simplest video project may be too much work to handle alone, so the first step is to find some assistants. The sidebar *Small Video Crews* describes three **crews**. The crew duties listed should give you an idea of how to assign responsibilities to your crew members.

Small Video Crews

Video production crews can be as large as 20 members or more, each performing specialized tasks. Most small-scale projects, however, are crewed by just a few people —or even produced by a single person. For obvious reasons, members of small crews often do several jobs at once. The job divisions suggested are only typical.

2-Person Crew	
Title	**Responsibilities**
Producer/ director/ videographer	**Producing:** Organizing and scheduling production, casting. **Directing:** Determining camera setups and shaping the performances of cast. **Videography:** Operating camera. **Lighting:** Designing and executing lighting with reflectors and/or lighting units.
Assistant	**Preproduction management:** tracking cast members. **Sound recording:** Miking talent. Wielding the microphone boom. Controlling sound levels with production audio mixer. **Camera/lighting assistant:** Helping transport and set up video equipment. Setting and adjusting reflectors and lights as directed by producer. **Continuity:** Keeping track of shots and setups. Ensuring consistency of shot contents and action from shot to shot. Recording shot information for editor. **Transportation:** Taking people and equipment to and from locations, as necessary.

4-Person Crew	
Title	**Responsibilities**
Producer/ director	**Producing:** Organizing and scheduling production. **Directing:** Determining camera setups and shaping the performances of cast.
Videographer	**Videography:** Operating camera. **Lighting:** Designing and executing lighting with reflectors and/or lighting units.
Video crew	**Sound recording:** Miking talent. Wielding the microphone boom. Controlling sound levels with production audio mixer. **Camera/lighting assistant:** Setting and adjusting reflectors and lights as directed by producer.
Production Manager	**Continuity:** Keeping track of shots and setups. Ensuring consistency of shot contents and action from shot to shot. Recording shot information for editor. **Management:** Organization and tracking of shooting schedule and all contributing components. **Makeup/costumes/production design:** Designing and applying cast makeup. Selecting, fitting, and managing cast costumes. Determining overall visual effect of production. **Transportation:** Taking people and equipment to and from locations, as necessary.

10-Person Crew	
Title	**Responsibilities**
Producer	**Producing:** Organizing and scheduling production.
Director	**Directing:** Determining camera setups and shaping the performances of cast.
Videographer	**Videography:** Operating camera. **Lighting:** Designing and executing lighting with reflectors and/or lighting units.
Gaffer	**Lighting assistance:** Setting and adjusting reflectors and lights as directed by producer.
Asst. Camera/Grip	**Camera assistance:** Help with camera setups, pull focus, perform scene carpentry.
Sound Recordist	**Sound recording:** Miking talent. Wielding the microphone boom. Controlling sound levels with production audio mixer.
Script Supervisor	**Continuity:** Keeping track of shots and setups. Ensuring consistency of shot contents and action from shot to shot. Recording shot information for editor.
Production Manager	**Management:** Organization and tracking of shooting schedule and all contributing components. **Transportation:** Taking people and equipment to and from locations, as necessary.
Makeup/ Costume	**Makeup:** Designing and applying cast makeup. **Costume:** Selecting, fitting, and managing cast costumes.
Production Designer	**Design:** Determining overall visual effect of production. **Props:** Dressing location and/or set shooting environments with properties.

Where do crew members come from? The first resource is always friends and family, especially for jobs that do not require too much technical expertise. For example, a camera operator needs to know some techniques for obtaining good quality images, **Figure 9-2**, but a production manager can draw upon skills learned in almost any managerial position.

Figure 9-2.
Video hobbyists are likely candidates for your crew.

When you do need technical expertise, the first place to look is in community theater or local clubs that feature music groups. Both activities attract talented amateurs to design and operate lighting schemes and mix multi-track audio. If your project is for an organization — whether a business, a church, a school, or a community group — look for assistants within that organization. After all, group members are likely to be interested in the success of your project because their organization stands to benefit from it.

In the case of the McKinley Boosters (introduced in the sidebar, *Case Study: The McKinley Boosters Club*), you might find a member who is interested in audio recording to become your sound person. A local amateur theater technician might want to learn video lighting. The business and professional members should offer any number of executives willing to manage the production (particularly if given a title like Producer). Other members might be called on to help provide transportation, hold reflectors during outdoor shooting, and perform other nontechnical duties. Still other club members, of course, will provide most of your on-camera talent: the cast, **Figure 9-3.**

Figure 9-3.
Local theater groups are good sources of talent.(Corel)

Casting the Production

In personal and entry-level professional productions, you may not have much choice in casting the parts in your production. Your strategy is to make the most of the choices that you do have. To cast your show successfully:

● Do not always cast the obvious person. For roles (unlike "Father" or "Mother") that are not gender-specific, cast males and females even-handedly.

● In casting a real-world character, do not limit your choice to the actual person. For example, the current president of the McKinley Boosters Club is a nice man but not a very dynamic speaker. The former president, however, is a woman with a fine platform presence and an ability to read speeches convincingly. For these reasons, you cast her as the president and spokesperson in your video. (After all, by the time the video is completed and released, the current president will be out of office too, so it makes no difference whom you cast in the role.)

● Find out in advance whether people have other obligations that might conflict with your shooting schedule. No-show actors can bring your entire production to a halt.

In this book "actor" refers to both genders.

Conducting Effective Auditions

Though you may have no choice in "casting" a personal family program or a professional job like a wedding, many video projects require you to find appropriate people to fill on-screen roles. To match these

Case Study: The McKinley Boosters Club

Throughout this chapter we will illustrate the discussion with a fictional organization called the McKinley Boosters Club.

President McKinley welcomes visitors to the Plaza.

In the small city of McKinley, the Boosters Club is an organization of business and professional men and women who meet for lunch weekly to discuss civic beautification and other urban improvements. The Boosters conduct fund-raisers for park benches, playground equipment, and landscaping projects. They work to save historic buildings and return them to productive use. On weekends, they spread out in squads to collect litter, clean up graffiti, and paint houses in low-income areas.

Now, they want a ten-minute video program to explain their activities, in order to recruit more members, raise money, and generally increase civic awareness of what they do. Imagine that, as a proud member of the McKinley Boosters Club, you have volunteered to produce this show for them.

The McKinley Boosters perform civic improvement projects, such as planting flowers in the Plaza.

roles to the right performers, you may wish to hold auditions at which people try out for parts in the program. You can simplify the tryout process by using these suggestions:

- Ensure privacy. Never ask people to read for a role in front of other applicants for the same part. Instead, have applicants wait in one room while you hold tryouts in another.

- Videotape all acting candidates to see how they look on screen. People often appear different on video, sometimes surprisingly so. Also, by recording tryouts you can later refresh your memory of each applicant (and they do tend to blur in your mind very quickly). Finally, you can edit the footage of various candidates to see how they look together. Suppose, for instance, that you have chosen your Romeo, but three different actors might make good Juliets. By intercutting audition shots of Romeo with footage of each different Juliet, you can see which combination works best.

- Tell actors not to look at the camcorder— and then see whether they can follow this direction. Some amateurs will spoil take after take by unconsciously looking into the lens.

- Give auditioners simple things to do, such as entering a room and sitting down or pouring and serving a glass of water. This will show you how naturally they can behave on camera.

Handling Talent

Auditions are psychologically punishing to all actors because they involve so much rejection, **Figure 9-4.** Only one applicant can be chosen for each role, so if ten people try out for a part, you will have to reject *90 percent* of them. In doing so, you appear to be rejecting them, not as performers but as people.

Think of it this way: if you turn down an applicant for a lathe operator position you are judging her metalworking skills. If you do not select a violin player for your orchestra you are evaluating his skills as an instrumentalist. But an actor's instrument is not a lathe or a violin; it is his appearance, his voice, his personality — in short, his entire self. By rejecting the actor you may appear to reject the

Figure 9-4.
Auditioning can be stressful for performers.

Figure 9-5.
Keep careful casting notes.

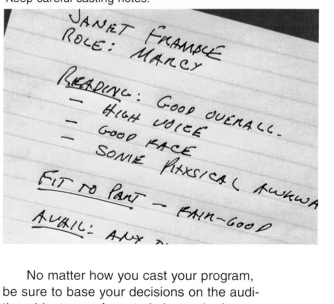

whole person. For this reason, it is important to support the people who audition for you.

First, give them adequate time. Even if you can see at once that applicants are unsuitable, give them time to show what they can do. It makes them feel that they have been taken seriously — and it often reveals talent that you may want for a later production.

Tell auditioners very simply what you want them to do. An audition is not the place for elaborate explanations of character. For example, if the role is that of an unsuitable job applicant, simply tell the actor something like this: "You want this job so badly that you can't help talking too much." A talented applicant will know what to do with this direction.

Finally, show that you are paying close attention to their efforts. Watch them as you listen to them read. Use their names frequently in conversation. Find something in every performance that you can praise.

By treating auditioners decently, you also enhance your own reputation. Whether a production is cast from a village's amateur theater crowd or the ranks of Hollywood professionals, the performing community is always small and the word gets around. By proving yourself sensitive to actors' feelings, you will make them wish to work for you, both now and in future productions.

Evaluating Audition Results

When auditions are over, you will need to select your cast. Some video makers systematically list and judge the pros and cons of each applicant, **Figure 9-5;** others rely completely on instinct for placing the best person in each role.

No matter how you cast your program, be sure to base your decisions on the audition videotapes. As noted above, the impressions people make on tape are often quite different from the way they appear in real life. People who are dynamic and forceful in person may seem dull on screen, while others who are not impressive in life are remarkably effective on tape. It is said that "the camera loves" these people; you can evaluate that affection only by studying the audition tapes.

Places: Scouting Locations

In scouting a shooting location, you contact the local people whose help you will need, determine the suitability of the place for shooting, and look for potential problems that must be solved in order to conduct a successful shoot there.

Scouting People

First and foremost, you need to establish productive relationships with key people at the location. If they are on your side, these people can give you substantial help, but if they are uncooperative they can make life very difficult.

Cultivate the custodian or building engineer, who knows more about the facility than anyone else, including the locations of the electrical power box, spare furniture and other potential props and set decorations, **Figure 9-6**. For example, the McKinley Boosters Club can avoid high rental costs at their regular meeting room in the McKinley Arms Hotel by borrowing a lectern with the

Managing Volunteer Helpers

Unreliable help is one of the biggest problems in producing personal or entry-level professional videos. If you have made videos with volunteers, you have probably experienced behavior like this:

- People arrive late and then announce that they must leave before the day's shooting is over.
- Crew members do not fulfill promises to do preproduction chores, such as finding props and costumes.
- Actors appear for later shooting sessions in clothes that do not match the outfits they wore in previous sessions.
- Crew members work slowly, or refuse to do jobs that do not appeal to them.
- Actors fail to memorize their lines, or, sometimes, even to read the script.
- Cast and crew members alike develop last-minute things to do instead, and fail to show up for shooting sessions.

Studio shoot, day one.

Day two (wrong shirt).

Why do volunteers often let the production down like this? Because they are not video professionals and do not pretend to be. Professionals have three powerful motivations for responsible behavior: they are being paid for their work, they will not be rehired if they develop a reputation for irresponsibility, and they enjoy their crafts and take personal pride in practicing them well. Amateurs, however, are motivated only by friendship with you, personal ego, and sometimes an interest in making a successful program.

Obtaining Loyalty

You may not be able to pay your cast and crew, but you can give them rewards that will help motivate them to work reliably and hard. These rewards are importance, attention, praise, credit, and ownership.

- *Importance*. Stress to cast members, in particular, that they are so essential to the production that when they are not present the production literally stops. So if they do not show up, many other volunteers like themselves are forced to stand idle. (Be careful in using this idea with certain actors, who may secretly enjoy this power to stop and start the whole production.)
- *Attention*. No matter how busy you may be, pay honest attention to the ideas and suggestions made by cast and crew. When people feel that their contributions are ignored, they lose their willingness to help in all areas.
- *Praise*. Notice and acknowledge good work. Praising actors is not too difficult, but your volunteer crew also needs recognition. A simple compliment like, "Great lighting setup — very realistic," may be all the pay that your lighting assistant will get.
- *Credit*. Before production starts, emphasize that cast and crew will receive on-screen credit for their contributions. People love to see their names in the credits.
- *Ownership*. Above all, create the idea that this is a team effort and the production belongs to everybody. In Shakespeare's *Henry V*, the king motivates his troops before a battle by calling them, "We few, we happy few, we band of brothers." That psychology works just as well today.

hotel logo on it and using it to stage the president's on-camera remarks at another location, outside the hotel. Who knows how to get hold of that lectern? The hotel's maintenance supervisor.

production area for storing equipment, costumes and props; for recharging camcorder and light batteries; for changing costumes, **Figure 9-7.** Is this area secure? . Is there a phone that you are allowed to use?

Figure 9-6.
Maintenance people know a building's systems.

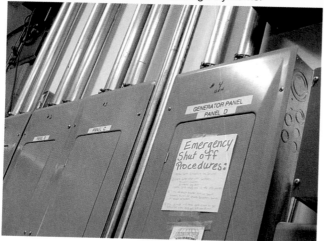

Figure 9-7.
A secure place for recharging batteries is essential.

If your location is a public place, you may also need to coordinate with one or two other key people. See the executive in charge for permission to use the facility. For example, the Boosters Club might need to ask the hotel manager for permission to shoot establishing shots at a luncheon meeting. Often, management will supply a person to accompany you throughout your shoot at the location, or at least to be on call when needed. For instance, the McKinley Arms Hotel might deputize the Assistant Manager for Banquets and Meetings to accompany the production crew in order to help out.

Consulting key people is important on personal projects as well. For instance, before moving furniture to get better camera angles on a birthday party, you might want to clear the idea with the party's host.

Scouting Facilities

You scout the facilities to ensure that you will have everything you need for production. First, check out the space where you will be shooting. Is there enough room? Can you create in it the on-screen environment you need (hotel room, office, dungeon, desert island)? Next, ensure that you will have access to a

Also, check the electrical service, starting with the power supply. Will the electricity fed to the shooting area power your camcorder, audio equipment, and above all, lighting? If not, can you obtain power by running a cable to the main service box? Verify that enough wall outlets are available for your use.

Tapping an electrical distribution box is strictly a job for a professional lighting person, unless a crew member happens to be a qualified electrician.

Finally, scout parking for cast and crew. Even a small production can involve a dozen cars that may have to be expensively garaged, or else parked far from the location.

Scouting Video Problems

Perhaps the most important scouting task is checking the location for camera problems, especially lighting difficulties. In many cases, the shooting area is too dark for good-quality video. By scouting, you can decide whether to bring in movie lights, increase the power of the available lighting, or even recommend moving to a better-lit area.

Another problem is excessive contrast: too much difference between the lightest and darkest parts of the scene. Camcorders cannot record high-quality video in environments where the contrast is extreme. In those conditions, the lightest areas "burn out" to glaring white or else the darkest areas "block up" to pure black.

Take, for example, the video scene in which the mayor of McKinley praises the civic activities of the Boosters Club. This sequence is to be shot with the mayor sitting at his desk in his office. The problem is that the desk is backed by a wall of windows that are very bright. In this contrasty environment, the mayor at his desk will record as a black silhouette, **Figure 9-8.**

By scouting for camera problems, you realize that you can place your camera where it will exclude the bright windows, as you can see from the office plan in **Figure 9-8B**. Simply direct the mayor to open the sequence facing forward and then swing his chair around to face the camera.

Another potential problem is mismatched light colors. In the mayor's office, light from a big desk lamp has a distinctly orange cast, while the window light is quite bluish. Noting this problem, you can plan to provide blue filtration to convert the lamp output to the color of daylight.

The same scouting trip will also reveal that you have a big problem in getting enough camera angles. Shooting at right angles to the window will give you one setup, but you will be unable to move to the side without running into the wall or else including the bright windows. After inspecting the location, you can solve the problem by planning to move the mayor's desk forward enough to permit a side angle on his face, **Figure 9-8C.** (The shift will not be noticeable to the viewers.)

Finally, many video problems arise because the camera must be placed too far from the subject. This is often true, for example, in wedding videos, where cameras and their operators are prohibited in certain parts of places of worship. By discovering that you will be far from the action, you can plan to bring a long lens or lens extender, plus a wireless microphone for the wedding couple, **Figure 9-9.**

Scouting Audio Problems

A distant sound source is one of several problems in recording quality audio. Although so-called zoom microphones are available, they have nowhere near a lens' ability to zoom in for more detail and less background. If you catch the problem, you might provide

Figure 9-9.
Wedding setups often require long lenses and wireless microphones.

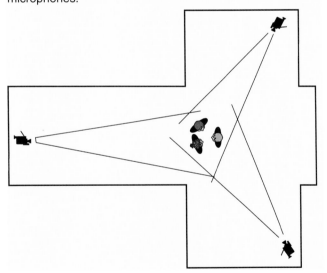

Figure 9-8.
A—In front of a bright window, the mayor is a silhouette. B—Repositioning the camera avoids the bright windows. C—Moving the desk allows extra camera angles.

A

B

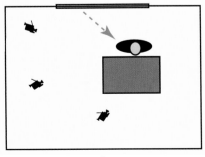

C

wireless mikes, as suggested earlier. Or you may be able to feed sound from the facility's own public address system.

A second major audio problem is background noise, and here the McKinley Booster project is in serious trouble. Most of the shooting locations are outdoors at public buildings or in the town plaza. Traffic noise is almost impossible to eliminate, since it reflects from all sides. You can control the problem by staging important scenes with the worst traffic behind the camera and microphone. Alternatively, you could establish the scene in the noisy location and then tape all the close shots of talking in a matching but quieter background, **Figure 9-10.**

Wireless microphones can sometimes add as many sound problems as they solve, especially if they pick up interference. Auto ignitions and other electrical sources can cause static, and your microphones may share frequencies with some radios and even cordless telephones. High-quality wireless microphones have fewer interference problems, but they can cost several hundred dollars apiece. So if you plan to use wireless mikes, take them on your scouting trips and test them at each location.

Things: Equipment and Supplies

After people and places, the most complex components of any production are *things*: cameras and lights and sound equipment, furniture, props, and set decorations. Without planning and careful management, looking after things can cause major problems.

Production Equipment

Where simple personal or entry-level professional productions are concerned, preproduction work with video equipment means ensuring that everything is present and in good working order. To do this, make a list of every piece of equipment, even if you have only a very simple video outfit. You would be surprised at how easy it is for small accessories and other items to be overlooked. Easily forgotten items include:

● Batteries and cables if you use external microphones.
● Camera quick-release components, **Figure 9-11.** One half may still be attached to the tripod, but is the other half on the camcorder?
● Spare lamps for movie lights (since their special bulbs cannot just be bought at any supermarket).

Figure 9-11.
Quick release plates can become separated from their tripods.

Figure 9-10.
Moving the subject away from noisy backgrounds will often improve the audio quality. (Sue Stinson)

Next make sure that all your equipment is functioning properly by repairing problems as soon as you notice them. If the tripod lock is defective or if the zoom lens control is stiff, get it fixed before you forget it. It is all too common to arrive at a new shoot with equipment that has not been repaired.

Pay particular attention to power for the camcorder and for lights, if you use any. Check to see that all camera batteries are fully charged and that the charger is included in your gear for use on location. Have plenty of industrial grade extension cords for movie lights.

Equipment planning also covers special items that you rent or buy for this shoot. Such items might include teleconverter accessories for shooting athletic events or special filters for creating optical effects.

Finally, ensure that you have an ample supply of videotapes ready for shooting. As explained in the sidebar, *Preparing Videotapes for Use*, tapes should be pre-blacked. Since this task must be completed in real time (a one-hour tape takes a full hour to black) it has to be done before actual production begins.

Sets, Properties, Costumes, and Makeup

Simple productions rarely involve actual set building, but you will often want to **dress** locations to make them look better on screen. To anticipate set-dressing needs, collect an assortment of potted plants, wall decorations, small furniture pieces, and other items to utilize if needed. It is also a good idea to have a roll of masking tape or double-faced tape.

Properties (usually shortened to "props") are all the items that are called for in the script: the glasses and silverware, the spectacles, the tire iron, the chocolate chip cookies — anything and everything that will appear in your program. To make sure you have every prop, make a list of them and check them off twice: once before you leave for location and again before you shoot.

Preparing Videotapes for Use

To simplify editing later, you should prepare each new videotape for recording by a process called **blacking the tape.** This means recording the whole length of the tape, without any video or audio program signal. Blacking a tape does two important things. First, it lays down a continuous reference signal for locating and identifying shots:

● In all digital formats, blacking the tape records time code, giving every individual frame a unique address. For instance, 00:22:12:25 identifies the single frame that is located zero hours, 22 minutes, 12 seconds, and 25 frames from the first frame of code placed on the tape.

● In nonprofessional analog formats such as VHS, blacking the tape records a control track of pulses at one-second intervals that make the tape counter function. If you review a "blank" tape and the counter does not advance, you know that the control track is not present and the tape has not been blacked.

Time code (or control track) is also laid down again with every shot recorded. The reason for prerecording it throughout the length of the tape is to provide readable code for any blank spots between recordings.

Second, blacking a tape lets you catch tape or camcorder problems in advance. By playing portions of the blacked tape, you can see (by the patterns on the screen) whether the tape is defective or the camcorder is failing to operate perfectly. The easiest way to black a tape is by placing it in a camcorder and pressing RECORD, with no video or audio signal coming in. To assure perfectly blank results from an amateur camcorder, black the tape with the lens cap on and a mini-plug converter inserted in the camera's external microphone jack. This will disable the built-in microphone.

If you have the required equipment, it is preferable to actually record a "reference black" color, rather than a blank signal. Most professional camcorders can generate their own reference black.

A miniplug is used to disable the camcorder's internal microphone.

Ext. mic.

Nothing is more frustrating than being unable to shoot for an hour while someone runs all over town, frantically searching for a forgotten prop.

In the McKinley Boosters Club program, a Certificate of Merit is a key prop, because the president will be seen presenting it to a homeowner for an exceptionally beautiful front yard. In this case, the actual certificate will not be ready in time for shooting, so you will need to fake one with a certificate form and a laser printer. From a distance, the camcorder will be unable to tell the difference.

In simple productions, costumes are usually provided by the actors, **Figure 9-12**, but you must include them in preplanning by using a costume inventory and check list. Before every scheduled shoot, call all cast members and remind them of the costume items for which they are responsible. (Perhaps the biggest source of delays in personal and small-scale professional production is actors who do not return in the same outfit they wore during the previous shooting session.)

Figure 9-12.
Performers often provide their own costumes.

Like costumes, makeup is usually the responsibility of individual actors. The sidebar *A Basic Makeup Kit* suggests a simple kit that you may want to assemble and have ready to use for touch-ups if needed.

Releases and Permissions

If you are making a program for purely personal or family use, you do not need to obtain permission to show any person, place, or thing, or to include published music on your sound track. But if you are making your video for profit and/or public showing, you risk being prosecuted if you fail to get the necessary releases and rights. What does the phrase "for profit and/or public showing" mean? It includes one or more of the following uses for your program:

● Your program will be used by a corporate client for internal training purposes, and you were paid for producing it.

● Your program will be offered for public sale.

● Your program will be shown to the public via broadcast, cable, satellite, the Internet, screening, or any other method.

Note that a program qualifies if it is *either* for profit *or* public. The private corporate video is for profit because you were paid to make it. A showing outside your home is public even if no one receives compensation for it.

The McKinley Boosters Club video falls into this second category. You will not make a penny for your work on this program and the club will not sell tapes or charge admission to showings. However, they will screen it all over town in order to develop support for the club's activities. For that reason, you must obtain permission to use people's likenesses (recognizable images) and music written by others.

At this simple production level obtaining permission means getting everyone who appears in the program to sign a talent release, a legal document that appears in the sidebar *Talent Release Forms*. Make sure that every performer completes a talent release form before actual shooting begins, and you will have discharged your legal obligations to them.

Plans: Production Logistics

Logistics is the overall task of organizing and supplying the shoot. In an elaborate production, this can be a formidable job; for simpler programs, the biggest tasks are creating a shooting schedule and providing support services.

Scheduling

Scheduling is the process of deciding which scenes to shoot in which order. The task seems straightforward until the production manager runs into problems like these:

A Basic Makeup Kit

Very little makeup is used in most personal and entry-level professional videos. Female cast members generally wear their normal street makeup. Men usually wear none at all. Nevertheless, you should have at least the following items to use for touching up your talent:

- Neutral powder for eliminating skin shine
- Light- and medium-toned powders for minimizing skin imperfections
- One or two powder brushes
- Neutral blemish spotter in a variety of skin tones
- Facial tissues
- Mirror
- Hairbrush, comb
- Hair spray, to keep hair in place
- Trim scissors
- Small plastic tool or tackle box to hold everything

If your programs include performers of different ethnicities, you will want to customize your powder and spotter colors to suit. In most larger cities, you can buy makeup at theatrical supply houses. In smaller cities and towns, try stores that sell dance supplies or party and Halloween costumes. You can obtain simple products at any drug or discount store makeup counter.

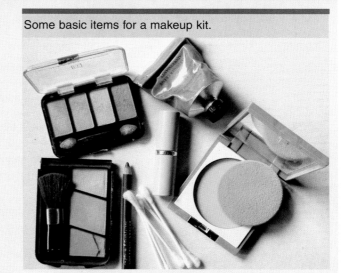

Some basic items for a makeup kit.

With your supplies assembled, here are some tips for using makeup in your programs:

- Use as little as possible.
- Fold tissues around collars to keep powder off costumes.
- Use makeup only to cover things up (shine, blemishes), not to alter a performer's appearance.
- Let women apply their own makeup and both women and men fix their own hair. They know themselves better than you do.
- Check the effect of makeup on an external color monitor before taping.

- For a scene between them, the Mayor cannot work on Wednesday and the Boosters Club President is unavailable on Thursday.
- The bulldozer for a dump cleanup sequence is available only on weekends, when it is not in use; but the city personnel who drive it do not work weekends.
- The statue illumination ceremony has to be shot at night, **Figure 9-13**.

Juggling several conflicting demands at once can make scheduling a frustrating business. Fortunately, there is a well-developed system for organizing a shoot. To sort out shooting priorities, the production manager lists certain characteristics for every scene in the script. (A scene is a single piece of action that happens in a single place at a single time.) Key characteristics of scenes include:

- *Places.* For obvious reasons, it is more efficient to shoot every scene that takes place at one location before moving on to the next location. Try to group scenes together by location, to minimize moving

Figure 9-13.
Night shooting requires careful planning.

the production from one place to another, then back again.

- *People.* At each place, different performers may be needed at different times; so scenes in which the same

Talent Release Forms

Most larger camera stores sell pads of standard photographic releases, or you can customize the following sample.

Performer Release

My signature below attests that I, _____, have read this release and that I understand and agree to the following:

1. I permit recordings of my voice and likeness to be made in connection with a media project currently titled _____.

2. I authorize _____, the proprietor(s) of this project, in perpetuity, to process, store, reproduce, distribute, and display recordings of my voice and likeness made in connection with this project, in whatever ways, forms, and media, and by whatever methods and technologies they may choose.

3. I waive, in perpetuity, the rights to any and all compensation for these recordings, other than such rights as may be set forth in other written agreements between myself and the proprietor(s) of this project.

_____   _____
Performer signature   Witness signature

_____   _____
Performer printed name   Witness printed name

_____   _____
Date   Date

As it appears here, this sample release may not be a legal document in your area. If you do not use the standard commercial releases designed specifically for your state or province, you should modify this sample or create your own form with the help of an attorney.

actors perform together should be scheduled consecutively.

- *Things.* Properties and large items such as special automobiles may be available only briefly, so the scenes in which they appear should be grouped together.

- *Conditions.* Daylight or darkness, sunshine or overcast, some natural conditions are called for in the script. You can sometimes shoot night scenes during the day and even vice versa, but the process is complex and expensive. So, for each location, schedule night or sunset scenes together, **Figure 9-14**.

A typical production breakdown will prioritize scenes as follows:

1. All scenes at location X.

1.1 All location X scenes at special times, especially night.

1.1.1 All location X night scenes with performer A.

Figure 9-14.
Downtown McKinley. The conditions before sunset called the "magic hour."

If key performers can work only at certain times, you may be forced to organize the shoot around their schedules, even if it means returning to the same locations.

Support Services

Even on small productions, support services can make a big difference in the morale and enthusiasm of cast and crew. Parking is especially important, and if the production is big enough to require supply trucks for lighting and other equipment, close and convenient parking is essential.

Food is equally important. It is good to have light snacks, coffee, and soft drinks available, especially for early morning or late evening shoots. In addition, meal breaks should be scheduled and adhered to. If public eating facilities are not easily available, meals should be provided.

Finally, attend to everyone's comfort. Since all production involves considerable waiting, especially for the performers, provide a comfortable lounging area (often called a "green room"). At interior locations, this may be just a room or other quiet area out of the way. Outdoors, it may be as simple as an area supplied with folding chairs and shaded by a tarpaulin. Restroom facilities are important too, and, if you are shooting at an outdoor location, may be required by local ordinance. If you are working, say, in the desert, you will need a water supply for washing as well as drinking, along with appropriate portable toilets.

Budgets: Production Costs

All video production costs money. Anticipating and controlling expenses is as vital to the success of a project as writing, directing, or videography. The formal process of identifying these production costs and allocating funds to pay them is *budgeting*. Typically, a project budget is created early in production planning and then refined and updated throughout the course of the production. Though budgets can sometimes be complex, the principles that govern them are simple:

- Identify every item that will cost money, including salaries, rentals, purchases, services, and rights.
- Estimate the amount of each item that will be needed.
- Determine the exact unit cost for each item.

- Multiply the item amount by the unit cost to determine the total cost for that item.
- Add the item totals together to determine the overall expected costs.

Figure 9-15 illustrates this process with three types of budget items: a salary, a rental, and a purchase. (Simpler projects will, of course, cost less.)

Figure 9-15.
Budget line items.

ITEM	AMOUNT	UNIT COST	TOTAL
actor	4 days	$300/day	$1,200
camera dolly	9 days	$120/day	$1,080
gaffer tape	2 rolls	$12/roll	$24

Standard Production Budgets

Even simple productions can have so many expenses that it is difficult to identify every one in advance. For this reason, most established production houses develop or buy preorganized budget breakdowns. These are usually computer spreadsheet or database programs developed for film and video budgeting, **Figure 9-16.**

To customize these standard forms, you delete line items that do not apply to your project, add any specialized items that may be unique to your production, and then fill in the amount and rate for every item. Typically, the software calculates totals, sales tax, and similar charges when applicable.

If you have some experience in developing spreadsheets or other databases, you may find it productive to build your own custom system for production planning, scheduling, and budgeting. In addition to spreadsheets and databases, some project management software packages include financial functions.

Contingency funds

Since video production is always vulnerable to unexpected events and expenses, every budget should include a contingency fund: an amount of money set aside to cover unforseen costs. A contingency amount is typically calculated as a percentage of the total production budget — anywhere from one percent to perhaps 15 percent. A five-percent contingency in a $10,000 budget would be $500, a relatively modest sum.

To determine how to set your contingency fund, evaluate the uncertainties (like weather) that might prolong production, and adjust your rate proportionally. For example, a training video on how to perform an assembly line procedure might be safe with a very small contingency budget item. But if you are shooting a nature program on the elusive mountain lion in its natural habitat, provide enough extra money for many additional shooting days.

Ready to Shoot

At this point you may think that planning even a simple video requires a great amount of work. To put preproduction in perspective, remember that many of the requirements covered in this chapter are unnecessary for short, simple videos — although all programs will benefit from a certain amount of systematic preparation. If you plan to make professional programs of even modest scope, you will find that careful production planning is essential to success.

Technical Terms

Blacking the tape: Prerecording an entire tape with a pure-black picture, no sound, and time code (or in analog formats, a control track).

Budgeting: Predicting the costs of every aspect of a production and allocating funds to cover it.

Crew: Production staff members who work behind the camera. In larger professional productions, the producer, director, and management staff are not considered "crew."

Dress: To add decorative items to a set or location. Such items are called "set dressing."

Talent: Every production member who performs for the camera.

Figure 9-16:
Summary page of a sample budget. (Movie Magic Budgeting, Creative Planet)

Acct#	Category Title	Page	Total
	TOTAL PRODUCTION		**818,957**
5100	Editing	10	28,259
5200	Post-Production Film/Lab	11	77,052
5300	Post-Production Sound	11	0
5400	Music	11	0
5500	Titles	12	0
5600	Opticals	12	0
5700	Post-Production Video	12	0
5800	Facilities	13	0
5900	Post-Prod Travel/Living	13	0
	TOTAL POST PRODUCTION		**105,311**
6100	Insurance	13	0
6200	Legal Costs	13	0
6300	Publicity	13	14,468
6400	Miscellaneous	13	0
	TOTAL OTHER		**14,468**
	Completion Bond: 0.00% (0 excluded)		0
	Contingency: 0.00% (0 excluded)		0
	Overhead: 0.00% (0 excluded)		0
	Insurance: 0.00% (0 excluded)		0
	Total Above-The-Line		13,267
	Total Below-The-Line		938,736
	Total Above and Below-The-Line		952,003
	Grand Total		952,003

10 Camera Systems

Contents

About Camera Systems
Camera Functions
Camera Support Systems
Camcorder Setup
Lens Setup

Objectives

After studying this chapter, you will be able to:

- ❏ Explain the functions of major camcorder controls.
- ❏ Describe the major camcorder support systems.
- ❏ Prepare camera equipment for shooting.
- ❏ Operate all camcorder systems.

(JVC Corporation)

About Camera Systems

The camcorder is, of course, the one indispensable tool for video makers. If you understand how it works and how to use it effectively, you are on your way to professional production. Camcorders include many different systems and controls. To make sense of all these features it is helpful to separate the camcorder into its two fundamental halves.

The word "camcorder" is a combination of "camera" and "recorder," because the unit contains both components:

● The *camera* section converts incoming light into images and sound into audio, both coded in the form of electrical signals.

● The *recorder* section copies those signals onto magnetic tape and then plays them back on demand. The recorder section works exactly like a VCR deck; indeed, you can connect an analog camcorder to a TV set and play back footage directly. Many camcorders have a two-position switch. In one position, the unit functions as a camera/recorder. In the other position it becomes a VCR/editor.

Some video recording systems use disk or flash memory cards rather than tape; and in some television studio setups, you may use a video camera that sends its signal to a separate recorder.

Not only does a camcorder include two types of machines, it also records two completely different kinds of information:

● *Video* (picture) information is converted into the video signal by the imaging chip, called a **charge-coupled device (CCD).**

● *Audio* (sound) information is converted into the audio signal by a microphone, either built into or plugged into the camcorder. Each type of information has its own controls and requires its own procedures, so it will be helpful if you think of video and audio separately.

Audio recording, which is also performed by the camcorder, is covered separately in Chapter 14.

Camera Functions

The job of the camera half of a camcorder is to convert incoming light into coherent optical images (recognizable pictures) and then translate those optical images into an electrical video signal. Here is how the video signal is created:

● Light passes through the camcorder lens, which organizes it into a coherent image and projects it onto the surface of the CCD, **Figure 10-1**.

The CCD is sometimes referred to simply as "the chip," despite the fact that it is only one of several solid state chips in the camcorder.

Figure 10-1.
The lens projects an optical image on the imaging chip. (Canon USA)

● The CCD contains hundreds of thousands of microscopic sensors. Each sensor responds differently to the amount and color of light striking it, so each sensor creates a different electrical signal.

● The thousands of separate signals are processed by electronic circuits that combine them into the composite signal for one complete image called a frame.

● This process repeats 25 or 30 times each second, to create a video track coded in electronic form.

In the North American video display format (NTSC), each frame is electronically divided into two separate 1/60 second **fields,** one containing all the even-numbered picture lines and the other all the odd ones. The two fields are combined to make one frame by a process called "interlacing."

Each frame of the video signal lasts only 1/30 second before it is replaced by the next frame. This means that the signal must be displayed as it is created or it will be lost forever.

One Chip or Three?

Most modern camcorders convert optical images into electronic signals by means of microchips called "charge coupled devices" or "CCDs" or just "chips."

The imaging chip is a Charge-Coupled Device (CCD).

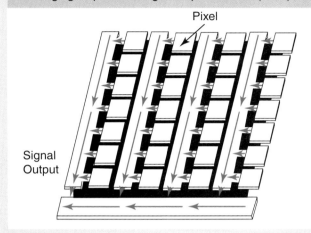

Pixel

Signal Output

Every color in the spectrum can be created by combining the red, green, and blue primary colors.

How a chip works

A CCD is a grid of tiny solar cells —so small that 400,000 or more can fit on a rectangle about one-quarter inch wide, measured diagonally. Like all solar cells, each of these minute sensors converts light into electricity— the brighter the light, the stronger the current. Sixty times each second (in NTSC video), electronic circuits drain the energy generated in these cells and send the pattern of charges to the recording mechanism. It is this pattern of light and dark that makes the picture.

Recording colors

Since the strength of the current generated by CCD cells depends on the brightness of the light, rather than its wavelength, these solar collectors cannot distinguish colors. To a cell, a certain amount of blue light "looks" much like the same amount of green or red light.

To record color information, each full-color picture unit is created by not one but three sensors working together. Each light collecting surface is covered with a different colored filter, red, green, or blue. The red-filtered sensor responds only to red light, the green-filtered one to green, and the blue-filtered one to blue. As a result, each sensor creates a slightly different amount of current.

Though visible light contains a theoretically infinite number of different colors, they can all be created by combining different intensities of the primary hues: red, green, and blue. By analyzing the currents produced by the three sensors, the camcorder circuits deduce the color striking each sensor. When you consider that this analysis takes place 60 times per second on hundreds of thousands of cell triplets, you can appreciate the engineering miracle in every camcorder.

This three-cell design has drawbacks, too. Because it is so difficult to lay these near-microscopic color filters

precisely over individual cells, they are not always perfectly positioned, and color inaccuracies result. And because three cells are needed for every one color element, the chip has only one-third the resolution (sharpness) that would theoretically be possible if every cell were recording a separate part of the image. That is why the more sophisticated camcorders use not one chip but three.

Three-chip cameras

In a three-chip camcorder, the entire surface of each chip is covered with a single primary color filter: red, green, or blue. This approach eliminates filter registration problems and increases picture sharpness. Professionals also prefer three-chip models because each chip can be supplied with its own electrical circuitry. That makes it possible to fine-tune the balance among the three chips to obtain the most accurate color rendition.

Three-chip camcorders have one problem: in order to direct the incoming light to three different surfaces, it must be divided into thirds by optical elements called beam splitters. Because some light is lost in this more complex processing, less gets through to the imaging chips. As a result, three-chip camcorders do not usually perform as well as their one-chip cousins do in very low light. In most professional applications, this is not a drawback because production companies typically light their scenes.

A three-chip imaging system. (Canon USA)

Blue chip

Light path

Red chip

Beam splitters

Green chip

Recorder Functions

To preserve short-lived video images, engineers developed the videotape recorder to record them. Combined in one unit with the camera, the recorder forms the "corder" part of the camcorder package.

Interlaced Scanning. Traditionally, video cameras produce "interlaced" frames, in which the odd-numbered lines of each frame are recorded as one field and the even-numbered lines as a second field.

Here is how a videotape recorder handles interlaced images:

● The electrically encoded information about each video field (one-half frame) is sent to a record head spinning on a drum in the recorder.

● The record head preserves the signal by selectively magnetizing metallic particles on the videotape that moves across its path.

VCR drums actually have at least two video record and two video playback heads. To create a two-field frame, each head records or plays a single field.

● When set to playback, the recorder passes the tape across the spinning drum again. This time, separate playback heads recreate field from the magnetically-coded tape particles.

● Sent at a rate of 60 per second to a playback unit, these fields are interlaced line-by-line to create 30 complete images displayed on the surface of a picture tube or LCD display, **Figure 10-2**.

In short, the "corder" section of a camcorder is a very compact VCR, with all the usual tape controls. Because of their sophisticated recording features, camcorders are often used in editing, as either source or assembly decks.

Some digital camcorder systems record every line in the video picture, in order, instead of dividing odd and even lines into separate fields. This single-pass recording system is called "progressive scan."

Digital Camcorders

Analog camera systems are giving way to cameras that record audio and video signals digitally. This change is vitally important to

Figure 10-2.
A standard TV image is created by "interlacing" the lines of Fields A and B.

Field A...   plus Field B...

= 1 frame

video postproduction, but it does not greatly alter the basic processes of shooting with the camcorder. In most ways, digital camcorders work much like analog models. The lens, focus, shutter, and aperture admit and process light into images, and the CCD converts those light images to coded electrical signals. The recording system preserves the results on videotape.

The one major difference is inside the camera, between the CCD and the recording mechanism. There, an analog-to-digital *(A/D)* chip converts the electrical signal from the continuously varying voltage of an analog waveform to the characteristic on/off pulses of digitally coded current. The recorder section captures this signal as digital video.

In some ways, digital recording does affect the way a videographer uses the camcorder. For example, digital signal processing allows extensive control over white balance and color. For this reason, it is sometimes possible to obtain acceptable image quality in working environments with mediocre lighting conditions, **Figure 10-3**.

Digital video also permits the recording of finer detail. The mini DV format that is popular in amateur and entry-level-professional camcorders captures images superior to similar analog formats. In fact, the resolution is so superior that mini DV digital camcorders are now used in many industrial and ENG (Electronic News Gathering) applications, as well as in a number of independent feature films.

Figure 10-3.
Even severe color casts...

can often be corrected by a digital camcorder.

Camera Support Systems

With the principal camcorder functions explained, we can survey the major equipment systems, starting from the ground up, with camcorder support. Camcorders are supported by *tripods*, *stabilizers*, or *dollies*.

Tripods

Tripods are by far the most common camera support. They have three legs instead of four because a three-point support will not wobble on uneven ground.

To see the problem with four legs, try leveling a card table outdoors.

To deploy a camera tripod, set up the feet, the legs, and the head, **Figure 10-4**, in that order. Most tripods have two sets of feet: soft, non-skid pads for smooth surfaces like floors and pointed pins for softer outdoor surfaces. It is easier to select one set or the other first, while the tripod is still collapsed. Unless you are setting up a low-angle shot with the tripod legs unextended, start by extending them fully. Different models use different methods for locking the leg sections.

Before you can adjust the tripod head you need to level it on the legs. Professional tripods let you unlock the head, tilt it until a bubble level shows that the head is level, and then lock it, **Figure 10-5**.

With less expensive units, you must level the head by adjusting the legs. First, use the bubble level to locate the high side of the tripod; then point one leg directly at that side.

Figure 10-4.
A tripod head designed for a lightweight video camcorder. (Manfrotto/Bogen)

Shorten the high-side leg until the bubble level indicates that the head is level.

Adjusting the Head

With the tripod set up and leveled, the next task is to set various controls so that the head operates smoothly when you move it and does not move by itself, **Figure 10-6**.

Quick release mechanism. If your camera and tripod connect via a quick release system, make sure that the camcorder and tripod head are tightly screwed to their docking plates. This helps prevent camera wobble.

Pan handle. Generally speaking, you want the pan handle installed on whichever side of the tripod head gives you easiest access to camcorder controls. Normally, the

Figure 10-5.
A—A ball level.

B—This ball-level mechanism can be added to lightweight tripods, between the head and legs. (Manfrotto/Bogen)

Figure 10-6.
A professional tripod head. (Gitzo/Bogen)

handle is installed on the right side because the viewfinder is on the left. However, if the camcorder's only record button is on the right-side hand grip, you may need to install the pan handle on the left.

Avoid using the camcorder's hand grip while working on a tripod. Turning the unit with the pan handle makes for smoother movement and less stress on the camcorder.

Camera balance. Some tripods allow you to balance the weight of the camcorder, either by sliding the unit forward or backward on the head, or by adjusting a built-in counterbalancing mechanism. Adjust the balance until your camera remains level even when the tilt lock and tilt drag controls are completely disengaged.

Tilt lock. A tilt lock prevents an unattended camcorder from tipping forward or backward. (Some tripod heads lack balancing mechanisms, and even those that have them may also provide a tilt lock, for extra security.) At the

start of the shooting session, engage and disengage this lock to ensure that it is working properly.

Tilt and pan drag. You execute vertical and horizontal camera swings more smoothly if you are pushing against resistance (called *drag)*. Too little drag is ineffective, while too much makes for jerky movements. Adjust the horizontal drag control to your taste; then disengage the tilt lock and do the same for the vertical drag control. That way, you will not waste time on setup when the equipment is needed.

Stabilizers

If you will be using a ***camera stabilizer,*** you should preassemble, adjust, and test it at the beginning of the shooting session. Camera stabilizers are systems designed to smooth hand-held shots, **Figure 10-7.** The most popular types are available in sizes to fit every camera from consumer mini-camcorders to large professional models.

Unlike internal stabilizers, which steady the image being recorded, camera stabilizers are external hardware designed to steady the entire camcorder.

Figure 10-7.
A camera stabilizer in operation. (Hollywood Lite)

Though various camera stabilizers differ in their design and engineering, most of them consist of four parts:

- The head, which supports the camera.
- The counterweight system, which balances the camera.
- The pivot system, which allows the camera and counterweight to move freely.
- The view screen, which allows the operator to frame and follow action without touching the camera's internal viewfinder.

In some systems, the view screen and/or external battery is part of the counterbalance system.

Well-adjusted and competently used, stabilizers work amazingly well, delivering footage as steady as dolly shots, while allowing the camera operator to follow the action with a flexibility that dollies cannot match. See **Figure 10-8.**

Figure 10-8.
The paths of the subject and the camera operator. A—The camera starts close to the car... B—pulls back as the subject emerges... C—climbs one step to the sidewalk... D—plus six steps to the archway... E—moves to one side... F—begins to draw ahead of the subject... G—who stops at the fountain... H—while the camera continues to the other end of the courtyard.

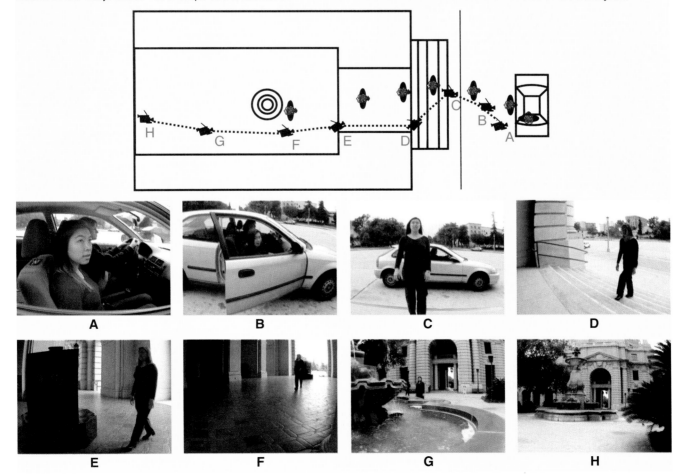

On the other hand, stabilizers can be time-consuming to set up and to counterbalance, and they may need frequent fine-tuning to work properly. Also, they require considerable practice to operate.

In feature film production, camera stabilizer operators are specialists who are hired solely to provide stabilized shots. Often, they receive screen credit for their work.

Dollies

Camera dollies are wheeled platforms used to make smooth moving shots. Dollies are classified by two sets of criteria: design and wheel system. There are two major types of camera dolly designs. **Pedestal** dollies consist of a camera head mounted on a telescoping center column. The column, in turn, is supported by a wheeled base. Pedestal dollies can be smoothly moved up or down ("pedestaled") during a shot. **Cart** dollies are essentially rolling platforms fitted with tripods. Heavier, more expensive types allow booming via a crane arm that moves up and down, but simpler cart dollies generally lack this feature. Some ultra-light dollies consist of tripods supplied with wheels and mounted on rails, **Figure 10-9.**

Dollies may be fitted with two different types of wheels. Floor wheels are designed to roll directly on smooth surfaces like interior floors. Most systems allow the dolly to change the direction in mid-shot by swiveling as they roll. The most sophisticated systems have four-wheel steer, so that all four wheels can be turned at once and the dolly can "crab" sideways. When used with rails, the Fisher dolly (see Figure 10-9) maintains alignment using the small horizontal guide wheels visible in the illustration. Rail wheels, by contrast,

work like train wheels, fitting over rails designed for the purpose. Floor wheel systems are quicker to set up (there are no rails to lay and align) and more flexible (the camera can change direction in mid-shot). On the other hand, rail wheel systems permit dolly shots outside and on floors too uneven for wheeled dollies.

Camcorder Setup

With camera support ready, the next task is to set up the camcorder itself, including the power supply, the external monitor (if present), and the videotapes.

To avoid repetition, the aperture and shutter systems are covered in the following chapter, though they too are camcorder components.

Power Supply

All major camcorder systems run on electrical power. Even the lens needs electricity for its zoom motor. Typically, a wall plug and cord supply 120 volt AC power to a charger/converter. The charger/converter changes the high-power AC to low-voltage DC power and sends it to the camcorder to run its systems and charge its battery.

Many countries use 240 volt AC power, rather than the 120 volt that is standard in North America. Many professional camera systems can be set for either voltage.

Though all power originates as 120 volt AC, you will operate your camcorder on battery power much of the time, except in studio-type situations where camera movement is restricted and wall power is conveniently close. Running on DC power, you may be

Figure 10-9.
Some track and dolly systems are extremely portable. (Microdolly Hollywood)… A large studio dolly. (J.L. Fisher Corp.) A wheeled spreader can convert a lightweight tripod into a dolly. (Manfrotto/Bogen)

using any of three different types of battery types. Brick batteries fit on or in the camcorder itself, **Figure 10-10**. They are light and convenient, but their capacity is relatively small. Block batteries are carried in cases on shoulder straps. Their capacity is often greater but they are heavy and relatively clumsy. Belt batteries are as powerful as block batteries, but more convenient to wear because their weight is distributed around the videographer's waist.

Brick, block, or belt styles are all suitable for news, documentary, and event (wedding) videography, especially if you also use battery-powered lights. Whichever battery type you select, you should have an external recharger and enough spare batteries to continue shooting while recharging.

Viewfinder

The viewfinder shows you the world as your camcorder sees it, because all finders display essentially the same image that is recorded on tape. Viewfinders come in two basic styles: internal and external.

An internal finder is basically a tiny monitor inside a housing on the camcorder. Internal viewfinders have several advantages. They are fitted with magnifying lenses to make critical focusing easier. These lenses can also be adjusted so that people with vision problems can see the finder clearly without glasses. Safe inside their housings, they are shielded from image-degrading light (like a bright light falling on a TV screen). Because they are actual TV tubes, they show color and contrast much as they will appear on playback.

External viewfinders, **Figure 10-11**, are small LCD (liquid crystal display) monitors attached to the camcorder body.

External finders also have advantages. Their larger image can be easier to see, except in very bright light. Because they can be seen from a wide range of angles, they permit greater flexibility in positioning the camcorder. By freeing the videographer from pressing the internal finder to one eye, they greatly reduce fatigue during lengthy shoots. Because they are obviously TV screens, the user tends to look *at* them rather than

Figure 10-10.
Professional batteries mount externally. (Anton Bauer)

Camcorder Power Checklist

Before shooting, use this checklist to ensure that you will have reliable power.

AC power
1. Locate power outlets.
2. Supply power cord and extension as needed.
3. Hook up and test power supply to camcorder.

Battery power
1. Set up battery charger and check condition of all batteries.
2. Mount fully charged battery on camcorder and test.
3. Recharge second battery for later use.

To decide how many batteries you need for continuous shooting, determine the time required to fully recharge a completely discharged battery. Then calculate how long a battery lasts in a typical shooting situation, where you are not recording continuously. For example, if a battery typically lasts one hour, but recharging takes twice as long, you can shoot continuously if you have three batteries and two external chargers.

A two-charger system for batteries A, B, and C.

Hour	1	2	3	4	5	6	7	8	9
In camera	A	B	C	A	B	C	A	B	C
In charger 1	B	A	A	C	C	B	B	A	A
In charger 2	C	C	B	B	A	A	C	C	B

Figure 10-11.
An external LCD viewfinder.

through them. This makes it easier to evaluate images as two-dimensional compositions, rather than as the real world viewed through a tiny window.

External viewfinders have some problems as well. Their color, contrast, and sharpness cannot equal those of a tube display, so they deliver a less accurate representation of the image being taped. Also, their picture is easily washed out in bright light.

Many external viewfinders can be fitted with hoods for outdoor use; and some newer screen designs can be viewed in bright light.

Whether internal or external, all viewfinders display information about what the camcorder is doing. Different models show different data, but the finder information in **Figure 10-12** is typical.

Figure 10-12.
Typical viewfinder information.

The information display is yet another reason for looking at the viewfinder rather than through it. Because it warns you that your battery is out of power or that you have neglected to insert a tape, the viewfinder display can often avert major problems.

Most camera viewfinders are adjustable. At the start of each shooting session, set up the:

- *Displays.* To minimize the text overlays that can obscure parts of the image, program your finder to show only the information you want.
- *Brightness and contrast.* Set these values to match the light in which you are shooting..
- **Diopter correction.** For internal finders, customize the focus to your eyesight by adjusting the diopter control until the finder screen is sharp.

In setting diopter correction, sharpen the text overlaid on the viewfinder rather than the image beneath it. Remember that you are not trying to focus the picture on the screen but the screen itself.

Monitor

If you are shooting at the advanced amateur level, an external color monitor is highly desirable; if your production is professional, it is indispensable. A standalone production monitor should have at least a nine-inch screen, and a 13-inch model is better, **Figure 10-13.** Camera-mounted LCD monitors are useful, but they are too small and low-resolution to use in evaluating video quality.

An external monitor performs two vital tasks. It lets you check exposure, lighting, color, and sharpness as shots are being taped; and it allows other people (like a director or script supervisor) to see exactly what is being recorded.

Separate monitors may be impractical for programs such as weddings and documentaries. Also, when making long or complex moving shots, you may need to disconnect the monitor cable from the camcorder.

To ensure accurate color display, the monitor should be set up at the start of each shooting session. All professional and many consumer camcorders can output standard color bars for use in adjusting the monitor. If your camcorder cannot generate bars, set it up as follows:

Figure 10-13.
A reference monitor. (JVC Corporation)

- Set the white balance on the camera, as discussed later in this chapter.
- Aim the camcorder at a standard color model card, obtainable at most larger camera stores.
- Adjust the monitor for most pleasing picture.

High-quality professional production monitors offer both AC and battery operation, and can be calibrated to the same standards as studio monitors. For less-elaborate productions, nine- or 13-inch consumer-grade monitors are available, **Figure 10-14,** at far lower cost, with AC/DC power and the composite and/or S-video inputs required for a quality picture.

Avoid monitors that have only RF connectors, since most camcorders cannot use RF cables.

Figure 10-14.
An AC/DC TV set can be used as a location monitor.

Videotape

Set up and test recording tapes as carefully as any other component of your videographer's kit. In particular, verify that the tape has been blacked, that it will record a signal properly, and that it is identified with a unique label. To double-check that a tape has been blacked, play back a few minutes of it from the start of the tape and verify that the screen is black and the time counter or time code readout is functioning.

Preblacking recording tapes is discussed in Chapter 9.

Next, verify that the tape will record properly by taping any convenient subject and then playing it back. If the tape is defective, the horizontal lines and/or rolling picture will warn you of the problem before you record actual program footage. If you see any problems, mark the tape defective and discard at once.

Finally, make sure that the tape is properly labeled, as suggested in the sidebar, *Identifying Videotapes.* By systematically labeling every single tape, you can help prevent the disaster of destroying previously recorded material by mistakenly reusing a tape.

To further prevent taping over existing material, it is essential to start each session by "rolling down to raw stock." If it is a new tape, play from the head of the tape to about one minute in order to verify that it is blank. If it has footage on it, roll through the recorded material until you are certain that you are past the last shot and into blank tape.

In either case, begin your new recording session at that point on the tape.

White Balance

With the videotape prepared, the next task is to adjust the camcorder's various exposure systems to suit the shooting conditions. You begin this process by setting the white balance. ***White balance*** refers to the overall color cast of the light in which you are shooting. Outdoor light tends to be slightly bluish, **Figure 10-15,** while light bulbs cast a warmer, redder light. To the human eye, a sheet of paper looks equally white in both kinds of light because the brain automatically compensates for differences in color tint. Unlike a brain, however, a camcorder can only record colors exactly as its chip and circuits receive them. Without

Identifying Videotapes

Many beginners are casual about labeling videocassettes, until they are taught a painful lesson by an accident like these: a used but unlabeled tape is reused, thereby erasing the original footage, or a tape is misplaced because its contents are not evident from its label. Here are some guidelines for the proper identification of both full-size and miniature videocassettes.

Full-size face labels

The large face label on every tape should carry the following information (sample information is in italics):
- **Producer/company:** *Jenna Jones Productions*
- **Program work title:** *Sidewinder Drill*
- **Date:** *06/22/04*
- **Time code start:** *03:00:00:00*. Some systems allow you to set the hour at which the time code begins. By selecting a different hour for each tape, you can shoot up to 24 one-hour tapes without repeating time codes.
- **Tape type:** *Camera orig*
- **Tape number:** *#03*
- **Total tapes of** *[blank]*. This information cannot be added until shooting is over. If the production should use 14 tapes in all, this particular label would eventually say *Camera Orig #03 of 14.*

Full-size spine labels
- **Program work title:** *Sidewinder Drill*
- **Tape type and number:** *Camera orig #03*

Miniature face labels

Small format tapes offer very little writing space, so give the production a code instead of a title.
- **Program work title:** *Prod. 013*
- **Tape type and number:** *Cam orig #03*

Miniature spine labels
- **Program work title:** *013*
- **Tape type and number:** *Orig #03*

Full-size tape cassette labels.

Identifying the tape's purpose (*camera original*) may seem unnecessary when shooting; but later, when you edit the program, you will need to distinguish camera tapes from assembly tapes, work tapes, and other types.

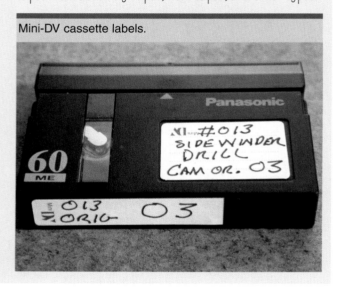

Mini-DV cassette labels.

adjustable white balance, outdoor scenes would look too blue and/or indoor scenes too red. The videographer's job is to set the camera's white balance to match the color of the light at each new location.

Different levels of camcorders offer different degrees of white balance control. Simpler models set white balance automatically. Circuits in the camera analyze the incoming light, determine its overall color cast, and adjust color sensitivity to produce a tint-free white on playback. You do not have to think about white balance at all, but you must accept whatever setting the camcorder makes.

More flexible camcorders include a white balance switch for selecting outdoor, indoor, or fully automatic settings. Some cameras

Figure 10-15.
Outdoor light is naturally bluish.

include a separate position for fluorescent light. With this type of white balance control, try using the automatic setting only when you are forced to shoot too fast to worry about subtleties of color balance. In many camcorders, the individual settings will usually deliver better-looking results.

Still more sophisticated camcorders include fully manual white balance. To use it, hold a white card so that its image fills the entire frame. See **Figure 10-16.**

Figure 10-16.
Setting white balance manually.

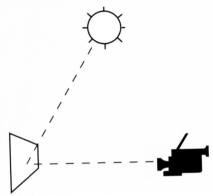

When you activate the white balance circuitry, the camcorder reads the light reflected from the card and sets itself to record it as neutral white. A professional videographer will typically set white balance to match every shooting location.

Even if you usually use the automatic setting, there are situations in which manual white balance is preferable. When the main light source is an odd color, such as yellowish sodium vapor or bluish mercury lighting, hold the card so that it reflects light only from the colored source. Or, when a colored surface tints the light reflected onto the scene, set white balance while aligning the card so that it picks up the colored reflections. This method can reduce or even eliminate the color cast from the strongly colored surface.

The best white balance systems add fully-adjustable override controls. Once you have set the white balance, you can gradually make the overall tint warmer or cooler until you obtain exactly the color you prefer. When making adjustments, use a good external color monitor to check the effect. Whatever your system, it is essential to select (or at least check) the white balance setting each time you move to a new shooting location.

Poor white balance can be corrected some-what in postproduction, but the results are rarely as good as if the camera had been set correctly in the first place.

Color Temperature

The overall color cast of a light source is described as its **color temperature**, and is expressed in degrees on the Kelvin temperature scale. The higher the color temperature, the bluer the light. Here are some typical light sources and their color temperatures ("K" is read as "degrees Kelvin."):

Typical color temperatures.

The daylight or outdoor white balance setting usually matches the 5,000-5,500K of sunlight and the indoor or incandescent setting matches the 3,200K of halogen movie lights. (Almost all halogen bulbs, including work lights and home bulbs are 3,200K.)

Many modern camcorders have separate white balance settings for fluorescent lights. Fluorescent light differs from both natural and incandescent (light bulb) illumination. Try both fluorescent and outdoor settings when shooting in fluorescent light, observing the effect on a color monitor. With warm fluorescent tubes and/or yellowed light fixture diffusion panels, you may find that the indoor setting yields the most pleasing color. If you have full manual white balance, use it instead, to match the fluorescent lighting precisely.

Lens Setup

The process of recording video images begins at the camcorder's lens, which gathers light rays reflected from subjects and focuses them on the imaging chip, **Figure 10-17.**

Most general purpose video camcorders are fitted with zoom lenses that allow you to change image sizes, either between shots or continuously while shooting.

Lens Mount

On simpler cameras, the lens is perma-nently attached. More sophisticated models

Figure 10-17.
Cutaway of a zoom lens with optical stabilization. (Canon USA)

exchange a general-purpose zoom lens (perhaps 5mm-60mm in some formats) for another zoom with a much longer range (such as 40mm-480mm) in order to shoot wildlife at great distances from the camera.

If your camcorder does have interchangeable lenses, you should always check to see that the lens is firmly attached to its mount, without any wiggle ("play").

Front Element

The next task is to set up the front end of your lens, including cleaning, installing a filter, and mounting a lens hood.

Cleaning. Visually inspect the lens to ensure that it is free of dust and smudges. Dust can be spritzed away with a blower bulb and brushed off with a lens brush. Smudges should be removed by cleaning, as described in the sidebar *Cleaning the Lens.* Any dirt on a lens will degrade its quality; in bright light, the depth of field (focus) of the lens may be so great that the front element (glass) of the lens itself is sharp, including all the dust and smudges on it. Also, a dirty lens increases light flare.

often have lens mounts that permit you to replace one lens with another, **Figure 10-18.** However, changing lenses during a shooting session is uncommon, for two reasons. First, the alignment between a lens and the imaging chips behind it is so critical that it is often safer to mount and calibrate a lens in a studio or lab.

All camcorders with interchangeable lenses are three-chip designs. Certain models, notably from Canon, are designed to allow changing lenses in the field.

Second, lenses are usually changed to accommodate the demands of very different shooting situations. For example, you may

Filter. If your lens is not recessed behind a protective glass window (and if it is threaded to receive filters) you should mount a "transparent lens cap" called a UV, 1A, or skylight filter to keep the lens clean. In very bright lighting conditions, a ***neutral density filter*** can replace the clear model. Neutral density filters reduce the light intensity without affecting color. A ***polarizing filter,*** **Figure 10-19,** can be installed to enhance the appearance of the sky. Never install more than one filter at a time, to avoid degrading image quality and showing the filter edge in the picture. A filter should be cleaned exactly like the lens itself.

Lens hood. If the lens is mounted outside the camera body and the front end is threaded, you may wish to mount a lens hood to help keep direct light off the lens. When selecting a lens hood, check it to verify that it does not appear in the picture when the lens is in the extreme wide angle zoom position. If it does, use the hood only for telephoto applications like sports and wildlife videography.

If you have mounted a filter, screw the lens hood onto the filter's front threads.

Figure 10-18.
A camcorder with interchangeable lenses. (Canon USA)

Figure 10-19.
A polarizing filter.

Clouds in a blue sky...

are enhanced by a polarizer. (Tiffen)

Focus and Aperture

For setup purposes, decide whether to use the autofocus system or focus the lens manually, **Figure 10-20**. Most camcorders default to autofocus, so you set manual focus by disabling the auto mechanism. In the same way, the camera defaults to auto-exposure mode. If you wish to adjust the aperture manually, disable the autoexposure system. Make sure that you are in manual mode by looking for an exposure readout in the viewfinder. Some camcorders display actual f-stops (2.0, 2.8, 4.0, 5.6, etc.), while others display increments above or below the automatically determined aperture (+1, +2, +3; -1, -2, -3, etc.). Check your camcorder manual to learn whether each increment is one-half or one-third stop.

Zoom

Always check your zoom lens to verify that it is functioning correctly. If the zoom is motor-driven only, a malfunction means that the camera is essentially inoperative. If the

Figure 10-20.
Auto/manual focus controls. (Canon USA)

zoom can be operated manually (usually by a ring and handle on the lens) it is less likely to malfunction.

Image stabilization

Image stabilization is a mechanism for automatically steadying shaky pictures. Stabilization systems use sophisticated circuitry to detect camera shake by comparing each frame with the one that preceded it. (Some systems analyze the actual camcorder motion rather than changes in the images.) If just some of the pixels are different from those in the preceding frame, the system concludes that the subject is moving and no compensation is required. In frames A and B in **Figure 10-21,** the pixels recording the subject have moved with her, but the background remains the same.

If all the pixels have shifted in the same direction, the system identifies camera shake and moves the pixels back to their original locations in the frame for recording. An image stabilizing system would recognize frame D of Figure 10-21 as *camera shake* because the entire image has shifted. (So-called "fuzzy logic" functions can recognize when all pixels are shifting because the camera is moving, rather than just shaking.)

Image stabilization should not be confused with camera stabilizers, which reduce camera shake rather than compensate for shaking's effect on the image.

There are two different systems of image stabilization, optical and electronic. Optical stabilization shifts the path of the light on its way through the camera lens, so that the same image strikes the CCD. See **Figure 10-22.** Electronic stabilization records on only part of an oversize CCD. As

Figure 10-21.
An image stabilization system can distinguish subject movement (A and B)...

A

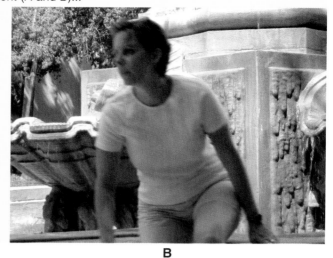

B

from camera shake (C and D).

C

D

Figure 10-22.
An optical image-stabilizing system. (Canon USA)

Variable
angle prism

Prism deflects image
element back to
original position

Image
element
shifts

the image shakes, the active recording area shifts in the opposite direction to compensate.

Both systems work very well, and image stabilization is a highly desirable feature on any camcorder. If you have image stabilization, by all means use it for hand-held work.

Some manufacturers recommend disabling stabilization when the camcorder is mounted on a tripod. You should test your particular system and decide whether or not to do this.

All Systems Ready

With the major camcorder systems set up and checked out, you are ready to begin the actual process of videography. That is the subject of *Chapter 11, Camera Operation.*

Cleaning the Lens

No matter how careful you are, you will have to clean your lens from time to time; so here are the supplies and techniques you will need. Cleaning supplies include lens fluid, lens cleaning tissues, and a blower bulb tipped with a soft brush. You can often find these items sold as a kit.

The lens is the most delicate component of a camcorder. (JVC Corporation)

A combination brush and blower.

In lens care, a good rule of thumb is, never do more than the minimum required to get the surface clean. To observe this rule, use the following methods in order, continuing to the next method only if the previous one fails to complete the job.

1. Making sure that your mouth is dry, blow short puffs of air *across* the lens to blow away loose dust.

2. Wipe the brush in concentric circles around the lens, starting from the center, while repeatedly squeezing the bulb to blow air through the brush.

3. Dispense a single drop of lens cleaning fluid onto the center of the lens; then crumple a sheet of lens tissue, grasp it between thumb and two fingers, and gently wipe the lens in a spiral motion, beginning in the center. When you reach the rim, crumple a second tissue and gently dry the lens, using the same spiral motion.

Never use facial tissues or paper towels instead of lens tissues, because they can leave lint on the lens or even scratch it. Also, avoid the cloths sold for cleaning eyeglasses if they have been chemically treated; however, *microfiber lens cloths* are effective and will not harm the lens coating.

Brush the lens in an outward spiral pattern.

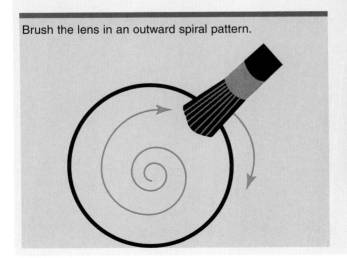

Used gently, microcloths intended for cleaning glasses are safe and effective on lenses.

Technical Terms

CCD (Charge-Coupled Device): The camcorder imaging chip that converts optical images into electronic signals.

Camera dolly: A rolling camera support. A cart dolly resembles a wagon; a pedestal dolly mounts the camera on a central post.

Color temperature: The overall color cast of nominally "white" light, expressed in degrees on the Kelvin scale. Sunlight color temperature (5,200K) is cooler (more bluish) than halogen light color temperature (3,200K).

Image stabilization: Compensation to minimize the effects of camera shake. Electronic stabilization shifts the image on the chip to counter movement; optical stabilization shifts parts of the lens instead.

Tripod: A three-legged camera support that permits leveling and turning the camera.

White balance: The camera setting selected to compensate for the color temperature of the light source that is illuminating the subject.

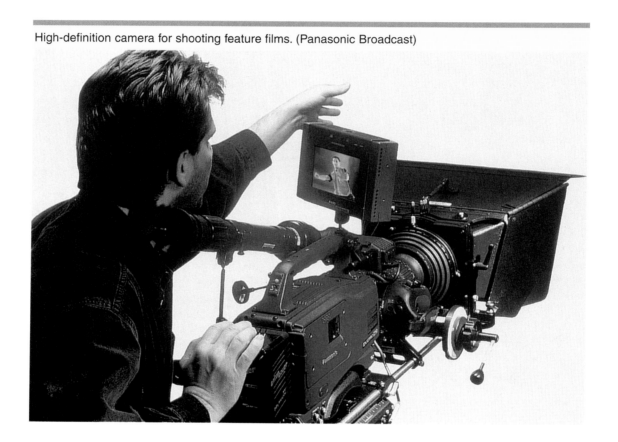

High-definition camera for shooting feature films. (Panasonic Broadcast)

11 Camera Operation

Contents

About Camera Operation
Working with Lenses
Setting Focus
Controlling Exposure
Operating the Camera

Objectives

After studying this chapter, you will be able to:

❑ Operate all camcorder systems
❑ Establish and adjust camera settings as needed for each shot
❑ Obtain pleasing pictorial compositions

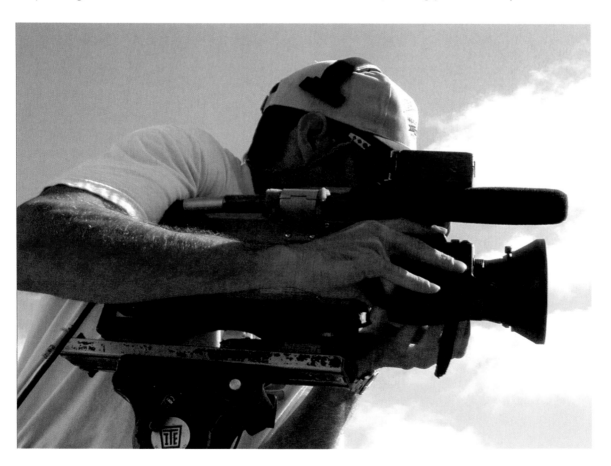

About Camera Operation

Just as gourmet foods are more than the recipes on which they are based, quality videography is greater than the sum of its taping techniques. The process is more art than science, and watching skilled videographers at work is like observing chefs in their kitchens. What makes them artists? What is the difference between a true videographer and a casual snapshooter? The answer has to do with the characteristics of the footage recorded: its quality, quantity, and usefulness.

Footage Quality

Professionally videotaped images display high technical and esthetic quality. That quality comes not only from technique but from attitude. Good videographers are fanatical about achieving the best images possible. This is their area of expertise and they love to utilize their skills and experience. They are never satisfied. Setup position, lighting, focus, and camera movement can always be improved. For a good videographer there is no such thing as "good enough."

Footage Quantity

Amateurs typically videotape everything only once. They record a view or a piece of action and then move on to the next one. Videographers are just the opposite, often shooting far more material than will appear in the finished program. They know that when shots are less than adequate (or omitted accidentally), they often cannot be taped at some later date. A wise videographer ensures that everything is recorded, and recorded properly, the first time, **Figure 11-1.**

Footage Utility

Though good videographers are fanatical about quality and patient about shooting enough footage to achieve it, they never forget that the whole purpose of their art is to enhance the effectiveness of the overall program. Videographers are not working alone but reinforcing the intentions of the director, the writer, and in most professional work, the client. Working in teams does not mean that videographers cannot be creative, but they exercise their creativity in productive collaboration with their colleagues and in service to the needs of the production.

Figure 11-1.
A project can never have "too much" footage.

In short, professional quality videotaping results not only from skill with the hardware but from an attitude toward the work. Having said that, we can begin to look at the techniques of videography. We will cover working with lenses; setting focus; controlling aperture, shutter, filtration, and gain; moving the camera; and composing the shot.

Working with Lenses

Video recording starts at the camcorder lens, which turns light rays into visual images and determines the pictorial qualities that those images will display.

Lens Focal Length

The way in which a lens renders images is determined by its focal length. The **focal length** of a lens is the distance (expressed in millimeters) from the front element of the lens to the focal *point*, the point at which the light rays intersect on their way to the focal *plane*, where the CCD is positioned, **Figure 11-2.**

Lenses are named according to focal length, for example, a "5mm lens" or a "75mm" lens. Originally, the focal length of every lens was fixed. To change focal lengths, a photographer had to dismount one lens and replace it with another. Today, however, almost all video optics are zoom lenses, whose focal lengths can be varied continuously between their shortest and longest positions. In the Mini-DV format, for instance, the focal length of a zoom lens might range from 3mm to 48mm. Since the

Figure 11-2.
The principal dimensions used in describing lenses.

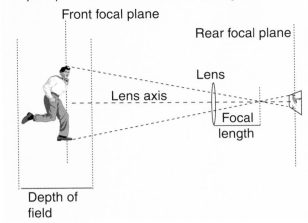

ratio of 48 to 3 is 16/1, this lens would be described as a "16-to-1 zoom."

As explained in the sidebar Wide Angle or Telephoto?, zoom ranges are dependent on the size of the imaging chip. Most of this discussion uses mini-DV focal lengths as examples.

Within a zoom range, the number of focal lengths is infinite. With a 3mm to 48mm zoom you could, theoretically, set the focal length at, say, 35mm or 35.2mm or 35.205mm (though you would need optical calibration equipment to do so). In actual production, however, professionals rarely refer to lenses by exact focal length. Instead, they divide them into three broad groups of focal lengths: wide angle, normal, and telephoto.

- **Normal** focal length lenses produce images that closely resemble human vision.
- **Wide angle** focal lengths include a wider field of view than normal lenses.
- **Telephoto** focal lengths show a narrower, more restricted field of view.

For proper contrast with "wide angle," long focal length lenses should probably be called "narrow angle" instead of telephoto.

Though wide angle, normal, and telephoto settings are actually just focal lengths within the zoom range of a single lens, they are usually discussed as if they were separate lenses. So when you read "telephoto lens" or "wide angle lens," remember that this typically refers to a setting on a zoom lens. As we discuss the optical qualities of wide, normal, and telephoto lenses, keep in mind that each category includes a whole range of individual

focal lengths. In our Mini-DV example, 3mm, 3.5mm, and 4mm are all different degrees of wide angle lens, and 14mm, 26mm, and 45mm are all telephoto focal lengths.

Finally, remember that the optical qualities of a particular focal length are dependent on the size of the camera CCD on which the image is created. For example, the 8mm focal length that is considered "normal" on a 1/4" chip would be an ultra-wide angle "fisheye" lens on a 35mm still camera. This is explained more fully in the sidebar *Wide Angle or Telephoto?*

Lens Characteristics

All lenses have three characteristics that affect the way the videographer uses them: angle of view, maximum aperture, and depth of field.

Angle of view

Every lens "sees" within a certain arc or **angle of view, Figure 11-3***:
- Wide angle lenses typically cover 70-140 degrees.
- Normal lenses cover 35-70 degrees.
- Telephoto lenses cover 18-35 degrees.

These distinctions are somewhat arbitrary — a "normal" lens that covers 69 degrees is not significantly different from a "wide angle" lens that covers 70 degrees.

Because of their broader coverage, wide angle lenses are useful in confined shooting areas, where longer focal lengths would not cover the whole action area.

Figure 11-3.
Angles of view of typical lenses.

Wide angle: 70°-140°

Normal: 35°-70° degrees

Telephoto: 18°-35°

Wide Angle or Telephoto?

Whether a lens is wide angle, normal, or telephoto depends on the size of the imaging area for which it is intended. The image created by the lens must cover the whole area of the CCD that is recording it. Since lens images are circular, while video frames are rectangular, the minimum image diameter must slightly exceed the diagonal of the frame, as you can see from the following illustration.

CCD chips for different visual formats.

1/4″ chip: 3.75 × 5mm

1/2″ chip: 7.5 × 10mm

35mm film: 24 × 36mm

(**Note:** Diagram is larger than actual size.)

The diameter of the lens must be slightly greater than the diagonal of the frame.

Lens imaging area →

CCD →

CCD diagonal measurement →

As a rule of thumb, a lens focal length slightly longer than the image diagonal produces a "normal" perspective. Shorter focal lengths yield wide angle images and longer ones create telephoto images. Since the visual perspective of any focal length depends on the area upon which the image is formed, a focal length that is wide angle on a frame of 35mm still film is telephoto on a 1/4″ CCD. To illustrate this, here are typical focal lengths for three image formats:

● A nominally 1/4″ CCD for a mini-DV camcorder.
● A 1/2″ CCD for a full-size professional camcorder.
● A 24mm x 36mm frame of 35mm still film.

The still camera is included because many people are familiar with the lenses typically used on it.

By comparing 35mm focal lengths to those of different video CCDs, you can get a relative idea of how different focal lengths behave in different image formats. As you look at the chart, notice three things:

● The 35mm focal lengths vary somewhat from straight multiples (like 17.5mm, 35mm, 70mm, 140mm) because still camera lenses are more typically designed in slightly different focal lengths (18mm, 35mm, 70mm, 135mm).

● The comparisons are not exact because the 3-to-2 proportions of the 35mm frame are different from the 4-to-3 proportions of the video frame.

● Because of the mathematics of optical design, the difference (expressed in millimeters) between focal lengths is quite small at the wide angle end of the spectrum, but much larger at the telephoto end. For example, a 4mm wide angle lens produces an image twice as large as a 2mm, though the difference between them is only 2mm. At the telephoto end, a 48mm lens also has twice the magnification of a 24mm lens; but the increase in focal length required to double the image size is 24mm, rather than just 2mm.

1/4″ Chip Focal Length	1/2″ Chip Focal Length	35mm Focal Length	Lens Characteristics
2mm	4mm	18mm	extreme wide angle
3mm	6mm	28mm	wide angle
4mm	8mm	35mm	mild wide angle
6mm	12mm	45mm	short normal
8mm	16mm	55mm	normal
12mm	24mm	70mm	long normal
16mm	32mm	105mm	short telephoto
24mm	48mm	135mm	telephoto
32mm	64mm	200mm	long telephoto
48mm	96mm	300mm	very long telephoto

Maximum aperture

As a rule, normal and wide angle lenses have larger maximum **apertures** (lens openings) than telephoto designs. That is because the "speed" (light gathering ability) of a lens depends on both the lens diameter and the focal length. For a lens of any diameter, the shorter the focal length, the larger the maximum potential aperture.

In fixed focal length designs, wide angle lenses should theoretically have larger maximum apertures than normal lenses. Because of other constraints in designing wide angle lenses, however, normal focal lengths typically have the largest maximum apertures.

Since a zoom lens has a fixed diameter but a variable focal length, its maximum aperture often will become smaller as the lens zooms from wide angle to telephoto. For example, a lens that can open to f/1.4 in the wide angle position may open only to f/2.8 at full telephoto. That is why you will often see identification markings on lenses like "f/1.4–2.8." This indicates f/1.4 is the maximum aperture at full wide angle, while f/2.8 is the maximum at full telephoto.

Some professional zoom lenses are designed to maintain the same maximum aperture throughout their zoom ranges.

Understanding how maximum apertures work in zoom lenses will help you use them effectively. In low light levels, for example, you may wish to restrict yourself to normal or wide angle lens settings, because their larger maximum apertures admit more light. They will yield better quality images in dim illumination.

Depth of field

Depth of field is the distance, in front of and behind the plane on which the lens is focused, in which objects in the image appear sharp, **Figure 11-4.** Like maximum aperture, depth of field grows smaller as the lens focal length grows longer. At any given aperture and distance from the subject, wide angle lenses have the deepest depth of field and telephoto focal lengths have the shallowest.

You need to be aware of these characteristics when following sports or other action in telephoto mode, and when setting focus for zooming. A scene that looks perfectly sharp in wide angle may turn soft when you zoom to telephoto. That is because the wide angle setting's greater depth of field includes the distant subjects, but the telephoto setting's shallower range does not.

The Pictorial Qualities of Lenses

The only true optical difference among lens focal lengths is angle of view: the arc within which a lens gathers light to form images. All other seeming differences are merely appearances. Nonetheless, those appearances are quite visible to viewers, and videographers use them to shape the images they create. We may call these appearances the *pictorial qualities* of lenses. They include *magnification*, *perspective*, *movement*, and *distortion*.

Figure 11-4.
A—Depth of field. B—In this telephoto shot, depth of field is limited to the area between the red lines.

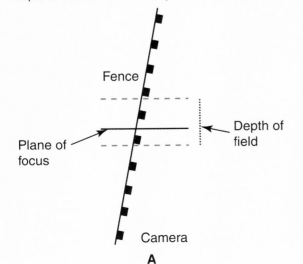

Fence

Plane of focus

Depth of field

Camera

A

B

Apertures and f-stops

How much light gets through a lens depends on two factors:

- Its *focal length* (such as 10mm or 100mm or 200mm)
- Its *maximum aperture*: the full diameter of the lens opening.

The light-gathering ability of a lens is called its *speed*; a sensitive design is called a *fast lens*. The speed of a lens is determined by a simple formula:

$$\frac{\text{focal length}}{\text{maximum aperture}} = \text{lens speed}$$

According to this formula, if a lens has a focal length of 100mm and a diameter of 50mm, then its speed would be 100 divided by 50, or f/2.

$$\frac{100mm}{50mm} = f/2$$

(By convention, apertures are indicated with a lower-case "f" and referred to as **f-stops**.)

A 200mm lens with the same 50mm diameter would have a speed of f/4.

$$\frac{200mm}{50mm} = f/4$$

An iris diaphragm varies the effective aperture.

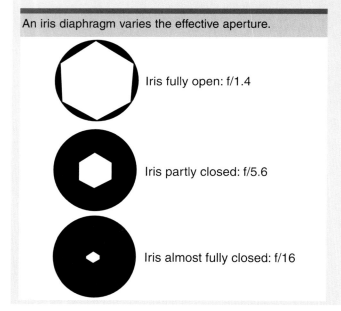

Iris fully open: f/1.4

Iris partly closed: f/5.6

Iris almost fully closed: f/16

Aperture range

Every lens includes an internal **iris diaphragm** (*"iris"* for short) that can be adjusted to progressively reduce the diameter of the lens opening. For this reason, a lens has a whole range of apertures.

Each reduction in aperture changes the result of the equation, so

$$\frac{100mm}{50mm \text{ (iris wide open)}} = f/2$$

$$\frac{100mm}{12.5mm \text{ (iris partially closed)}} = f/8$$

Apertures on most lenses have been standardized at f/1.4, f/2, f/2.8, f/4, f/5.6, f/8, f/11, f/16, f/22. Though these numbers seem arbitrary, a moment's study will reveal that they are all based on square roots.

Smaller equals higher

As you can see from the diagram, the smaller the f-stop number, the *larger* the aperture. Commonly, f/1.4 is the largest aperture and f/22 is the smallest (though certain specialized lenses can "stop down" to f/64). By another convention, the speed of a lens is expressed as its maximum aperture. Thus, an f/2 lens is said to be "two stops faster" than an f/4 lens because it includes the two extra stops (f/2.8 and f/2) below f/4.

Apertures grow smaller as their f-stop numbers grow bigger.

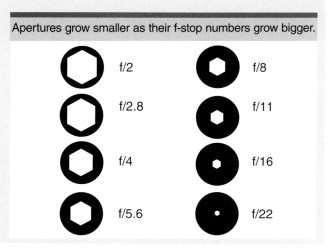

f/2   f/8

f/2.8   f/11

f/4   f/16

f/5.6   f/22

Magnification

The most obvious difference between wide angle and telephoto lenses is **magnification.** An object that appears tiny in wide angle may loom huge in telephoto. In comparison to human vision:

- *Normal* lenses make objects seem about the size they would appear to the human eye.

- *Telephoto* lenses make objects seem bigger.
- *Wide angle* lenses make objects seem smaller.

Apparent magnification is an effect of angle of view, because every lens must fill the frame from edge to edge. Since the screen size does not change, filling it with a 5-degree view will make objects appear much larger than filling it with a 90-degree view. This concept is illustrated in **Figure 11-5.**

First-time camcorder users quickly discover that zooming from wide angle to telephoto enlarges the subject in the frame.

Perspective

Perspective is the illusion of depth in the picture, the apparent distance from the camcorder to the farthest part of the scene. Wide angle lenses exaggerate this virtual depth, making distances seem greater and faraway objects seem smaller. Telephoto lenses reduce apparent depth, seemingly bringing distant objects closer. **Figure 11-6** shows the same setup photographed with both wide angle and telephoto lenses. Notice that much of the scene is excluded from the

telephoto shot because of the lens' narrow angle of view. Objects in the telephoto image are much larger than in the wide angle view, and the buildings appear squeezed together.

In Figure 11-6, the lens remains the same distance from the subject at both wide angle and telephoto settings. But if you move the camera you will achieve a quite different effect. **Figure 11-7** shows the setups used to shoot the two frames in Figure 11-8. In **Figure 11-8A**, the two subjects are photographed with a wide angle lens. In **Figure 11-8B**, the same subjects are photographed with a telephoto lens, but with the camera placed much farther away. As a result, the near subject is exactly the same size as in the previous wide angle setting, but the far subject appears much larger and closer.

Figure 11-5.
Wide angle and telephoto lens fields of view. Because the frame remains the same size, filling it with a telephoto view makes the subject larger.

Figure 11-6.
Lenses change perspective. A—Wide angle lens. B—Telephoto lens.

A

B

Figure 11-7.
Setup used to photograph Figure 11-8.

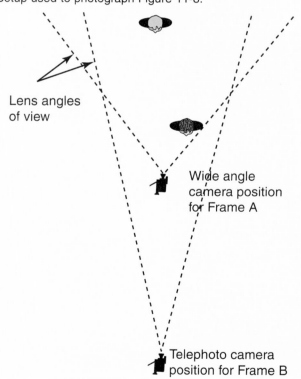

Lens angles of view

Wide angle camera position for Frame A

Telephoto camera position for Frame B

Figure 11-8.
A—Wide angle image. B—Telephoto image with camera moved to maintain the foreground subject size.

A

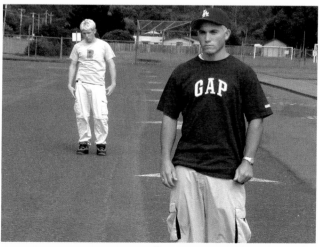

B

Movement

Because wide angle and telephoto lenses affect the apparent depth of an image, they also modify apparent movement toward or away from the lens. In wide angle shots, moving people and objects seem to rush quickly toward the camera or away, **Figure 11-9.** In telephoto shots however, fore-and-aft movement is minimized, and people do not change size

Figure 11-9.
In a wide angle shot, the truck grows dramatically as it approaches the camera.

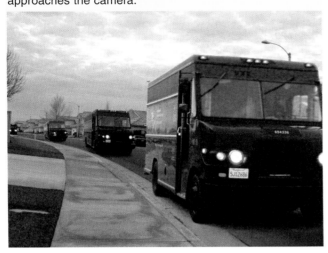

dramatically as they move forward or backward. For these reasons, wide angle lenses are useful for dynamic action scenes like fights and chases, while telephoto lenses convey a contrasting sense of distance and detachment.

Distortion

Since wide angle and telephoto lenses affect the way objects "shrink" and "grow," depending on their distance from the camera, they also can distort the shapes of those objects. Note how the wide angle lens in **Figure 11-10** makes the vehicle look longer and more powerful, while the telephoto shot seems to squeeze it together.

Be careful in using wide angle lenses on the human body. **Figure 11-11** shows what happens when wide angle perspective stretches arms and legs. For the same reason, try to avoid wide angle lenses in portraiture, since the extra depth can distort chins and noses unpleasantly.

Moderate telephoto settings are generally preferable for portraits of women. However, a mild wide angle lens can make a male portrait look more rugged.

Focal length and composition

To arrange images effectively with wide angle and telephoto lenses, first decide whether you want to create a composition in three dimensions or two. Wide angle lenses help you enhance the illusion of a third dimension in a composition by emphasizing apparent depth. Telephoto lenses let you organize compositions on the screen surface, rather than "behind" it. As you can see from **Figure 11-12**, both approaches can yield very effective compositions.

Finally, keep in mind that the lens focal lengths most like human vision are in the so-called normal range. When you want viewers to subconsciously think that they are looking directly at the action, rather than at a TV screen, normal focal lengths render images without the exaggerations and distortions that announce the presence of a lens.

Figure 11-10.
Lens distortion. A—The wide angle lens elongates the vehicle. B—The telephoto lens appears to squeeze it together.

A

B

Figure 11-11.
Wide angle lenses can distort human proportions and make unpleasant-looking portraits.

Figure 11-12.
A—Choose a wide angle lens to enhance the illusion of depth. B—A telephoto lens creates the composition on the surface of the screen.

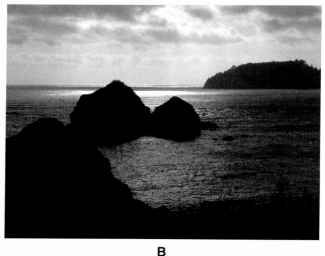

A   B

Operating the Zoom

As a rule, use the zoom sparingly, because the seconds required to move between the start and end compositions are sometimes a waste of screen time. When you zoom, try to set the shot up in such a way that the editor can remove the zoom by cutting directly from the start to the finish, **Figure 11-13**.

A zoom cannot be easily removed if it contains action. For example, if you shoot someone walking, removing the zoom will result in a jump cut, as you can see from **Figure 11-14.**

The solution is to follow the shot by reshooting the same action from a different angle, beginning before the zoom started in the previous shot, to keep the action continuous, **Figure 11-15.**

Zooming techniques

Skilled videographers often prefer to zoom manually, for better control. (If your motorized zoom lacks a manual mode, it probably offers variable speed operations.) Here is a technique for professional looking zooms: begin slowly, accelerate during the first half of the zoom, then decelerate during the second half. Finish the zoom slowly and come to a stop. Never correct a zoom after you have initially stopped by "bumping" it a bit closer or farther away. Either accept the end composition where you first halted or else retake the shot.

Optical vs Pictorial Lens Qualities

Photographers know that wide angle and telephoto lenses render image magnification, perspective, movement, and distortion in markedly different ways. Optical engineers, however, insist that there is only one difference between wide angle and telephoto lenses: angle of view. All other seeming differences are merely illusions.

Which side is right? Both. On the one hand, the many photos in this chapter clearly show the pictorial differences between wide angle and telephoto images. On the other hand, if you enlarge the center of a wide angle image until it matches the angle of view of a telephoto, the perspective of the two shots will be almost identical.

In the photo panel, A is a wide angle scenic and B is a telephoto shot made from exactly the same spot. Photo C is the very center of the wide angle image, enlarged to match the telephoto picture (hence its relatively poor quality).

Studying the building doors and railings, notice that the scale and perspective in the blowup are essentially the same as that of the telephoto shot. From an optical standpoint, there is no difference between wide and long lenses except angle of view. •

A—Wide angle shot. B—Telephoto shot. C—Center portion of the wide angle shot.

A B C

Figure 11-13.
With no action in the shot, it is easy to cut the zoom from wide angle to telephoto.

At one time, zooms were rarely used in feature films. Nowadays, though, the prejudice against them has lessened.

Digital Zoom

Digital zoom is an electronic feature that can magnify images beyond the ability of the lens to enlarge them. True zoom, called *optical zoom,* adjusts the lens to fill the entire imaging chip with a smaller and smaller angle of view. Because the entire chip is always used to form the image, the picture quality always remains the same. Digital zoom, by contrast, works by selecting a smaller and smaller percentage of the image on the chip and electronically enlarging it to fill the whole frame. Since the number of pixels is fixed by

Figure 11-14.
Omitting the zoom from an action shot creates a jump cut.

Figure 11-15.
A—Before the zoom. B—Covering the action during the zoom. C—Shot A resumes after the zoom.

A   **B**   **C**

the total number on the chip, using just part of the chip requires filling the frame with fewer pixels. The fewer the pixels, the worse the image quality, **Figure 11-16.**

Pixels (short for "picture elements) are the dots that make up the image.

Because image quality is degraded by digital zooming, this technique should be used only when subjects are too far away to be magnified adequately by optical means alone. Common applications for digital zoom include nature videography, shooting sports from the sidelines, and surveillance.

Figure 11-16.
Zooming in on a distant subject...   optical zoom maintains full image quality...   digital zoom degrades image quality.

Special Lens Filters

The front elements of professional lenses are machined with threads to receive screw-on filters. (The lenses of some compact format cameras such as Mini-DV may not have filter threads.) Many filters used in film photography (such as starburst and color shift effects) are not employed as often in video because their effects can be supplied by software during the process of computerized editing.

As a rule, it is better to record the best possible unmodified images and then filter them digitally in postproduction. Any effect that modifies an original camera recording is permanent. Two types of filtration, however, can be achieved only in the camera: *neutral density* and *polarization*.

Neutral density filters

Gray-colored **neutral density filters** are used to cut down the incoming light, either to reduce the intensity of an exceptionally bright scene, or to force the aperture wider open in order to reduce depth of field.

Polarizing filters

A polarizing filter, or **polarizer,** is a sandwich of two rings. The back one threads onto the lens and the front one, holding the filter, rotates freely. By changing the orientation of the filter with respect to the lens, you can suppress small, bright glints of light (called **specular reflections**) from surfaces like metal, glass, water, and shiny paint. You can also reduce unwanted reflections on window glass, as shown in the accompanying illustration. Polarizers can also darken blue skies to make clouds stand out. A polarizer can do extra duty as a variable-strength neutral density filter. Generally, (though not always) the more you rotate the filter, the less light you admit to the lens.

A polarizing filter can reduce reflections, such as the glare off this store window.

Setting Focus

Setting focus is the process of adjusting the lens so that subjects at a certain distance from the camera appear sharp on the focal plane. Since the imaging chip (CCD) is located on that plane, objects in focus there will be sharp in the video image. Of course, focus must be changeable because subjects may be videotaped at many different distances: a postcard six inches away from the lens, a group of people six feet away, a distant mountain six miles away.

Like your own eyes, optical systems cannot always keep everything from a few inches to the horizon in focus at the same time.

In very bright light and at wide angle lens settings, every object from the postcard to the mountain may be in reasonably sharp focus. On the other hand, when shooting in dim light with a telephoto lens, the depth of field (range of focus) may be as shallow as an inch or two. The reasons for this are explained in the sidebar *Depth of Field.* Almost all camcorders can compute and set focus automatically, and modern autofocus systems work remarkably well. But they are not perfect.

Autofocus

Autofocus is a camcorder system that adjusts the lens continuously and automatically to keep objects in the image sharp.

Depth of Field

Mathematically speaking, objects in an image are in perfect focus only if they lie on an imaginary plane surface that is precisely a certain distance from the lens. Objects that are behind or in front of that plane — even as little as a fraction of an inch — are not in theoretically perfect focus, as shown in the diagram. (Technically, this imaginary plane of perfect focus is called the "front focal plane" while the plane on which the CCD lies is called the "rear focal plane.")

In reality, however, objects up to a certain distance behind and in front of the plane of "perfect" focus are also acceptably sharp, because they appear that way to viewers. This acceptably focused zone is called the *depth of field*. (Note

that the depth of field in front of the plane of focus is shallower than the depth of field behind it, as illustrated. This is always the case.)

The depth of field in an image is determined by three factors working together: lens *focal length*, lens *aperture*, and the *distance* from the lens to the theoretical plane of focus.

Lens focal length

The longer the lens focal length, the shallower the depth of field. If you set up two camcorders with a 4mm lens and a 16mm lens, both at the same distance from the subject and using the same aperture (f-stop), the 4mm lens will yield a greater depth of field than the 16mm lens.

In theory, only a single mathematical plane is in perfect focus. In fact, the range of acceptable sharpness extends before and behind the plane.

The "plane of focus" is the only distance from the camera that is theoretically perfectly sharp.

Depth of field is the range of distances through which subjects appear sharp to the viewer

The longer the lens focal length, the shallower the depth of field.

16mm lens

4mm lens

Though different camcorders employ different approaches to autofocus, most of them involve the same basic procedure. The system calculates the distance to objects inside a focusing zone within the image — usually the central portion — and a servo motor in the lens adjusts focus to the calculated distance. Most camcorders default to the autofocus setting, **Figure 11-17.**

Autofocus has several limitations that can make it unsuitable for professional shooting. If the subject is not within the focusing zone, it may be out of focus. If the camera and/or subject moves, the autofocus may not respond quickly enough to maintain uninterrupted sharpness. If unimportant objects move into the focusing zone, the system may focus on them, rather than on the center of interest.

Figure 11-17.
Many camcorders use the center of the image for focusing. (Sue Stinson)

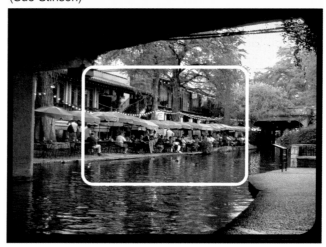

Lens aperture

The wider the lens aperture, the shallower the depth of field. If you set up those same two camcorders, both at the same distance from the subject and both using the same lens focal length, an f/16 aperture will produce the greater depth of field and an f/1.4 stop will produce the lesser.

Lens distance

The shorter the lens-to-subject distance, the shallower the depth of field. If your two camcorder lenses have both the same focal length and the same aperture, but one camera is set closer to the subject than the other, the more distant camera will realize the greater depth of field and the closer one the lesser.

Depth of field can be confusing to calculate because it is determined by focal length, aperture, and distance, all working at once. For example, some people think that if the depth of field produced by a telephoto setting is too shallow, they can fix the problem by switching to a wide angle setting with its inherently greater depth of field. The problem is that in order to match the view of the telephoto lens, they would have to move the wide angle lens closer to the subject. Since moving closer reduces depth of field, the eventual wide angle focus would be no deeper than the original telephoto focus.

The shorter the distance, the shallower the depth of field.

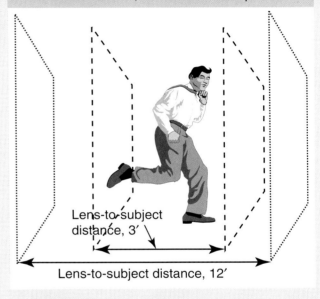

Lens-to-subject distance, 3′

Lens-to-subject distance, 12′

The wider the aperture, the shallower the depth of field.

Aperture f/4

Aperture f/16

For these reasons, better camcorders offer three alternate ways to maintain focus: autofocus lock, manual focus, and pulling focus.

Autofocus lock

Autofocus lock uses the automatic mechanism to focus on a subject and then prevents that setting from changing, even if the subject moves. To use the autofocus lock system, focus on the subject, then engage the focus lock control on the camcorder.

When the shot is complete, remember to disable the focus-locking mechanism.

Locking the autofocus function is especially useful when the center of interest is outside the focusing area. Simply center the frame on the subject, focus the lens, lock the focus, and recompose the shot. The subject will stay sharp.

You can also use autofocus lock when unimportant foreground objects "steal" the focus from your subject matter. If you lock focus on the subject, the focusing system will ignore the intruding objects. In **Figure 11-18**, for example, the subject is taped as she moves along a sidewalk behind a series of hedges.

The autofocus system does not always work reliably during zooms, because the depth of field narrows as you zoom in. This means that a focus setting made at a wide angle focal length may lose sharpness as you zoom into a distant part of the scene. This is especially true of a zoom in, where

Figure 11-18.
A—The subject is sharp as she starts to walk behind a hedge. B—As the foreground hedge fills the screen, the autofocus system shifts the focus to it, softening the subject. C—Locking the focus on the subject prevents this unwanted shift.

A   **B**   **C**

the autofocus system has set focus in the wide angle start position, **Figure 11-19.** (In a zoom out, the start focus will be properly set and the system will usually adjust itself satisfactorily as the shot widens.)

For this reason, you should use the autofocus lock option to set up every zoom in, as shown in **Figure 11-20.** In most situations this procedure will keep your shot sharp throughout the range of the zoom.

Figure 11-19.
A scene focused at a wide angle setting...

may not stay in focus at the end of a zoom-in.

 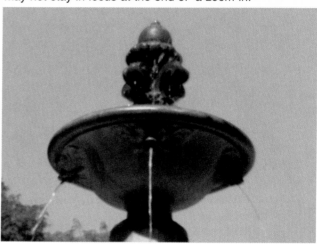

Figure 11-20.
Zoom to full telephoto, allowing the autofocus system to focus. Lock the focus.

Zoom out to your start position.

Manual focus

In some situations, the autofocus lock method will not work because the autofocus mechanism fails to get a fix on the subject. This can happen in low light, when shooting through a window, or when the subject lacks features that the focusing system needs for reference. The procedure for focusing manually is similar to focusing for a zoom:

● Disable the autofocus system.

● Zoom to the full telephoto position to obtain the shallowest depth of field.

● Manually adjust the focus until the subject is sharp.

● Zoom back out to the desired composition.

Except in news and sports applications, most professional videographers use manual focus whenever practical.

In low light levels, a long zoom may require pulling focus, as described below.

Pulling focus

Pulling focus is the technique of shifting manually from one focal setting to another during the shot.

This procedure is also called "follow focus," "racking focus," and other names.

Pulling focus is practical only when the camera has an external zoom lens fitted with a focus ring. It usually requires an assistant to revolve that ring to change focus. To prepare a shot for pulling focus:

● Wrap a narrow piece of white tape around the lens barrel, next to the focus ring.

● Focus the lens at the starting position and mark a reference line on the tape.

● Repeat the process for each additional focus position, **Figure 11-21.**

Focus pulling is often used to keep a moving subject sharp. To do this when the subject approaches the camera, set focus points at the far, middle, and near points of the movement. As the subject moves toward the camera, shift the focus continuously, using the reference marks on the tape.

Exposure

Setting exposure means literally *exposing* the camcorder circuits to the exact amount

Figure 11-21.
White tape marked with interim focus points.

of light required to form a quality image. If the imaging chip (CCD) receives too much light, the picture will be too light (overexposed) or even "burnt out" to white. With too little light, the image will be too dark (underexposed) or "blocked up" to black. Sometimes the camcorder cannot handle the ultra-bright light in an environment like a beach or a ski slope. On the other hand, when taping at night or in a dark room, there may be too little light to form a good image. To solve the problems of too much or too little light, the camcorder relies on four exposure control systems: *aperture, shutter, gain,* and *filtration.*

Aperture

As explained in the section on lenses, the aperture is the hole through which light enters the camcorder. The bigger this hole, the more light gets in. The aperture is set by an *iris,* a circular opening inside the camera lens that can be expanded to nearly the full diameter of the lens or contracted until it is almost completely closed.

The aperture is usually polygonal rather than truly circular. That is why lens flares (from shooting into the sun or other bright lights) appear as multiple polygons.

Aperture Exposure Control

The autoexposure system built into every camcorder works by adjusting the aperture.

Automatic aperture

In auto mode, your camcorder sets exposure by analyzing the intensity of the incoming light and automatically changing the size of the lens opening, so that the same amount of light reaches the CCD, regardless of the light level outside. Autoexposure systems adjust aperture only, leaving the shutter at its default speed. Autoexposure systems work so well that you can use them much of the time, as long as you avoid panning too quickly from, say, a very bright scene to a dark one.

When light levels are too different, try restaging the action to avoid the light change, or get a cutaway shot to replace the badly exposed transitional section later when you edit the scene.

Manual aperture

Many amateur and all professional camcorders also allow you to set the aperture manually. One way to do this is by locking the exposure:

● In auto mode, frame the scene that you wish to expose for.

● Lock the aperture.

● Make the shot.

Figure 11-22 shows a typical exposure problem that can be solved by this method. Notice that it is very similar to the focus problem discussed previously.

You can also set aperture in full manual mode to fine-tune overall exposure. This is especially useful when backlighting is a problem or when the center of the frame is much brighter than the rest of the image. Excessively bright areas are more irritating, visually, than overly dark ones. For this reason, it is often better to correct backlighting problems by lighting the foreground subject or moving it away from the bright background. However, when it is the subject

that is too bright you can expose for it and allow the darker areas to "block up." To do this:

● Zoom in until the bright subject fills the frame.

● Lock the autoexposure.

● Zoom back out to the original composition.

● Make the shot.

Programmed aperture

Most camcorders offer programmed aperture settings to address various exposure problems. Though different models offer different programs, two of the more popular aperture-based options are *backlight* and *spotlight*.

Backlight. Backlight programs automatically open the aperture a certain amount to increase the exposure for dark subjects in front of bright backgrounds. Unfortunately, many backlight programs have only one setting. If it doesn't match the situation exactly, the results may not be satisfactory. If your camcorder has manual aperture control, it is better to compensate for backlighting by increasing exposure in small steps until you are satisfied with the exposure.

Spotlight. The spotlight program is the opposite of back light. It is intended for theater performances and other situations in which the subject is brightly illuminated against a much darker background. The spotlight program reduces the contrast between the two elements, and improves the picture considerably.

Shutter

While the aperture controls the size of the opening through which light is admitted to the camcorder, the ***shutter*** controls the amount of time allotted to forming each video frame (image). In a film camera, the

Figure 11-22.
Original exposure.

Autoexposure increases exposure for the archway, overexposing the subject.

Manual aperture retains original exposure.

Overexposure Zebras

Many professional cameras warn the operator when part or all of the scene is too bright to record properly. Typically, this warning overlays the too-bright portions of the image in the viewfinder with a striped pattern. For this reason, it is called a *zebra*.

The most common form of zebra warning appears when part of the image is brighter than 100% of the camera's ability to record it. Another type is programmed to appear when the center of the image is too bright to record Caucasian flesh tones properly (about 70% of maximum brightness).

A striped overlay identifies the overexposed portion of the image.

Some cameras can be set to offer warnings in the viewfinder when skin tones are overexposed. (JVC)

shutter is an actual window that opens and shuts for each image. In video, however, the shutter is a set of circuits that control how long the incoming light is allowed to build up electrical charges on the chip before they are removed and sent on to be processed and recorded on tape.

A few professional cameras do use mechanical shutters, but not as film cameras employ them.

NTSC video is displayed at 30 frames per second, with every frame made up of two interlaced fields. This means that the effective normal shutter speed is 1/60 second. That is, when the shutter circuits are in "normal" mode, they allow the CCD to build up electrical charges for each field for 1/60 second before collecting them and starting over.

Some interlaced systems combine the information from adjacent scan lines. This electronic processing can increase the effective exposure from 1/60 to 1/30 second. In terms of recording movement, however, the shutter speed is still 1/60.

Shutter speed usually remains locked at 1/60 second so that exposure control is

handled entirely by the aperture. There are special situations, however, in which you may want to change shutter speed. For this purpose, many camcorders offer shutter control programs.

Programmed Shutter

Like exposure programs, shutter programs adjust one or more camcorder settings for you automatically. All you do is select the effect you want and the circuitry does the rest. Shutter programs have three purposes: forcing open the aperture, freezing rapid motion, and compensating for extreme light levels.

Portrait

The portrait program increases shutter speed moderately in order to force the aperture wider open. The wider aperture reduces depth of field so you can keep your portrait or still life subject sharp in the foreground while throwing a distracting background out of focus, **Figure 11-23**.

As explained in the sidebar Apertures and f-stops, each time you double shutter speed, the aperture opens by one f-stop to compensate.

Figure 11-23.
The portrait program opens the aperture to throw backgrounds out of focus. (Sue Stinson)

Sports

The sports program increases shutter speed more than the portrait program in order to sharpen fast action that might be blurred at the normal shutter speed. Sharpening the image improves detail but can make movement look jerky.

High light levels

The high light level program (often called "sand and snow" or some other proprietary term) increases shutter speed when outside conditions are so bright that the smallest aperture still admits too much light. Since each doubling of the shutter speed reduces incoming light by one full f-stop, a moderate shutter increase (say, to 1/125 second) is usually enough to compensate for the brightest scene. See **Figure 11-24**.

Most professional camcorders control excessive brightness by reducing the gain setting, enabling a built-in neutral density filter, or both.

Low light levels

Some shutters can be set *slower* than normal, typically at 1/15 of a second. This allows the CCD four times as long to form an image in very low light. The drawback is an obvious blurring of the action; and since the circuitry must record each frame twice for normal playback speed, the result is quite jerky. In general, a slow shutter should be used only when the light is otherwise too dim to record an image. A slow shutter can create an eerie, dreamlike effect for music videos and other special-purpose applications.

Manual Shutter

Some camcorders allow you to change shutter speed manually. For instance, you can manually control depth of field in a portrait shot more precisely than with an automatic portrait program. Very high shutter speeds are often useful for scientific analysis and similar purposes

As you manually adjust shutter speed, keep two important points in mind. First, increasing shutter speed always widens the aperture proportionately (in order to maintain the same exposure). This can seriously reduce depth of field, making it hard to hold focus at long telephoto settings . Second, shutter speeds faster than about 1/125 second jerk and strobe too much to yield normal-looking movement. Because of these

Figure 11-24.
The high light level program reduces overexposure. (Sue Stinson)

motion problems, exposure is adjusted less often by manual and programmed *shutter* settings than by *aperture* controls.

Gain

Gain is the electronic amplification of the video signal. In most camcorders this "video volume" can be turned up to compensate for low light levels. Unlike aperture and shutter, gain does not affect the amount of light used to form the image. Instead, it operates *after* the image has been coded as an electronic signal by increasing the strength of that signal. Gain control can operate in several different ways, depending on the sophistication of the camcorder:

- In simple units, the gain turns on automatically whenever light levels drop too low.
- Better models allow you to turn the gain on and off manually.
- Still more sophisticated cameras let you select different amounts of gain compensation, to suit lighting conditions precisely.

Professional video cameras are designed to operate in normal light with a certain amount of gain enabled. That way, the videographer can compensate for excessively bright conditions by reducing the gain instead of using filtration.

Gain control is useful where the situation is otherwise too dark for recording; but it cannot improve the poor quality of the image. It can only brighten it, and the result is often washed out color, coarse detail, and video noise that appears on the screen as "snow," **Figure 11-25.**

Filtration

The final way to regulate exposure is by placing a neutral density filter over the lens. This is a gray filter that reduces the brightness of the light without changing its color. Popular neutral density filters are offered in shades labeled ND3, ND6, ND9, and ND12, which reduce incoming light by 1, 2, 3, and 4 f-stops, respectively. In unusually bright shooting conditions, neutral density filters enable the camera to capture a good quality image. Used at normal light levels, they can reduce depth of field by widening the aperture without increasing the shutter speed.

Filters for bright conditions

Very bright sunshine in reflective locations can overpower your camcorder's chip and circuitry. The result is flares of white, and smeary colors that "bloom" beyond their proper borders. In these conditions, an appropriate neutral density filter will reduce the incoming light to a level that the electronic circuitry can handle, **Figure 11-26.**

Filters for aperture control

Even when brightness is not excessive, you may want to reduce the incoming light in order to force open the aperture. You could do this by increasing shutter speed, as explained previously, but fast shutters often result in undesirable stroboscopic effects. To widen the aperture without changing shutter speed, use a neutral density filter instead.

There are two reasons for working at a wider aperture: first, the reduced depth of field lets you separate your subject from the

Figure 11-25.
Gain control circuits can lighten the image, but the quality is often poor.

Figure 11-26.

Overexposure without filtration…	With an ND3 (one stop) neutral density filter.	With an ND6 (two stop) neutral density filter. (Sue Stinson)

background by keeping it sharp, while the area behind it is soft. Next, almost all photographic lenses record their best images at apertures in the middle of their range. If, for example, the apertures of a lens range from f/2 (widest) to f/22 (narrowest), the lens will perform best between about f/5.6 and f/11. Since even average sunshine may require a very small aperture, a neutral density filter can improve picture quality and help control depth of field.

If, for instance, the autoexposure system sets the lens aperture to f/22, an ND9 neutral density filter over the lens will reduce the aperture three f-stops, to f/8, where the depth of field is extensive but not excessive and the optical quality of the lens is at its best.

Since the gain control is enabled only in low light levels and most filters reduce light levels, the two controls are rarely employed at the same time.

Operating the Camera

Managing the camcorder capably is so important that fine camera operators are highly regarded. No matter how good the acting, costumes, sets, or lighting, a shot can be no better than the competence with which it is recorded. Basically, a camera operator's job is to frame (compose) the shot well, then to move the camera as needed to maintain an effective composition, **Figure 11-27.**

Framing the Shot

Framing a shot means creating a pleasing composition within the frame. The key to success is your ability to see the viewfinder not as a window but as a picture.

Visual composition is covered in Chapter 5.

Figure 11-27.
A professional videographer at work.

The floating frame

To compensate for movement within the image, the camera must move as well. Professional camera operators rarely lock the tripod's pan and tilt mechanisms. Even when the shot is supposed to be fixed, they are constantly moving the camera slightly, to maintain a good composition. In a skilled operator's hands, this camera movement is so smooth and unobtrusive that it is invisible to the audience. To achieve this fluid movement, you aim the lens much as a hunter aims at a constantly moving target. But instead of following the central subject, you "aim" at the entire composition within the frame.

Compensation

Frequently, you correct the composition to compensate for added or subtracted elements. Suppose you have a composition in which a second subject joins a first subject. **Figure 11-28** shows the effect without camera compensation.

Factors Affecting Exposure

Like focus, exposure is the result of several factors working together. In order of importance, these factors are aperture (f-stop), shutter speed, filtration, and gain. Filtration and gain operate only when you enable them, but aperture and shutter are always working.

A fixed amount of light

The key to understanding exposure is the idea that to make a good quality image, the camcorder must *always* receive exactly the same amount of light. Whether the original light is on a beach lit by the sun at noon or by a fire at midnight, the light that eventually reaches the CCD (imaging chip) must be at the same brightness level, even if the noon sunlight is 250 times as bright as the firelight.

The most common problem is to reduce excessively bright light so that it does not overwhelm the sensitive chip. To do this, the camcorder uses first the aperture and then, if necessary, the shutter.

Aperture

At its widest aperture (such as f/1.4) the lens admits nearly all the light that strikes it. If the raw light is too bright for the chip, the aperture grows smaller and smaller. Each full stop reduction in the aperture size is called one f-stop (or just "stop"), and each smaller stop admits one half as much light as the next wider one. The usual f-stops are 1.4, 2, 2.8, 4, 5.6, 8, 11, 16, and 22 (to control very bright light, some camcorder lenses will "stop down" to f/32). Most aperture control systems can change in partial stops, closing, say, from f/2 to f/2.4, which is half -way to the next full stop, f/2.8. More sophisticated models divide stops into one-third stop, rather than one-half stop increments.

Shutter

In situations where the aperture alone cannot fully control exposure, the shutter is brought into play. Typical shutter speeds are 1/60 second, 1/125, 1/250, 1/500, 1/1000, 1/2000, 1/4000, 1/8000. Each time you double the shutter speed, you reduce the light by half, because you allow the chip half as much time to form an image before it is removed and processed.

Aperture plus shutter equals exposure

The amount of light used to form an image depends first on how much is allowed to reach the chip (aperture) and how long the chip is allowed to soak it up (shutter speed). A one-stop decrease in aperture reduces the light by half and so does each doubling of shutter speed.

To see how aperture and shutter work together, imagine a sort of equation:

Aperture + shutter = correct exposure

Pretend that "correct exposure" has a value of 10, so,

Aperture + shutter = 10

Next, give the aperture fr/1.4 a value of 1, f/2 a value of 2, f/2.8 a value of 3, and so on, increasing the value by 1 for each full stop.

In the same way, give shutter speed 1/60 second a value of 1, 1/125 a value of 2, and so on, also increasing the value of each doubled speed by a value of 1. You can value both f-stops and shutter speeds in multiples of 1 because each change represents the same reduction in light. With these values, you can see that 1 + 9 = 10, 2 + 8 =10, 3 + 7 = 10, 4 + 6 = 10, 5 + 5 = 10. If you translate these numerical values back into apertures and shutter speeds, the result would look like this for bright sunlight:

Aperture		Shutter		Total light
1 (f/1.4)	+	9 (1/16000)	=	10
2 (f/2.0)	+	8 (1/8000)	=	10
3 (f/2.8)	+	7 (1/4000)	=	10
4 (f/4.0)	+	6 (1/2000)	=	10
5 (f/5.6)	+	5 1/1000)	=	10
6 (f/8.0)	+	4 (1/500)	=	10
7 (f/11.0)	+	3 (1/250)	=	10
8 (f/16.0)	+	2 (1/125)	=	10
9 (f/22.0)	+	1 (1/60)	=	10

In a darker environment like a living room at night, the available exposure combinations might resemble this:

Aperture		Shutter		Total light
1 (f/1.4)	+	9 (1/250)	=	10
2 (f/2.0)	+	8 (1/125)	=	10
3 (f/2.8)	+	7 (1/60)	=	10

In this darker location, f-stops smaller than f/2.8 and shutter speeds faster than 1/250 are not available because there is not enough light to allow them.

As you review these examples, keep in mind that "aperture plus shutter speed equals exposure" is not a true mathematical equation, but only a rough analogy.

Figure 11-28.
Without camera compensation, the new subject spoils the composition.

As you can see, failure to re-frame for the second subject ruins the composition. **Figure 11-29** shows correction for the second subject.

Look room

When framing people, allow more room on the side toward which they are facing. This avoids the claustrophobic feeling that they are boxed in by the frame. **Figure 11-30** compares two different compositions of a subject. Since people move as they speak, a common application for the floating frame is maintaining adequate look room.

Lead room

When subjects move so that the camera too must move to hold them in frame, look room turns into *lead* room. The idea is exactly the same: allow extra room on the side of the frame toward which people or objects are moving, to prevent them from crowding the frame line, **Figure 11-31.**

Framing Moving Shots

Maintaining lead room will keep a moving subject properly framed, but it will not guar-

antee a good composition. To do that, you need to consider the background as well as the subject. To ensure good composition overall, set up an effective start composition that accommodates both subject and background. Preframe an equal or better ending composition with the subject blocked to complete the move at the designated spot.

In video as in theater, a subject's predesigned and rehearsed movements are called blocking.

Moving the Camera

Composing moving shots naturally requires moving the camcorder, and this is not always as simple as it sounds. The operator must keep the move smooth, while maintaining a good frame and operating camera features like the zoom control. Whether pivoting the camera on its tripod or rolling on a dolly, the key to a professional-looking move is variable speed. Start the move slowly and then accelerate to the desired maximum speed; then slow smoothly and gradually to a stop.

Figure 11-29.
Camera compensation corrects the shot.

Figure 11-30.
Composition with inadequate look room.   Composition with good look room.

Figure 11-31.

| The subject is "crowding the frame." | Centering the subject improves the composition. | Ideally, the subject should be slightly "behind" the center line of the frame. |

Panning and tilting

When rotating the camera horizontally (panning) or vertically (tilting), follow these suggestions:

● Set the drag (resistance) on the tripod head so that you are pushing against it hard enough to smooth the move, but not hard enough to cause jerks in the motion.

● Position your body at the midpoint of the movement. By twisting first toward the start of the movement and then toward the end, you can make smooth pans of 180 degrees. See **Figure 11-32.**

● Use an external monitor, either camera-mounted or stand-alone. By not looking through the built-in viewfinder, you can position yourself far enough away from the camera to avoid impeding its free movement.

Dollying

These suggestions apply equally to moving the camera on a dolly. The main problem with dolly shots is keeping perfect pace with the moving subject so that the lead room remains constant. It is very distracting to have a moving subject shifting forward and backward in relation to the frame. To make dollying effective, remember that even the fastest-moving subject is standing still *in relation to the frame*. To give the shot a feeling of dynamic movement, be sure to include a distinctive background. On screen, it is the background that will fly by, not the subject.

Hand-holding

All the suggestions for smooth panning and dollying apply as well to hand-held moving shots. The challenge with these shots is to keep them smooth. Here are some tips for professional hand-holding:

● Use a wide angle lens setting to minimize the appearance of camera shake.

● Use an external view screen. This keeps your head from transmitting bumps to the camera, and it lets you use your peripheral vision to watch where you are going.

● Keep your arms away from your sides so that your bent elbows can act as shock absorbers.

● Walk with knees slightly flexed and try to glide along rather than striding.

Figure 11-32.
Start facing the center of the pan and twist your upper body to frame start of the pan. You can pan up to 180°.

● Carry the camcorder as if it were a very full and very hot cup of coffee.

If you combine these techniques with a good lens stabilization system, you can get hand-held shots that rival professional dolly work.

Roll Camera

At this point, you have worked your way through the basics of professional videography, and now you are ready to shoot. Just one final reminder: always roll at least five seconds of tape before signaling to begin the action; and keep on rolling at least five seconds after the action has ended or moved off-screen. The editor will thank you.

Technical Terms

Angle of view: The breadth of a lens' field of coverage, expressed as an arc of a circle, such as "10°."

Aperture: The opening in the lens that admits light. The iris diaphragm can vary the aperture from fully open to almost or completely closed.

Autofocus: The camcorder system that automatically adjusts the lens to keep subjects sharp.

Blocking: The predetermined movements that a subject makes during a shot. Camera movement is also blocked.

Depth of field: The distance range, near-to-far, within which subjects appear sharp in the image.

Digital zooming: Increasing the subject size by filling the frame with only the central part of the image.

f-stop: A particular aperture. Most lenses are designed with preset f-stops of f/1.4, f/2, f/2.8, f/4, f/5.6, f/8, f/11, f/16, and f/22.

Focal length: Technically, one design parameter of a lens, expressed in millimeters (4mm, 40mm). Informally, the name of any particular lens, such as, "a 40mm lens."

Gain: The electronic amplification of the signal made from an image, in order to increase its brightness.

Iris diaphragm (iris): A mechanism inside a lens (usually a ring of overlapping blades) that varies the size of the lens opening (aperture).

Magnification: The apparent increase or decrease in subject size of an image, compared to the same subject as seen by the human eye. Telephoto lenses magnify subjects; wide angle lenses reduce them.

Optical zoom: Changing a lens' angle of view (wide angle to telephoto) continuously by moving internal parts of the lens.

Pulling focus (following focus, racking focus): Changing the lens focus during a shot to keep a moving subject sharp.

Setting focus: Adjusting the lens to make the subject appear clear and sharp.

Shutter: The electronic circuitry that determines how long each frame of picture will accumulate on the imaging chip before processing. The standard shutter speed is 1/60 per second for NTSC format video.

Specular reflections: Hard, bright reflections from surfaces such as water, glass, metal, and automobile paint that create points of light on the image. Often controllable by a polarizer.

Speed: The light-gathering ability of a lens, expressed as its maximum aperture. Thus, an f/1.4 lens is "two stops faster" (more light sensitive) than an f/2.8 lens.

12 Lighting Design

Contents

About Lighting Design
Lighting Quality
Lighting Character
Lighting Tools

Objectives

After studying this chapter, you will be able to:

❑ Explain the basic procedures of video lighting.

❑ Describe the principal styles of lighting.

❑ Select and use common lighting tools appropriately.

(Lowel Corporation)

About Lighting Design

Considered from one perspective, video is about *light*. You may think you are taping beautiful backgrounds, exciting action, and expressive performers, but you are not. What you are actually recording is only the light that bounces off your subjects, streams through the lens, and strikes the imaging chip. Since that light is all that your camera sees, you can shape video images by controlling the light that illuminates them.

Because camcorders can capture a satisfactory image in almost any quantity and quality of illumination, it is possible to make videos without paying much attention to lighting. But if you ignore lighting, you neglect one of your most powerful tools. One difference between a casual shooter and a video artist is that the beginner merely *records* images while the videographer *creates* them — in part, by managing light.

Video lighting, then, is the art of creating images with light. To do this, of course, you must know the lighting tools at your disposal and how to employ them in a variety of situations. But before you can deal with the technicalities of lighting, you need to start at the beginning by considering what lighting does and why it does it. Briefly, video lighting determines the *quality* of the light on a scene and also creates its *character*.

Lighting Quality

To record high-quality images, your camcorder needs high-quality light. That means light of exactly the right *quantity*, *contrast*, and *color*.

Light Quantity

As explained in the chapters on videography, the camera's imaging chip (or chips) must receive exactly the right quantity of light in order to form a high-quality image. Too much light makes colors smear and "bloom" and forces the aperture to very small f-stops (openings). Too little light makes a murky picture with dull colors and little detail and may push the electronic gain compensation up to a level that creates grainy, noisy images. The videography chapters showed how to adjust the camera to suit the light. This chapter shows just the opposite: how to adjust the light to suit the camera.

Decreasing the quantity

To reduce excess light, you can either block it or screen it, **Figure 12-1.** To block light entirely, you place an opaque shield such as a reflector or lighting "flag" between the light source and the subject. This technique works when there is enough light from other sources to illuminate the blocked area of the subject.

You can also screen the light instead of blocking it. Where blocking cuts all the light, screening it merely reduces it to a more pleasing level. Typically, you screen a light source with a large, framed screen of mesh placed either horizontally above the subject or vertically beside it.

Increasing the quantity

Sometimes the problem is not too much light but too little, and your job is to increase the quantity of illumination, **Figure 12-2.** You

Figure 12-1.
Decreasing light quantity. A—This closeup was made in direct sunlight. B— Direct sun blocked by a flag. C— Sunlight filtered by a screen.

A

B

C

Figure 12-2.
Using a reflector. A—Direct sunlight. B—Shadow filled with a reflector.

A

B

have two options: redirect existing light or add new light. To redirect light that is already present, you use **reflectors.** Reflectors are quick, cheap, simple solutions for outdoor lighting especially, and they can be used indoors as well.

Adding new light to the available illumination means using electric lighting instruments.

In the technical vocabulary of lighting, a bulb is called a *lamp*, a light is called an *instrument*, and all the instruments together are called *lights*.

Except on large productions, electric lighting is usually an indoor-only option, for several reasons. Electrical power can be hard to find outdoors unless the production has an expensive generator. Because of the naturally high level of outdoor ambient light, very large, heavy, power-hungry lights are required to add enough brightness to balance the daylight. Most electric lights must be filtered to match the color temperature of daylight, a process that reduces their output and so requires more lighting units.

Electric lighting can be as simple as an on-camera fill light or as elaborate as a set lit with fifty instruments. In professional video work, almost all interior locations are lit for shooting, often by supplementing the existing light at the location.

Light Contrast

After quantity, the biggest lighting problem is contrast. **Contrast** is the difference in brightness between the lightest and darkest areas in the image. Too little contrast makes subjects appear flat and bland. Too much contrast makes light areas appear stark white or dark areas solid black, or, in extreme cases, both at once. See **Figure 12-3.**

Lighting contrast is expressed as a ratio. A "four-to-one" ratio indicates that the lightest areas are four times as bright as the darkest ones.

Regardless of the lighting mood or style, a well-lit image has an even range of brightness levels:

● True black in the darkest areas.
● Shadows with details visible in them.
● Several gradations of brightness in the middle range.
● Highlights that retain some detail.
● True white in the lightest areas.

You control contrast by reducing or increasing the light, as described in the section on quantity, until the lightest-to-darkest ratio is suitable. You can also reduce contrast by diffusing the light, scattering the straight-line rays of a light source so that they bounce around the subject. You can diffuse direct light by screening it with cloth or plastic sheeting; reflected light can be softened by using white reflectors instead of metallic ones.

Figure 12-3.
Lighting contrast. A—Too much contrast. B—Contrast reduced.

A   B

Light Color

To completely control the quality of light, you need to manage not only its brightness and contrast, but its color as well. Commonly, this means setting and maintaining white balance, as discussed in the videography

chapters. But there are special situations in which you will want to exercise highly selective control over color. For example, many locations require mixing light sources of different color temperatures, whether combining incandescent and fluorescent lights or managing daylight coming through a window, **Figure 12-4**.

In other situations, you may want to simulate the warmth of a sunset or fireplace. Or you may need to imitate cool moonlight to make daytime footage look like night. Whether creating special effects, balancing multiple color tints, or simply setting white balance, you are always dealing with the color of light.

Estimating Contrast

Our human eyes are not reliable in judging contrast for video because we are far better at handling wide differences between the lightest and darkest areas of an image. In many cases, humans can see details in highlights and shadows that even the best video systems record as blank white or black. For this reason, it is important to check contrast on a monitor. Conventional monitors are reliable, but even the best small LCD screens cannot display accurate contrast, especially in bright lighting conditions.

If you have no external monitor, you can estimate the contrast of the image to be recorded by using an old photographer's trick:

1. Look at the scene to be taped.
2. Close one eye completely.
3. Squint the other eye until it is almost shut and its eyelashes form a sort of filter.
4. Look at the darkest parts of the scene.

If you cannot make out details in the shadow areas, the contrast is too great. Though this improvisation is no substitute for an accurate monitor, it can give you a rough approximation of the scene contrast as the camcorder will record it.

Figure 12-4.
The window light coming from the right is bluer than the supplementary movie lights.

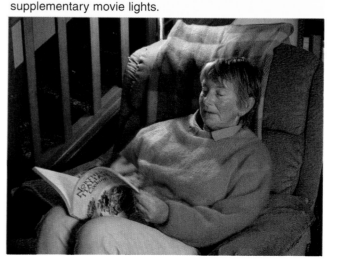

Lighting Character

If you master the quality of light, your images may be well-illuminated, attractively colored, and pleasing to look at, but they may not contribute much to the program. To pull its weight artistically, lighting must also have character. *Lighting character* is the set of traits that individualizes the look of the scene by giving it a distinctive *mood* and *style*.

Mood and Style

Though these terms may appear confusingly similar, they really mean quite different things. *Mood* is the emotional feeling of the image: cheerful or gloomy, frightening or reassuring, exciting or soothing.

Style is the lighting approach used to create a mood. A mood can be created by any of several different lighting styles. As you can see from **Figure 12-5,** the mood in two images can be similar, though the styles used to create it are quite different.

To put it another way, mood is the emotional effect of the lighting, and style is the way in which lighting is used to create that effect.

Over the centuries, painters, stage designers, photographers, and cinematographers have evolved many approaches to lighting. Though there is no standard classification, we may distinguish several basic lighting styles and label them *naturalism*, *realism*, *pictorial realism*, *magic realism*, and *expressionism*.

Although these terms are not universally agreed upon, they are common in critical writings about art, theater, film, and photography.

Classifying lighting styles is not just a theoretical exercise. By choosing a basic approach to lighting and then customizing it to your personal taste, you can give your videography a consistent "look and feel," a distinctive quality that enhances its effectiveness and increases its professionalism.

Naturalism

Naturalism is the lighting style that most closely imitates human vision. A naturalistic scene does not look "lit." Instead, a naturalistic image makes you feel that you are looking directly at the scene rather than at an image of it on a screen. Naturalistic lighting uses the available light as much as possible and does not light anything to achieve an obvious effect. Naturalism is a useful style if you want your program to have the look of a straightforward documentary, **Figure 12-6.**

Figure 12-6.
Naturalistic lighting.

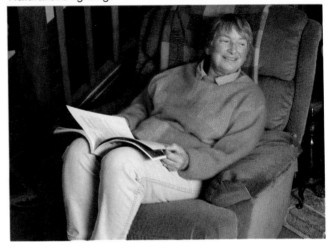

Figure 12-5.
A three-light portrait.

A one-light portrait.

Realism

Realism is naturalism heightened and intensified somewhat to add dramatic effect. Where naturalism records actual lighting conditions as far as possible, realism recreates actual-looking conditions through lighting. The average viewer may not notice it as lighting, but it is visible to an informed eye, **Figure 12-7.** Realism is the most common style for TV programs, whether police dramas shot on location or comedies taped in a studio. If you make program videos, you will work most often in the realistic style.

Pictorial Realism

Pictorial realism is a "painterly" style, in which the lighting effects are frankly visible, although they still imitate real-world lighting such as lamps, streetlights, headlights, sunlight, and moonlight. Through most of Hollywood's history, until the 1960s, pictorial realism was the most popular lighting style; and the simpler alternative of plain realism was largely confined to exterior shooting, where the lighting equipment and techniques needed for pictorial realism were often impractical.

At the height of the silent film period, so-called "Rembrandt lighting" was highly regarded; and during the era of classic studio sound films, an influential textbook on cinematography was titled Painting with Light.

Although pictorial realism sometimes looks artificial to modern viewers, it was accepted as realistic by the original audiences of classic Hollywood films. Today, pictorial realism is often used in commercials and music videos, where a purposely theatrical feel is required.

Magic Realism

Digital video image processing has led to a hybrid style that combines elements of realism, pictorial realism, and expressionism. Because its overall look is superficially realistic, but with a heightened, intensified quality, we may borrow a literary term and name it ***magic realism.***

Though not always manipulated by computer, images in magic realism typically look processed: colors may appear slightly more intense or more uniform than normal, **Figure 12-8.** Different picture components may be sharp or blurred in ways that do not match the focusing characteristics of lenses. Perspective may be skewed. Overall, the images seem to be combinations of photography and illustration.

Expressionism

Expressionism is the most frankly theatrical of the major lighting styles, and does not pretend to reflect reality at all. It is lighting for its own sake, in which any effect is acceptable as long as it *expresses* and intensifies the feeling of the scene. Often, though not always, expressionistic lighting is hyperdramatic, even extreme. Expressionism began as a movement in painting and theater in Europe, and then was adopted by film makers, notably in Germany. The most

Figure 12-7.
Although this room seems lit by natural daylight, the "hot spots" in the upper right reveal the lights above the frame border. (Sue Stinson).

Figure 12-8.
A cemetery scene that has been processed in a magic realism style.

influential expressionistic film is *The Cabinet of Dr. Caligari*. **Figure 12-9**. German directors brought expressionistic lighting and camera work to Hollywood in the 1920s and '30s.

Ironically, because of contemporary limitations in film emulsions and lighting techniques, the expressionistic design of this film was created more with scene paint than with light.

Like pictorial realism and magic realism, expressionism is often the style for commercials (especially humorous ones) and music videos.

Lighting Tools

Now that you have considered why lighting is important (for image quality) and what lighting is for (character created through mood and style), you are ready to practice the actual craft of lighting. To do this, you need to know the lighting tools available to you and the

Figure 12-9.
A scene from The Cabinet of Dr. Caligari.

techniques for using them effectively. There are three basic kinds of lighting resources: tools for controlling existing light, lighting instruments ("lights"), and lighting accessories.

An Anti-style

In addition to the other styles, there is a visual look that might be called an "anti-style," in which the images constantly remind the audience that they are looking at a video or film. We have placed this anti-style by itself because it involves not only lighting but every other aspect of videography as well.

This anti-style exploits the characteristics and limitations of the video medium:

- Shots are purposely set up so that light sources will strike the lens and create intentional flares.
- Dark scenes are shot in low light levels with the gain circuits enabled for a murky, grainy look.
- Exteriors are shot in available light. If light levels are too high, colors smear. If the contrast is too great, faces turn into silhouettes.

- Light levels are not equalized, so that the autoexposure system is visibly adjusting exposure as the camera moves.

This anti-style is similar to naturalism in that it strives to convince viewers that they are looking at unprocessed reality. The difference is that naturalism says, "Here is reality" while anti-style insists, "Here is a video *recording* of reality."

Some viewers think that this anti-style is an intrinsically honest approach to recording video images. Others find it pretentious and irritating. Either way, it can be powerfully effective in the right type of program.

Examples of "anti-style"—intentional sun flare and an ultra low-light shot. (Sue Stinson)

Tools for Available Light

In outdoor shooting, lighting often means controlling the existing light, modifying and redirecting it to improve the quality of the image. In working with available light you control its *quantity*, *direction*, and *color*.

Controlling quantity

Since you cannot add natural light, controlling quantity means subtracting light when it is too intense. Here, your principal tools are flags, screens, and silks.

Flags are flat, opaque, and usually constructed of metal, thin plywood, or fabric on a metal frame. Most are rectangular, though rounded edge flags can be used for special effects. Reflectors can serve as flags when set to block light rather than reflect it. Foam-core board, used mainly for reflectors, also works well as a flag. Flags may be held by crew members or clamped onto stands. Flags, of course, completely block the path of directional light, **Figure 12-10.**

Screens are large expanses of metal or plastic mesh stretched on frames, **Figure 12-11.** Small ones can be held by stands or by crew members, but most are mounted on support structures. Unlike flags, screens allow most of the light to reach the subject; unlike silks, they do not change the light's directionality or character. The screening material can be obtained in different densities, depending on how much light reduction is needed.

Silks look and work like screens, except that they are sheets of thin white synthetic fabric.

Actual silk fabric is rarely used on "silks" anymore.

Figure 12-11.
A screen reduces light intensity without altering its character.

Like screens, they reduce the intensity of light on the subject. But as you can see from **Figure 12-12**, silks also diffuse the light, changing it from a single, directional beam to an overall glow.

Because silks diffuse the light as well as reduce it, they could also be listed among the tools that control light direction.

Controlling direction

Reflectors are large boards with reflective surfaces that are positioned to receive light from natural sources and bounce it back onto subjects. Large studio-style reflectors are mounted on yoked stands, **Figure 12-13.** Because of their weight, they are stable in winds, but awkward to handle, transport, and store.

Hand-held reflectors have just the opposite advantages and disadvantages: light and

Figure 12-10.
A flag blocks light completely.

Figure 12-12.
A silk reduces and diffuses the light.

Figure 12-13.
A heavy-duty studio-style reflector.

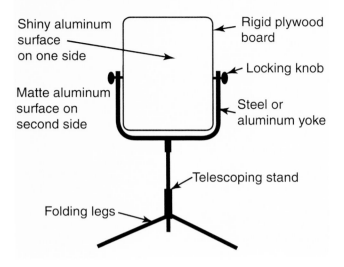

Shiny aluminum surface on one side

Matte aluminum surface on second side

Rigid plywood board

Locking knob

Steel or aluminum yoke

Telescoping stand

Folding legs

easy to handle, they tend to wobble in breezes, making the light on the subject waver unsuitably. The lightest reflectors are fabric stretched on wire hoops. These can be folded and stored in very small spaces.

Reflectors come in four main types:

- *Hard metallic*. Highly directional, these silver reflectors throw a light beam a long distance and/or fill a small subject area. They can be painfully bright when directed at actors' faces.

- *Soft metallic*. Less directional, these silver reflectors still throw light a long distance, but disperse it over a wider area.

- *White*. Extremely diffuse, these reflectors provide a soft, even fill light that does not hurt actors' eyes. The most common white reflector is made of **foam-core board**: a one-half-inch or one-inch sheet of rigid plastic foam laminated between two sheets of white paper. Stiff, light, and disposable, foam-core is an indispensable lighting tool.

- *Tinted*. Metal, cloth, or foam-core reflectors can be obtained in colors, notably gold tone for metallic models and pale amber or pale blue for paper. By changing the color of the reflected light, these reflectors can warm up flesh tones, simulate moonlight, and deliver other specialized tints.

Controlling color

Aside from tinted reflectors, the principal tools for altering available light color are filters. **Filters** selectively change the overall color of light sources.

Color correction and neutral density filters placed directly on the camera lens change all of the light entering the camera. Sheet filters, however, affect only the light sources that they are covering.

The most common light source filter is window gel, tinted plastic sheeting that comes in rolls big enough to cover entire windows. Window filtering gels are used for two purposes: to change color temperature and/or to reduce incoming light. If your interior lights and camcorder are set for incandescent color temperature (3200K), the daylight streaming through visible windows will look far too blue. Color correction filters positioned outside these windows will warm the cool daylight up to match the interior lights, **Figure 12-14.**

In addition to being bluer than interior light, daylight is typically much brighter. To prevent on-screen windows from burning out to pure white, neutral density filter plastic is applied over the windows. Neutral density filtration material is supplied in several strengths, coded ND3, ND6, ND9, etc. Since each number (1, 2, 3, etc.) represents 1/3 of one f-stop, an ND3 filter reduces light by one stop, an ND6 by two stops, and so-on. To control both intensity and color at once, color correction tinting is often added to neutral density filters.

Gelling a window is a time-consuming process, so it helps to determine the correct filtration before cutting and applying the plastic.

You can also change the color of existing artificial light (lamps and fluorescents) already

Figure 12-14.
For demonstration purposes, a single panel of this window has been covered with a color correction filter.

in use at a location. Sheet filters can be placed over fluorescent fixtures to match the warmer color of movie lights; or tube-shaped filters can be slipped over the fluorescent lamps themselves. Sometimes, the existing fluorescent tubes are replaced with special lamps that supply matching color temperature.

In practice, you will find that you can often achieve professional lighting results simply by controlling the light that is already available. Professional camcorders can adjust white balance over a very wide range of color tints,

and CCD recording systems are so sensitive that you can often shoot in well-lit interiors without much special movie lighting. The key to success is to study a good quality, well-adjusted monitor and remember that if it looks good, it *is* good.

Lighting Instruments

Professional lighting instruments can be confusing because there are so many to choose from. The lights of one manufacturer are designed differently from those of others;

Inexpensive Lighting Control Tools

If you are building an outdoor lighting kit on a limited budget, you can construct many of the most common lighting control tools.

Century stands

The exception is one or more Century stands, or C-stands, as they are called. **Century stands** are so versatile and so relatively inexpensive that to make an equivalent support would cost as much as buying one. C-stands are available from the mail order companies that advertise in video magazines, and from theatrical supply houses or commercial photo supply outlets in larger cities.

Toothed plates allow clamp to rotate and lock at any angle

Multipurpose heads

Clamp holds different sized pipes

Locking knob

Collar fits stand or pipe

Telescoping stand

Plates clamp reflectors and other cards

Feet rotate to fold

Century stand head

Century stand

Reflectors

Reflectors are easily constructed by taping aluminum foil over light plywood rectangles (a 24" × 36" sheet of 3/16" plywood is a good size). To create the hardest surface with the longest throw and brightest light, use spray adhesive to glue the foil, shiny side up, to the board. For a slightly softer surface, place the matte side of the foil up

instead. For a still more diffuse light, ball up the foil lightly and then spread it flat again before gluing. This will break up the surface into thousands of tiny facets that will refract the light and diffuse the overall reflection.

For soft fill effects, any white cardboard will do;

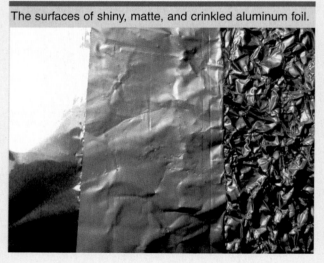

The surfaces of shiny, matte, and crinkled aluminum foil.

but white foam-core board is more rigid. For greater permanence, invest in one-inch board, rather than the thinner type.

The most common type of reflector combines a hard surface (shiny or matte aluminum) on one side with a soft surface (faceted aluminum or white) on the other side.

Flags

Reflectors of foam-core or plywood can also be used as flags to mask off unwanted light; however, the most versatile flag shape is a longer, thinner rectangle. Flags should be painted black, to minimize light bouncing off them. It is a good idea to construct a variety of black plywood flags.

Screens and silks

Screens reduce the intensity of light and silks diffuse it. Hand-held models are inexpensive enough and each vendor offers several competing families of lighting instruments with different characteristics engineered for different applications. In practice, many lighting designers eventually standardize on a particular vendor and family of lights simply because those are the ones they happened to have mastered.

For all their many differences in design features and accessories, most lighting instruments fall into one of three main types: *small source, large source,* and *specialty.*

Small source lights

These are spotlights whose light source is the diameter of the lamp and its reflector, **Figure 12-15.**

The small light source produces a highly directional light pattern. This means the light illuminates relatively small areas, casts distinct, hard-edged shadows, and is easily masked by barn doors or flags. Small source spotlights are often used as key (main) lights on subjects, or to simulate the light from

These flags are attached to a light by flexible shafts. (Lowel Corporation)

A frame made of inexpensive plastic pipe.

90 degree elbow

48" maximum length

1.25" PVC pipe

36"-48" maximum width

Fabric hemmed to receive pipe

Do not cement pipe, so that frame will come apart for storage

to buy, and you can find them at most larger camera stores. Stretched on wire hoops, these types fold into small areas for storage and transport. For larger models, you will need to construct a mounting frame. The diagram shows a frame of plastic pipe that disassembles for storage.

Old bedsheets make excellent silks. For screens, plant nurseries and large garden supply stores carry black plastic netting in large rolls. You can select the density of the screening, or double-layer lighter screens to block more light.

Weights

The great enemy of lighting control is wind, especially with screens and large reflectors. To hold down C-stands or screening frames, weights are essential accessories. Sandbags are cheap and effective weights, but they are heavy, dirty, and tend to leak. For this reason, some production companies use weights filled with water instead. By filling and emptying the bags at the location, they avoid transporting most of the weight.

Commercial water weights are available from production supply houses, but the collapsible plastic water bags sold for camping are inexpensive

and work just as well. They are typically supplied with handles and hooks to help hang them on light and reflector stands. If you need to improvise, one-gallon drinking water bottles are available at any supermarket at very low cost. They can be secured to stand bases with duct tape or bungee cords.

Water bags and even plastic drinking water bottles make excellent weights.

Taped to leg

1 gallon jugs filled with water

Figure 12-15.
A typical small-source light. (Lowel Corporation)

Figure 12-16.
Focusing a spotlight.

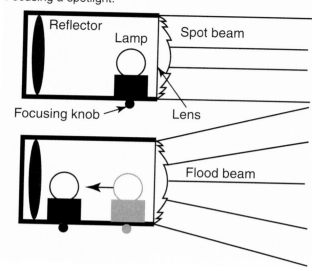

natural sources ranging from the sun to a table lamp.

A spotlight can be focused by moving its lamp forward or backward in relationship to the reflector behind it and/or the lens in front, **Figure 12-16.** Focusing changes the beam from narrow and intense to wider and less intense. The advantage of small-source lights is that they are very easy to control. On the other hand, small-source light beams are relatively harsh and several used together can throw unrealistic multiple shadows.

Large source lights

Large source lights, **Figure 12-17,** are commonly used to fill in shadows (often created by small source key lights) and to light backgrounds. Compared with small source lights, large instruments have the opposite advantages and drawbacks. On the positive side, their light is softer and less directional; their shadows are fainter or, with the largest sources, almost nonexistent; and their beam

pattern is broad and even. On the negative side, their intensity is less at any given part of the beam pattern and they are difficult to control by masking.

Specialty lights

Lighting instruments are also designed for numerous special applications. Two of the most common are camera lights and practicals. **Camera lights** are small spotlights or floodlights mounted on the camera for brightening foreground subjects.

So-called *"practicals"* are lights that will be seen by viewers, like table lamps or wall sconces, **Figure 12-18.** In set lighting, you will sometimes replace the lamp in a working practical to adjust its intensity, color temperature, or both. Practicals are easy to color-balance because 3200K halogen bulbs can be obtained with the medium screw-type bases used for household lighting. In cases involving car headlights or flashlights, you may establish

Figure 12-17.
Large source lights. A—Soft box floodlight. B—Broad floodlight. C— Fluorescent floodlight. (Lowel Corporation)

A

B

C

Figure 12-18.
The reading light is a *practical*.

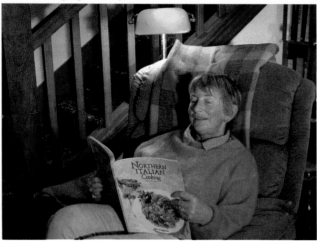

the practical in the scene, and then simulate its light with a more controllable spotlight when the source is not in the shot and the audience is seeing what the practical is supposedly illuminating.

The term *practical* comes from the theater, where on-stage lights that actors can actually turn on and off require special wiring that must be placed or removed with each scene change.

Production Lamps

The lightbulbs used in video lighting are called lamps, and there are three basic types: incandescent, halogen, and fluorescent.

Incandescent lamps

These lamps contain metal filaments glowing in a near-vacuum. They are universally found in household lighting. Ordinary incandescents have a color temperature (relative whiteness) of 2700K-2800K, while the special models sold for photographic lighting burn at 3200K, the white balance of a camcorder's "indoor" or "incandescent" setting. Older lighting instruments take incandescent lamps, but they have been largely replaced by halogen units.

Halogen lamps

Halogen lamps, **Figure 12-19**, contain metal filaments in a special mixture of gasses. All halogens burn at 3200K. Unlike incandescent light, halogen illumination does not grow more yellow as the lamps age. Halogen lamps are also smaller and emit more light, watt-for-watt, than incandescents. They are generally less expensive than 3200K incandescents, though more expensive than household lamps. Halogen lamps have one potential safety problem: a tendency to shatter.

For this reason, always follow precautions in working with them. Never use a halogen instrument that does not place the lamp behind a safety glass. Never touch a lamp with your fingers. Your natural skin oil can etch the quartz envelope of the lamp. When the lamp heats up, it can shatter at the etched area. To change a halogen lamp, wrap it in a facial tissue or use the foam sheet that is usually packed with it. Some

Inexpensive Lighting Instruments

If your budget is limited, halogen work lights can be very useful accessories.

Halogen work lights are available at most hardware and building supply stores at reasonable prices. Depending on your needs, you can select:

● Wattages from 150 to 1,000.
● Single- or double-head lights.
● Heads fitted with two separately switchable lamps.
● Lights on telescopic floor stands, short legs, or clamps.

Intended for light industrial use, these fixtures meet all code requirements for lamp safety, cord protection, and switches.

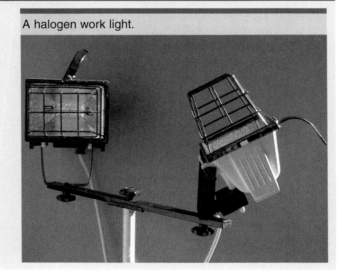

A halogen work light.

Figure 12-19.
A halogen lamp (bulb).

types of halogen lamp are enclosed in a second outer envelope that can be touched. Others are mounted within integral reflectors, which can also be handled safely.

Fluorescent lamps

Most camcorders have white balance settings optimized for standard fluorescent lights, and you can often obtain satisfactory video colors this way. But if you use fluorescents as movie lights, you will want to select specialized tubes that produce more pleasing color. When mixing fluorescent and halogen lights, use tubes rated at 3000K. If your whole lighting setup is fluorescent, you may get better results with "sunshine" fluorescent lights, whose 5000K color temperature closely matches that of direct sunlight.

When selecting fluorescent tubes, note that some manufacturers provide a "Color Rendering Index" (CRI) a scale from 1 to 100 that rates the ability of a fluorescent tube to deliver natural looking color. For example, inexpensive "shop light" tubes may have an index of 67. Better quality lamps have indexes in the 70s. The best sunlight tubes are rated at over 90.

For more consistent output, make sure that all your tubes are the same make and model and all are replaced at the same time.

Accessories for Lights

The beams from small source lights (spotlights and narrow floods) can be modified by accessories that fit on the front of the instrument to mask, reduce, or diffuse the light.

Light masking

The highly directional beams of spotlights can be masked to produce hard-edged cutoff patterns. Masking accessories include *barn doors* and *flags*. **Barn doors** are pairs of metal flaps hinged to the sides and/or top and bottom edges of the lamp, **Figure 12-20.** Small flags on movable arms can be positioned more flexibly than barn doors. As a rule, the farther a masking device is placed from the light, the harder-edged is its shadow. Barn doors attached to the light throw softer shadows than flags mounted on C-stands placed closer to the subjects.

Light reduction

Spotlights can be fitted with circular frames covered with nets (actually made of screen wire) to cut down the light intensity, **Figure 12-21.**

The most common nets are:

- *Singles*: One-layer nets for moderate light reduction.
- *Doubles*: Two-layer versions for stronger reduction.
- *Halves*: Frames with one half netted and the other half clear. By rotating a half net, you can selectively reduce the illumination on just part of the area lit by the beam. Half nets are also supplied in

Figure 12-20.
All four barn doors on this spotlight can be shaped for better control. (Lowell Corporation)

Figure 12-21.
This graduated screen uses 2, 1, and 0 layers of net. (Lowel Corporation)

Metal frame
No net
Single net
Double net

one- and two-layer versions, so a "half double" is a two-layered half-circle net.

Light Diffusion

Rings framing white material can diffuse the hard beams of small source instruments, but diffusion material is more effective on large-source floodlights.

White cloth sheeting is especially effective on fluorescent floodlights because they emit relatively little heat.

Smaller floodlights are often enclosed in so-called "soft boxes" in order to diffuse the light by increasing the apparent size of the light source, **Figure 12-22.**

Color

Lighting instruments are sometimes gelled with colored plastic to simulate firelight, moonlight, or other effects; or simply to warm or cool the light on an area.

Other Lighting Accessories

In addition to accessories placed on or in front of the lighting instruments, a wide variety of other lighting tools are available. Here is a summary of the more common accessories.

Light control

Stand-alone flags are used to mask light paths, and colored gels are sometimes placed out in front of lights instead of on them.

Patterns

Specially cut sheets are placed in front of spotlights to create patterns on walls and other surfaces. These *"cookies,"* as they are called, can simulate leaves, bare tree branches, Venetian blinds, **Figure 12-23,** or any other pattern required.

Some videographers carry small, actual mini-blinds that they suspend from a C-stand in front of a light and adjust to create the desired light pattern.

Mounts

Light stands are the most common accessories for supporting lights. To illuminate larger areas, horizontal overhead lighting

Figure 12-22.
A soft box uses opaque fabric on the sides and silk-like fabric in front for diffusion. (Lowel Corporation)

Figure 12-23.
A Venetian blind cookie.

pipes spanning the center of a set may be supported by heavy stands and hung with several instruments. Aside from light stands, the most useful mounting device is a Century stand. As noted, a C-stand can hold a light, a flag, a cookie, or just about anything else, It is such an indispensable lighting tool that large productions may have dozens of them.

Electrical Accessories

For location lighting, extension cables are essential. Make sure that your cables are safe:

- Wire gauge should be no thinner than No. 12; No. 10 is even better. (The lower the number, the thicker the wire.) See **Figure 12-24.**
- Extensions should not exceed 25 feet in length.
- Use single plugs, rather than multiple outlet boxes, to avoid overloading circuits.
- Use high-visibility yellow or orange cables for safety.
- Tape loose cable to the floor for additional safety. If tangled around a foot, a cable can topple a light on a stand, with disagreeable results.

Figure 12-24.
An appropriate cable for location lighting.

Heavy-duty plug with ground

Strain relief

Orange or yellow cable for visibility, #12 gauge or heavier

Dimmers can be used to reduce the output of a light. Dimming a light often warms up its color temperature, so dimming can be used to control color as well as output.

The kit of a professional gaffer (chief electrician) may contain hundreds of special-purpose accessories; but two items are universal: gloves and gaffer tape.

Gloves

Leather gloves are a must around hot lights. Find the heaviest industrial grade models you can, because incandescent lighting instruments can heat up to hundreds of degrees.

Gaffer tape

Gaffer tape looks just like ordinary duct tape but costs five times as much and works five times as well. It is sticky enough to tape light-weight instruments to walls and other surfaces. At the end of a shoot, it can be peeled from the wall (with patience) without lifting paint.

Gaffer tape is a special high-performance version of duct tape. It was originally offered for lighting use in 1959 by Ross Lowel, the founder of the Lowel-Light Manufacturing Company. Gaffer tape is available from video mail-order companies.

Lighting Evaluation Tools

In addition to an educated eye, two tools are useful for assessing a lighting design: a monitor and a light meter. Meters can be indispensable in certain situations, and a good monitor is essential for almost *all* types of shooting.

Monitors

No professional videographer likes to work without a reference monitor: a high-quality display that has been calibrated to show exactly what the camcorder is recording, **Figure 12-25.**

A good monitor delivers "what you see is what you get"(WYSIWYG) information about the lighting. With it, you can light a set using basic common sense: simply check the effect on the screen as you work and adjust the lighting until you are satisfied with the image.

Figure 12-25.
An AC/DC combination monitor/player is a useful location accessory.

Figure 12-26.
This incident light meter is reading foot-candle ("FC") units. (Mamiya/Sekonic).

Light meters

Even with a reference monitor, a light meter is a useful measurement tool. You can use it to regulate contrast by checking the relative brightness of different image areas and adjusting light levels until the meter indicates the desired contrast ratio.

You can also use a light meter for checking overall brightness levels, in order to calculate the f-stop at which your lens is working and determine whether to use neutral density filters (to reduce light) or the gain control (to amplify low-light signals).

Incident meters, like the Sekonic studio model in **Figure 12-26**, are aimed at the lights to measure illumination directly. **Reflective meters** are aimed at the subject to measure the light that reaches the camera lens.

A **color temperature meter** precisely measures the relative blueness or redness of "white" light at any point in a scene. This information is useful if you are working with a mixture of light sources, so that you can decide which ones to adjust for color, and how much adjustment to make.

Some videographers like the precision afforded by light meters, while others seldom use them, except in specialized and/or very difficult lighting situations.

From General to Specific

This chapter has discussed some general theories about lighting and reviewed many of the more commonly used lighting instruments and accessories. Now that these basics have been covered, we can explore some practical techniques used to apply them and some actual lighting problems and situations. The next chapter covers the specifics of video lighting.

Technical Terms

Barn doors: Metal flaps in sets of two or four, attached to the fronts of spotlights to control the edges of the beam.

Camera light: A small light mounted on the camera to provide foreground fill.

Century stand (C-stand): A telescoping floor stand fitted with a clamp and usually an adjustable arm, for supporting lights and accessories.

Color temperature meter: A light meter that measures the relative blueness or redness of nominally "white" light.

Contrast: The difference between the lightest and darkest parts of an image, expressed as a ratio (e.g. "four-to-one").

Cookie: A sheet cut into a specific pattern and placed in the beam of a light to throw distinctive shadows such as leaves or blinds.

Flag: A flat piece of opaque metal, wood, or foam-core placed to mask off part of a light beam.

Incident meter: A light meter that measures the illumination as it comes from the light sources.

Instrument: A unit of lighting hardware such as a spotlight or floodlight.

Lamp: The actual bulb in a lighting instrument.

Practical: An instrument that is included in shots and may be operated by the actors.

Reflective meter: A light meter that measures illumination as it bounces off the subjects and into the camera lens.

Reflector: A large silver, white, or colored surface used to bounce light onto a subject or scene.

Screen: A mesh material that reduces light intensity without markedly changing its character.

Silk: A fabric material that reduces both light intensity and directionality, producing a soft, directionless illumination.

A lighting kit in a suitcase. Compare its mixture of spot and floodlights to the kit on the opposite page. (Cool Lux)

13 Lighting Techniques

Contents

About Lighting Techniques
Lighting Principles
Lighting Applications

Objectives

After studying this chapter, you will be able to:

- ❏ Demonstrate basic lighting principles and techniques.
- ❏ Apply lighting methods to common shooting situations.

Lowel Corporation

About Lighting Techniques

This chapter applies the lighting theories covered in Chapter 12 to practical lighting problems in specific shooting situations. The section on lighting *principles* shows how to systematically build up a lighting design to achieve the look you want. The section on lighting *applications* addresses the problems you are likely to encounter in several common shooting environments. As you address the practicalities of video lighting, keep in mind that you are always lighting by employing a coherent *style* to achieve a particular *mood*.

Since theory and practice are two approaches to the same subject, there is some content overlap in this chapter and Chapter 12.

The Development of Video Lighting

Historically, film and TV scenes have been lit quite differently. Since video is a hybrid of both older technologies, it takes something from each and adds techniques of its own.

Film lighting

Despite its many advantages, film has, until recently, suffered from two major lighting problems: its relative insensitivity and its need to be processed and printed for viewing. The relatively slow speed (light sensitivity) of film meant that sets needed to be lit with many lighting instruments that consumed considerable power. Although today's color film is more sensitive than it was when film lighting methods were developed, these techniques are still widely practiced, so that film lighting tends to be a relatively elaborate procedure.

Because film must be processed and printed before it can be viewed, it is impossible to see the precise effect of film lighting during shooting.

On many film productions today, the lighting is previewed on video monitors, but these can only approximate the look of the actual film.

To overcome this inconvenience, professional cinematographers and lighting gaffers become experts at predicting how their lighting designs will look on film. To help in this process, they use specialized light meters to measure **incident light** and **reflected light** levels at important points in the scene. Nonetheless, even with these sophisticated metering instruments and today's sensitive emulsions, film lighting is an art that can take years of practice to master.

The gaffer is the boss of the lighting department on a shoot. The term is derived from an old British word meaning "grandfather," or simply, "old man."

Television lighting

Studio-based television also presents lighting problems, **Figure 13-1**. For many years, the tube-type cameras employed could not handle contrast competently. This meant that the darkest parts of the image had to be no less than about one-third as bright as the lightest parts. Moreover, television programs are recorded more or less continuously by multiple cameras shooting from different directions and often covering different parts of the set. For this reason, every subject, place, action, and angle must be lit at the same time. Although technical progress has allowed television studio lighting to improve substantially, the demands of low-contrast lighting and full-set coverage can still make television lighting more flat and bland than film lighting.

Figure 13-1.
TV studios use low-contrast lighting. (Corel)

Video lighting

Video is a true hybrid: a medium that combines the shooting techniques of film with the recording technology of television. Camcorders fitted with modern CCDs are more sensitive to light than many standard film stocks and accept wider contrast ratios than classic television cameras. Like TV lighting directors, videographers can see exactly what their images look like as they are setting them up and shooting them. For this reason, learning to light for video is easier than mastering film lighting. In effect, if it looks good on a quality reference monitor, it *is* good.

Perhaps the fairest assessment might be that today, all three visual media can support sophisticated lighting. While film and television continue using traditional methods with technical improvements, video lighting has evolved its own approach.

Lighting Principles

Before you start hanging lights and stringing cable, you need to size up each lighting assignment and develop a strategy for it. There are three general principles that apply to most lighting situations:

● Light the subjects, not the space.

● Use added light in moderation.

● Light to create a standard video image.

These principles are so important that they deserve discussion in some detail.

Light the Subjects, Not the Space

Images are created by light reflected into the lens from subjects in the frame. For this reason, you do not have to light every cubic inch of your location, but only those areas containing subject matter, **Figure 13-2.**

To light just the areas that will show on screen, follow this procedure:

1. Study the performers' positions and movement ("blocking").

2. Light the areas that they will use, paying special attention to places where they will stay, or at least pause. In other words, keep them adequately illuminated throughout their movement, and carefully lit at the more important action points.

We will use the term *action points* throughout this chapter.

3. Light the background (including furniture and any floor or ceiling areas) only where it will appear behind the subjects.

If there is considerable action to be shot from one setup, you may want to provide basic lighting for the entire blocking area, adding or adjusting instruments as needed to optimize the lighting for later setups that focus on different action points.

Use added light in moderation

The sensitivity and flexibility of video often allow it to capture good quality images in available light. When this is the case, let that "free" light work for you. Add lights and/or reflectors where the ambient light alone cannot create the mood and style that you want.

Figure 13-2.
Lighting the subject. A—Lighting plan for a moving subject. B—The subject is fully lit at the start and end positions.

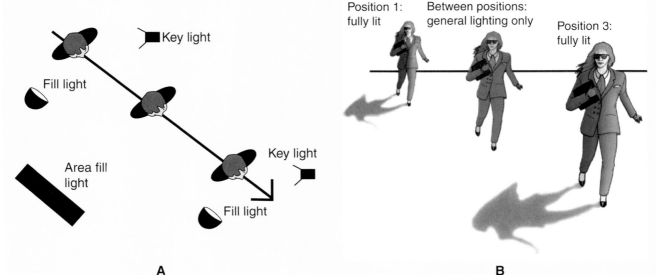

A

B

Light to create a standard video image

Most video postproduction uses digital technology that permits a wide range of adjustments to the image. Moonlit nights, sunsets, and other overall color tints are easy to add during editing. Contrast and brightness can be adjusted to change day shots to night.

It is generally safer to add such effects in postproduction than to record them as part of the original footage. That way, if you do not like an effect, you can always return to the original, unmodified version and try something different. In contrast, special lighting effects recorded as part of the original footage are harder to remove (though they can sometimes be modified digitally). For this reason, you should typically light and record a high-quality image with a neutral-looking white balance. In short, capture it accurately now; modify it later.

This rule is even more important with camera effects like mosaic and strobe, which cannot be undone by digital postproduction.

On the other hand, if you have colored light on just one part of your scene, it may well be easier to create the effect while shooting than to add it in postproduction. For example, the flashing red light of an offscreen "police car" colors only the left side of the subject in **Figure 13-3.**

Like all generalizations, these principles may not apply to every lighting situation that you will encounter, but it is wise to consider them in developing any lighting strategy.

Shooting Day for Night

Although you can use a camcorder in very low light levels, there are good reasons for shooting exterior night scenes during the day. Daytime shooting is more convenient for everyone. Daytime light levels are high enough for optimal imaging. Fewer lighting instruments and accessories are required. In some cases, you can shoot without electrical power.

In video, making daytime shots look like night is easy if you follow a few simple rules.

The shot recorded normally.

The completed day-for-night version.

Figure 13-3.
A—Simulating a police car's flashing red light.

Hand-held revolving light simulates off-screen police car.

A

B— The effect on screen.

B

The setup for the shot…

Set white balance for incandescent

Using an indoor white balance setting outdoors will lend an overall "moonlight" bluish cast to the footage, while rendering any incandescent lights as true white. You may also want to set exposure so that the natural shadows fill in as deep black. If you will edit digitally (and no incandescent lighting is used),

White balance set for incandescent (indoor) light.

you can create the color, exposure, and contrast of "night" in postproduction. In this situation, it is often safer to get conventionally balanced and exposed footage and then alter it later.

Use back-cross lighting

Instead of directing the main (key) light source at subjects from the front or partway to one side, position subjects and reflectors as needed to splash the brightest light from the rear, onto hair and shoulders, while the faces remain somewhat darker.

Back-cross lighting from the sun creates a rim light of "moonlight."

Frame off the sky

Unless you can darken the sky with a polarizing filter, use neutral or high angles to aim the camcorder away from the sky, which will appear much too light for a convincing night effect.

Including the daytime sky reveals the trick.

Include incandescent light

Finally, try to include some incandescent or halogen lighting in the shot, such as headlights, a street light, or light streaming out of a window or open door. Since the indoor white balance setting will render this light as "white," it will contrast convincingly with the "moonlight" cast of the overall scene.

Incandescent light completes the illusion.

Lighting Designs

With the three basic principles in mind, begin creating a lighting design by determining the mood of the scene—that is, the overall emotional effect you want to produce.

Briefly, the three principles are: 1. light the subject, not the space; 2. add lights in moderation, and 3. light to create a standard video image.

Is it warm or cold, frightening or reassuring, romantic or detached? Then decide whether to implement your design by *controlling* the light already available at the location, by *enhancing* that available light, or by *replacing* that light entirely with movie lighting.

Designs That Control Existing Light

At the simplest level, you can light a location by shaping and directing the light that is already there. To do this, you control the available light's *quantity*, *color*, *direction*, and *character*.

Controlling quantity

Controlling the amount of light on the scene means reducing it, since you cannot add to it.

The simplest way to reduce the light levels is to move the camera so that it frames a darker background, or to move the entire action to a darker area, Figure 13-4.

Figure 13-4.
Too much contrast throws the subject into silhouette.

Using a darker background reduces contrast.

To reduce the quantity of light, filter it through one or more screens. Screens mounted on frames can filter a wide area, while hand-held screens serve well for medium and close shots. Remember: since you are providing fully-designed lighting only for positions where the subject stands or pauses, you can screen just the area where a moving subject will stop.

To change the quality and direction of the light as well as its quantity, you can use diffusion instead of screening, as noted later in this chapter. To reduce the light level of the entire scene as the camera sees it, use a neutral density filter over the lens.

These tips are mainly for exterior locations, since interiors rarely offer excessive ambient light, except for daylight entering from outside. To reduce this light, cover windows from the outside with neutral density gel sheets.

Sheet filters of heat-resistant plastic are still called "gels" because they were once made of a gelatin material.

Controlling color

Windows are prime sources of color mismatches when shooting by interior available light. Mixing fluorescent and incandescent lights can give problems as well. To control color, follow this plan:

1. Decide which type of light will provide the main illumination. Suppose you have a room lit by fluorescents with a lamp on a table and a window to one side. Here, you might choose the fluorescent light as your main source, **Figure 13-5.**

2. Set white balance to match the fluorescent main source (preferably manually, if your camcorder permits).
3. Aim the camera to frame all three light sources (or at least, objects lit by them) and check the results on your production monitor.
4. If needed, place a neutral density gel over the window and surround the bulb of the lamp with a cool gel to match the fluorescents.

If your monitor shows that the table lamp casts an attractively warm glow on the desk, you may want to leave it unfiltered.

Figure 13-5.
Plan showing three types of light source.

Controlling direction

Controlling the direction of ambient light means using reflectors with hard metallic surfaces for long throws, soft metallic surfaces to reduce harshness and spread the beam, or white models to cast a diffuse glow. Use rigid, stand-mounted reflectors where practical, to eliminate movement that creates a wavering reflection on the subject. To control reflector intensity and beam diameter, change the distance from the subject, **Figure 13-6**.

A reflector need not be directly opposite the sun or other source that it is reflecting, but it will not work well if it is too far off to one side. As a rough rule of thumb, it is usually best to use the softest reflectors that the light source and throw distance allow, except for special tasks such as rim-lighting the subject.

A light or reflector's "throw" is the distance between it and the subject it is lighting.

Controlling character

The character of a lighting scheme is set mainly by the light's contrast and directness. Reflectors are usually put to work filling in shadows opposite the main light source, in order to reduce contrast. Contrast and light direction are closely linked because high-contrast lighting is the result of highly directional light, while low-contrast lighting is typically created with soft, less-directional light sources.

Even when lighting is limited to reflectors and screens, it is possible to light a location in more than one style. In the natural style, the fill light is purposely faint, so as to leave a natural-looking shadow. In the realistic style, the fill is stronger, but still moderate enough so that most viewers would not notice it. In the pictorial style, a rim light reflection is often added to separate subjects more dramatically from their backgrounds.

Designs That Enhance Existing Light

Although available light is sometimes bright enough to create a high-quality image, its character may not be appropriate to the style you want to achieve. To solve the problem, you can often enhance the ambient light with supplementary lighting.

Generally, the first step is to decide whether to use the existing illumination as the key light or the fill light. Commonly, window light is used to key a setup, while soft overhead lighting provides fill.

Enhancing an existing key light

In **Figure 13-7**, the woman is lit primarily by soft light from an offscreen sliding glass door. To add visual interest, while preserving the natural-looking design, an added practical (on-screen) light provides rim light.

Enhancing an existing fill light

In **Figure 13-8**, by contrast, the subject is lit primarily by soft fill from overhead fluorescent lights. A soft key light has been added,

Figure 13-6.
A—Control reflector beam size and intensity by changing reflector distance. B— Fill shadows on faces by placing reflectors below eye level.

A   **B**

High Key, Low Key

Classic Hollywood technique distinguished between two basic approaches to lighting: *high key* and *low key*. Simply put, a high key image is composed mainly of lighter values, punctuated with occasional dark areas. A low key image is the opposite: mainly dark, but usually with a lighter center of interest.

High key lighting was used for comedies, romantic movies, and action pictures. Low key lighting was used for crime and mystery films, intense dramas, and horror.

High and low key lighting can be designed in any style, especially in pictorial and magic realism. The so-called "film noir" style of the 1930s and 1940s executed low key lighting in the pictorial realism style, with great effectiveness.

Today, high key or low key lighting schemes are still used; but in the preferred styles of naturalism and realism, their effect is usually not as pronounced.

High key lighting.

Low key lighting (Corel).

Figure 13-7.
Natural key light plus rim light (practical).

Rim light from practical lamp

Key light from glass doors

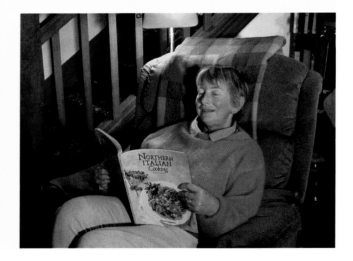

placed to the side and at eye level; small overhead lights provide modeling for the background (note the hot spot on the flowers).

Enhancing under-lit subjects

You can call the viewer's attention to your center of interest by making it just a bit brighter than objects around it. The method may be as simple as a small light mounted directly on the camera, **Figure 13-9.**

In **Figure 13-9,** notice how the extra front light slightly emphasizes the subject, without seeming to throw an obvious spotlight on him. Alternatively, you can do the same job with a small, stand-mounted spotlight.

On-camera lights with multiple power settings let you control the amount of front lighting you add.

Designs That Replace Existing Light

In a studio or a relatively dark location, you replace the available light entirely by over-powering it with movie lighting. Like controlling or enhancing existing light, creating designs

Figure 13-8.
Natural fill light plus key and rim lights.

Figure 13-9.
An on-camera light. (Lowel Corporation).   The lighting is murky.   An on-camera light adds front fill.

from scratch involves lighting the background and the subjects in front of it. Although the different styles of naturalism, realism, and pictorial realism achieve this through somewhat different approaches, all three styles rely on variations of a classic four-light scheme:

- Key light.
- Fill light.
- Rim (modeling) light.
- Background light.

Once you understand these four basic components, **Figure 13-10,** you can use them in any lighting style.

Key light

The **key light** provides the basic illumination for the image, **Figure 13-11**. Though it may be placed anywhere in a 180° arc around the front of the subject, the classic position delivers 3/4 facial lighting from a point higher than the subject. In pictorial realism, the key is usually a small source spotlight. In naturalism, it is likely to be a larger, softer source instead.

Figure 13-10.
The four basic types of light.

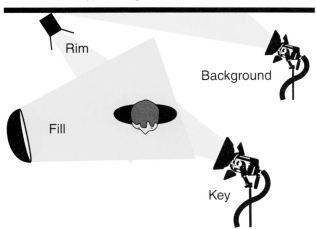

Fill light

The **fill light** moderates the shadows created by the key light, **Figure 13-12**. It is usually placed on the opposite side of the subject, and is not as high as the key light. Its lower position helps fill in shadows under the subject's eyebrows, nose, and chin.

Custom Cookies

A cookie (a short form of the theater word "cukaloris") is usually a sheet of opaque material with cutouts, mounted in front of a light to throw patterns on the set. Cookies are useful for varying the light on background walls. With an artist's knife and a sheet of foam-core, you can create any pattern you need.

This blank wall lacks character. A leaf cookie adds an attractive pattern.

Here are a few of the most popular cookie patterns.

Bare branch

A common wall pattern suggests the outline of a leafless tree.

A bare branch cookie.

Leaves

A leaf pattern cookie can throw the shadow of leaves on subjects (which makes it useful outdoors as well as inside). Keep the leaf cutouts small, for best results.

Special purpose

You can also cut a cookie to throw any shadow you need. A gallows is a simple (if melodramatic) example.

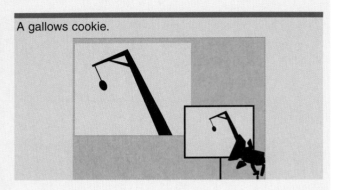

A gallows cookie.

Cookies are most believable in the styles of pictorial realism, magic realism, and expressionism. In naturalistic lighting, they tend to look excessively theatrical.

Using a cookie

To use cookies successfully, choose a hard-edged, **small-source** light to throw a sharp, distinctive shadow. Floodlights may not yield good results and soft boxes do not work well. Next, control the shadow character by the cookie's distance from the light. The closer the cookie is to the light, the bigger the shadow and the softer its edges. For smaller, sharp-edged patterns, place the cookie as far in front of the light source as practical.

Figure 13-11.
Key light only.

Figure 13-12.
Key and fill lights together.

Sometimes, you can replace the fill light with a large white card that bounces the key light back on the subject.

Rim light

The **rim light** is designed to splash the hair and shoulders of the subject from high and behind, in order to separate the performer from the background, **Figure 13-13.** A rim light should be a small source like a **spotlight** with barn doors, to control the light pattern closely and keep flare out of the camera lens.

A rim light may be called a *modeling light, back light, kicker,* or *any of several other names.*

Rim lighting is almost universal in the pictorial realist movies of classic Hollywood. In the modern realistic style, it is used less obviously, and in the naturalistic style it is often avoided altogether unless it is motivated by a practical (on-screen) light.

Background light

In many cases the subject lighting covers the background as well, but in larger shooting areas, the walls require their own lighting, **Figure 13-14.** If the only requirement is to illuminate broad areas, then **large-source floodlights** work well and look natural. For more control and better modeling, small-source spotlights with barn doors are often preferred.

Perfect background lighting can require considerable time and care. In Figure 13-14, note that the surface of the painting is reflecting the light. The problem could have been solved by repositioning the light or using a polarizing filter on the lens.

Figure 13-13.
Key, fill, and rim lights together.

Figure 13-14.
Key, fill, rim, and background lights.

As noted earlier, this basic scheme can be used with any of the major lighting styles. To show this, **Figure 13-15** places the four previous images together, each labeled with its style.

The basic lighting setup demonstrated here uses only one to four lights and covers only a space about the size of a single action point. In large shooting areas, the lighting can involve many more instruments, but they tend to be deployed in multiples of these basic layouts. Though it should not be noticeable to the viewer, a large shooting area will typically have:

- Key, fill, and (sometimes) rim lighting for each action point.
- Illumination for transitional areas between action points.
- Practical lights (light sources visible in the picture).
- Illumination for visible background areas.
- Decorative modeling/shadowing background lighting, according to the lighting style employed.

Once you understand lighting strategies in general, you can apply them in particular situations.

Lighting Applications

Since programs are made in many sorts of places and lighting conditions, it would be impractical to try to discuss all of them; so here are some of the most common production situations and some strategies for lighting them. These situations include outdoor locations, electronic news gathering ("ENG"), interviews, small indoor locations, and tabletop setups for teaching and training sequences.

Outdoor Locations

Most outdoor locations can be lit with reflectors.

Since outdoor lighting in general has already been covered, this section is just a brief summary.

The most common need is bounce fill light for shadows. Here, as with interior lighting, do not try to provide fill for every square foot of the action area. Instead, place your performers at key subject/action points within the shot and preset lighting in those positions, **Figure 13-16.**

Figure 13-15.
Lighting styles A—Naturalism. B— Realism. C— Pictorial realism. D— Expressionism.

A

B

C

D

Figure 13-16.
Outdoors, reflectors can fill important action spots.

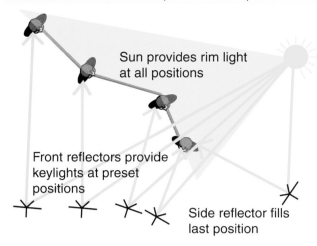

Sun provides rim light
at all positions

Front reflectors provide
keylights at preset
positions

Side reflector fills
last position

As you adjust fill levels by moving reflectors toward or away from their subjects, watch your monitor carefully to avoid over-filling. Also, position reflectors far enough to the side to avoid hurting performers' eyes and making them squint.

Screens are useful for moderating directional sunlight, but they have limitations. Large, framed overhead models are clumsy and time-consuming to place. They are most useful in static situations like stand-up narration or interviews in which performers remain basically in the same spot for an extended period. On the other hand, small models on steel hoops are good only for closeups, and tend to wobble so that the light on the subjects changes. One strategy is to use reflectors only for longer shots and then add a hand-held or stand-mounted screen for closeups.

Silks are less useful in this application because they soften and diffuse the light as well as reduce it. That will change the key light quality so that the closeup lighting will not match that of the longer shots. In addition to screening the key (sun) light for closeups, you can also use a soft white reflector to fill in shadows unobtrusively.

For closeups, subjects can sometimes hold their own reflectors, below the bottom frame line.

Electronic News Gathering (ENG)

Even at the broadcast TV level, reporters often go into the field with a single technician who must function as videographer, lighting

Lighting at "Magic Hour"

"Magic hour" is the brief period before sundown. On a sunny day, magic hour provides light qualities that look especially attractive on screen. Shadows from the low sun are long, molding objects and enhancing the impression of depth. The moisture in the air is often low, so everything appears exceptionally sharp and clear. The color temperature is warmer, lending a golden tone until near sundown, and then a distinctive sunset-orange tint.

McKinley at "magic hour."

Lighting for magic hour is simple because the low sun makes reflector placement easy. The problem lies in capturing all the footage required in the relatively brief time before the sun actually sets. For this reason, you may wish to design and rehearse several different camera setups, so that you can move quickly from one to the next as you shoot.

Another problem with magic hour is white balance, because the color temperature drops continuously as the sun goes down. One way to solve the problem is by compensating for the color shift while shooting. To do this, manually reset the white balance frequently. That way, you will capture the long shadows and clear light of magic hour, but all your original camera footage will have the same neutral color balance.

After you have edited a magic hour sequence, you can apply sunset tint to taste, or even warm the images up progressively as the sequence unfolds, to simulate an actual sunset. Be aware, however, that a digitally applied sunset color can have a mechanical, too-uniform quality. If you have the skill to capture it, there is no substitute for real magic hour light.

director, and sound recordist. To simplify lighting, this one-person crew will often work with just two tools: an on-camera light and a stand-mounted reflector.

The camera-mounted light is typically variable in light output and often powered by its own substantial battery. Even in daylight, a front fill light can highlight the reporter's face just enough to emphasize it against the background.

News camcorders are often fitted with batteries big enough to power a light as well.

An alternative is a stand-mounted reflector, **Figure 13-17.** Because the camera person must leave the reflector unattended while shooting, it needs to be heavy and relatively small, to resist the wind.

Night shooting requires a different deployment of lighting tools. The on-camera light continues to provide much of the illumination. A second, battery-powered light on a stand can fulfill the same function as a reflector, providing more modeling on the reporter's face, **Figure 13-18.** Backgrounds at night are generally dark; but look for lighted walls or windows to include in the shot, so that the image behind the reporter has some design to it.

Interviews

The modern style of video interview has the subject on-screen almost all the time, and the lighting style is usually realistic, **Figure 13-19.** Since interview subjects are rarely media professionals, lighting should be moderate and kept out of their eyes. Soft lights work well for both key and fill lights (place the fill light lower than the key and farther away). For a slightly more theatrical look, you can use a harder spotlight for a key light and add a rim light to separate subject from background.

Figure 13-18.
One- and two-light schemes.

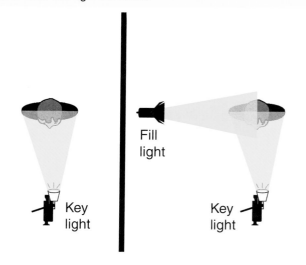

Figure 13-19.
A two-light interview setup.

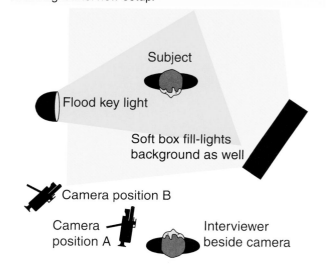

Figure 13-17.
Two approaches to fill-lighting a reporter outdoors. A—Reflector for both key and fill. B—Reflector for fill only.

A

B

On-camera interviewer

If your interviewer will appear on screen, you must light her or him as well. In establishing shots, the back view of the narrator in the foreground can often be lit by the lights on the interview subject, **Figure 13-20.**

For single shots of the interviewer asking questions or listening to answers, you have two different options. One is to light the interviewer separately for real-time recording with a second camera. To do this, position the reporter's camera to shoot over the interviewee's shoulder, so that both people are included in wider shots. Place the lights for both people so that they are outside the frame in both setups.

If space is restricted, or if some of the reporter's questions and reactions need to be reshot, you can relight and reset the camera after the main interview to pick up this material for later editing into the sequence.

If you shoot the interviewer separately, you can move him or her in front of whatever background looks best. The audience will be unable to tell that the interviewer has moved from the original interview position.

Interview backgrounds

Background lighting for interviews is sometimes created by spill from the key and fill lights. But if you have room to move the subject several feet forward, you can light the background separately, as you would in any other interior.

Small Location Interiors

Small interiors like offices are often lit by supplementing the light already available. The toughest task is often to hide these extra lights in the restricted floor space available.

Study your monitor very carefully for cables, which have a way of creeping into the shot.

Light stands work well in front and to the sides of the action area where they are safely off screen. To hide lights placed deeper in the set, deploy units that can be clipped or taped to moldings, curtain rods, door frames or the tops of open doors themselves. Fluorescent ceiling grids are also prime locations for clipping small lamps. See **Figure 13-21.**

Some lighting instruments have built-in clips; others mount on posts fitted with clips or flat surfaces for taping.

Figure 13-20.
Interviewer lighting. A—Shooting over the interviewer's shoulder. B—Close-up of the interviewee. C—A reverse setup features the interviewer. D—The interviewer's close-ups can be shot later.

| A | B | C | D |

Figure 13-21.
Light-mounting methods. A—Small lights can be gaffer-taped to walls. B—Larger lights can be clamped to walls and doors. C—Small lights can be supported almost anywhere. (Lowel Corporation)

| A | B | C |

Finally, keep in mind that you do not have to light all the action in a location at once. By lighting each shot individually, you can safely move lights into positions for close setups where they would be in the picture in wider angles.

Tabletop Videography

Tabletop videography involves shooting small objects and/or activities on a table, counter, or special photographic stand. This is a common procedure for science experiments, product demonstrations, and how-to training sequences.

Television cooking programs rely heavily on tabletop videography.

In shooting small subjects, camera and lighting problems generally arise from two causes. First, the short camera-to-subject distances (and/or telephoto lens settings) create very shallow depth of field. This makes small objects difficult to keep in sharp focus. Second, the hands, arms, and head of the demonstrator tend to get into the picture.

To help solve these questions, you need lights that are both very bright (to force smaller lens openings and thereby increase depth of field) and very soft (to eliminate or at least minimize shadows in the picture). Every situation has unique lighting requirements, of course, but **Figure 13-22** shows a solution for a typical product shot setup.

The subject and tabletop are bracketed by very large, bright fluorescent ***soft lights.***

Figure 13-22.
Tabletop setups use very large, soft lights.

These instruments are excellent for this application because:

- Their four-foot square shape provides an extremely large source, to reduce shadows.
- Their multiple 40-watt tubes provide a bright light, permitting smaller f-stops to create greater depth of field.
- Their power requirements are low enough for use in most locations.
- Their output is cool enough for subject comfort, and for delicate applications such as food demonstrations and biology experiments.

Where you want completely shadowless lighting (and do not require great depth of field) you can use ***tent*** lighting. By hanging a white sheet over and around your subject and aiming lights through it, you can create the softest possible lighting effects. Tenting techniques are also useful for lighting products in commercials. Tenting also works very well outdoors, with a sheet hung over a line, **Figure 13-23.**

Other Lighting Applications

The representative lighting solutions in this chapter cannot cover all the situations that you may encounter, but they do demonstrate how to use the basic ideas behind all lighting designs to analyze the situation, utilize the light available, and build upon it to create video lighting with style.

Technical Terms

Barn doors: Metal flaps in sets of two or four, attached to the fronts of spotlights to control the edges of the beam.

Camera light: A small light mounted on the camera, usually to provide foreground fill.

Century stand (C-stand): A telescoping floor stand fitted with a clamp and usually an adjustable arm, for supporting lights and accessories.

Color temperature meter: A light meter that measures the relative blueness or redness of nominally "white" light.

Contrast: The difference between the lightest and darkest parts of an image, expressed as a ratio (e.g. "four-to-one").

Cookie: A sheet cut into a specific pattern and placed in the beam of a light to throw distinctive shadows such as leaves or blinds.

Figure 13-23.
A—A simple tent setup outdoors, using a bedsheet. B—Many of the lights shown in this chapter were photographed in tent setups. (Lowel Corporation)

A B

Fill light: The light that lightens shadows created by the main (key) light.

Flag: A flat piece of opaque metal, wood, or foam-core placed to mask off part of a light beam.

Floodlight: A large-source instrument that typically lacks a lens, for lighting wide areas.

Gaffer: The chief lighting technician on a shoot.

Key light: The main illumination of a subject.

Large-source: Describing a lighting instrument, such as a scoop or other flood-light, with a big front area from which light is emitted. Light from large-source instruments is relatively soft and diffuse.

Practical: An instrument that is included in shots and may be operated by the actors.

Reflector: A large silver, white, or colored surface used to bounce light onto a subject or scene.

Rim light: A light placed high and behind a subject to create a rim of light on head and shoulders, to help separate subject and background.

Screen: A mesh material that reduces light intensity without markedly changing its character.

Silk: A fabric material that both reduces light intensity and directionality, producing a soft, directionless illumination.

Small-source: Describing a lighting instrument such as a spotlight, with a small front area from which light is emitted. Light from small-source instruments is generally hard-edged and tightly focused.

Soft light: A very large-source lighting instrument (as big as four feet square) that emits extremely soft, diffuse light that imitates natural light.

Spotlight: A small-source instrument that emits a narrow, hard-edged beam usually, but not always fitted with a lens to concentrate the light.

Tabletop: Videography of small subjects and activities on a table or counter.

Tent: A white fabric draped above a subject to diffuse lighting completely for a totally shadowless effect.

Some lighting designs are beyond human abilities. Here, good lighting technique means finding, recognizing, and extending what nature has provided.

14 Recording Audio

Contents

About Recording Audio
Types of Audio Recording
Microphones
Other Recording Equipment
Audio Recording Techniques

Objectives

After studying this chapter, you will be able to:

- ❏ Distinguish the different types and purposes of recording.
- ❏ Understand audio equipment and select it appropriately.
- ❏ Record quality audio tracks of all the major types.
- ❏ Solve the problems associated with common recording situations.

About Recording Audio

Audio, as we use the word here, is the recording and reproduction of sound in support of video. Chapter 7 explains how the sound track affects viewers and why it is such an important part of every video program. With this information in mind, we are ready to consider the techniques used to create that sound track: the techniques of professional audio recording.

The sound "track" gets its name from the film medium, where the audio, recorded along the edge of the film, appears as a visible track.

Professional camcorders allow manual control of audio recording. Consumer camcorders, however, record sound automatically. Automatic recording is simpler, but if you have heard the often mediocre results, you can see why obtaining quality audio requires effort and skill.

Audio recording must always deal with two problems. First, recording captures everything, whether it is wanted or not. Second, on playback, recorded sounds may seem distorted or even quite unlike the originals. Before learning about specific audio equipment and techniques, you need to understand how these fundamental problems affect audio recording.

Problem: Audio Records Everything

Like your own ears, microphones pick up every sound within their range. Sound from an outdoor scene might be a mix of spoken dialogue, background traffic noise, wind, shuffling feet, and even sounds made by the camcorder itself. See **Figure 14-1.**

The problem arises because of the way in which people process the sounds they hear. You may hear sounds with your ears, but you *listen* with your brain. Without noticing it, you suppress everything in the incoming sound mix except for the parts that interest you. For example, you may focus on the dialogue, while blocking out the background noises. Then, if you should notice trees waving in the wind, you might shift your mental focus to the wind sound, to the point where you no longer hear what is being said.

For reasons that are not perfectly understood, this mental sound filtration is more difficult to do with recordings than with live sounds. As a result, the dialogue in a video

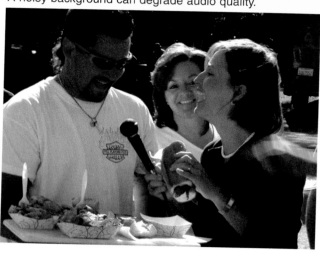

Figure 14-1.
A noisy background can degrade audio quality.

scene may be ruined by wind or other noises that you would not even notice in the real world.

Problem: Audio Distorts Sounds

The second problem is that recording a sound does not guarantee that it will be convincing or even recognizable on playback. Many factors affect the quality and character of recorded sound; it takes skill to listen to what the microphone is picking up and then adjust recording conditions to make the resulting signal sound natural.

Even when the sound is not actually distorted, an audio recording can still sound unnatural, especially if it does not match the visual environment. For instance, sound recorded in postproduction and then synchronized with a video scene in a metal aircraft hangar may sound muffled and "dead," when it should have a metallic echoing quality.

The most common problem with sound quality is inconsistency from one shot to the next. The sound character of a wide shot may not match that of close-ups made of the same sequence because the camera's broad field of view has forced the microphone farther away from the performers in order to keep it out of the shot. See **Figure 14-2.**

In real-world listening, we tend to ignore the difference, but in an edited video sequence that alternates between wide and close angles, the constantly changing sound quality will be obvious and annoying.

In the real world, of course, we do not abruptly change position every few seconds, as the camera does from one setup to the next.

Figure 14-2.
A wide shot may force the microphone far back from the subjects.

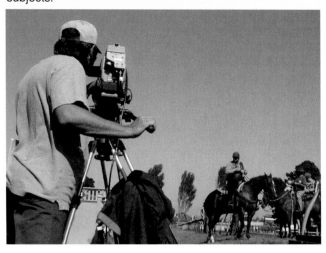

Figure 14-3.
Digital editing can handle dozens of audio tracks. (JVC Corporation)

Overcoming Audio Problems

To address these problems, professional audio recordists employ a well-proven strategy:

- Identify the separate types of sound that are wanted for a sequence (such as dialogue, sound effects, and background noises).
- Isolate each sound component and record it separately.
- Select, position, and adjust microphones to obtain consistent, high-quality, natural-sounding audio, regardless of the visual perspective.

With clean, separate audio tracks, a sound editor can place and balance audio components to duplicate the function of the listener's brain, calling attention to certain sounds and minimizing others, as required, **Figure 14-3.** A well-mixed sound track directs the ear, eliminates audio clutter, and enhances the realism of the program.

Sound track mixing is covered in the chapters on editing.

Providing the editor with clean, separate components is the sound recordist's fundamental job. To do this job, you need to know the basics of audio recording, the equipment used to do it, and the techniques required to obtain high-quality audio.

Types of Audio Recording

In recording raw sound for later editing, you must deal with several different types of track, each requiring its own set of recording techniques. At different times you may need to record production sound, background sound, sound effects, voice tracks, and music. The most common type of recording is production sound.

Production Sound

Production sound is, of course, the sound that is recorded with the video. While most amateur sound is recorded by the camcorder's built-in microphone, professional productions generally use separate mikes. Because the camera position is rarely the optimal location for miking the shot, separate video and audio recording devices allow each to be placed in the best spot, **Figure 14-4.**

Production sound calls for special care because mistakes may require another take of the whole shot. As an extreme example, if your first attempt to record the actual sound of a train derailing is unsatisfactory, you cannot re-record the effect without derailing another train.

Because actual recordings are often impractical, train derailments and similar sounds are usually simulated and recorded separately as sound effects and added to the video in postproduction.

Figure 14-4.
Fishpole mike supports are sometimes used in studio production. (Sennheiser)

Background Sounds

In the real world, individual sounds are heard against a background of more-or-less continuous noise. This noise may come from wind, waves, birds, traffic, heating and air conditioning, or people talking or doing things like coughing in a theater or rattling dishes in a restaurant. See **Figure 14-5.**

Even without any obvious background noise, no location is truly silent. If the editor cuts unwanted pieces out of the production track, the "emptiness" of the resulting soundless passages is clearly audible. To prevent this, you record "room tone," which sounds like nothing by itself, but is used to fill the holes left by deletions from the production track. See **Figure 14-6.**

Though in real life, we filter out most background noise, a movie sound track does this job for us. To minimize background noise:

● Turn off controllable sounds like heating ducts or background conversations during takes.

● Minimize uncontrollable noises like traffic or wind as much as possible during dialogue or effects recording.

● Make lengthy (up to five minutes long) recordings of ambient (background) sound alone.

In editing, the continuous ambient noise is then laid in under the dialogue and effects tracks, where it helps conceal any background noise that makes its way onto the dialogue tracks, and it minimizes the differences in quality between production tracks made from different mike positions. Professional sound libraries include prerecorded background tracks of a wide variety of locales. These tracks are often substituted for background sound recordings made during a shoot.

"Mit Out Sound!"

Unlike video, film production usually requires two separate machines for recording picture and sound. For this reason, shots in which audio would be difficult to record adequately or microphones would interfere with the visuals are often made with the film camera only, omitting the sound recorder. Shots filmed without sound are slated M.O.S.

Tradition holds that the acronym "M.O.S." stands for "Mit Out Sound," in the imperfect pronunciation of a famous European director who came to Hollywood at the beginning of the sound era and hated the new technology so much that he did everything he could to shoot "mit out" it.

In video, by contrast, picture and sound are captured together on the same tape, so sound of one sort or another is almost always recorded. Even if you think you will be unable to use the production audio in the finished video, you should still record it, at least with the camcorder's built-in mike. This will create a reference track, also called a "scratch" or "cue" track. In postproduction, you use a scratch track for several purposes: to synchronize replacement ("looped") dialogue with the original, to indicate the exact positions of sounds to be added from separately recorded sound effects, and to provide a record of minor dialogue changes, etc. that occurred during the shooting. For these reasons, it is always important to record the best quality production audio that is practical under the circumstances.

A waveform display simplifies identifying and editing effects.

Figure 14-5.
Heating and air conditioning are common sources of background noise.

Figure 14-6.
Room tone is used to fill gaps in the production track.

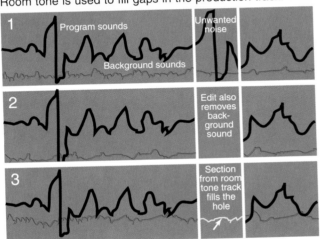

1 Program sounds
Unwanted noise
Background sounds

2 Edit also removes background sound

3 Section from room tone track fills the hole

An ambient track is used in long pieces to blend other tracks. A room tone recording (also called a presence track) is used in very short pieces, to fill gaps where the editor has removed parts of the production track.

Sound Effects

Sound effects are often recorded *"wild,"* meaning separately from the production track. This usually happens when using that track is impractical, often because it is impossible to place a microphone for good quality sound or because the actual sound would be disruptive (like gunshots on a busy street).

Audio was originally recorded directly on film in a machine separate from the camera. To synchronize the two machines, their motors were electrically "slaved" to a "master" motor. Thus, a machine recording sound effects independently of a camera was running "wild," rather than "slaved."

Sound effects that would be hard to get under any circumstances are available in sound effects libraries, some of which contain thousands of different noises. See **Figure 14-7.**

In every recording situation, deciding whether to use production track or wild sound effects depends on how many there are and how closely they are synchronized to the picture. For example, the sound of a car starting and driving away could easily be recorded as a wild effect and post-synchronized with the picture. On the other hand, the on-screen feet of a man and two women crossing a marble floor would be extremely tedious to record and lay individually one person, foot, and footstep at a time.

For situations like this, professionals use what is called a **Foley studio:** an environment in which technicians can make sounds while watching a shot on the screen and synchronizing the effects as they are recorded.

Voice Recording

Like sound effects, voices can be recorded separately from the production

Figure 14-7.
Continuous sounds like racing car engines are easy to record and use in postproduction. (Corel)

track. The most common application for this is narration recording. In a sound booth or small radio studio, the performer records all the narration in a program, leaving gaps between sections that allow the editor to select the best takes and lay each one in at its proper spot.

Dialogue replacement is also a common procedure. It works like Foley recording, only with voices rather than sound effects. One or more actors record their lines in a sound studio, while watching a dialogue scene on screen and listening to a reference production track through headphones.

Dialogue replacement is often still called "looping" because short lengths of movie film were once spliced end-to-end in loops for continuous projection while the watching performers rehearsed synchronizing the new dialogue.

Music

Music is seldom recorded with production sound. Instead, it is captured separately in studios designed to optimize musical sound, and then added to the sound track in editing. Music recording is a complex process that requires sophisticated microphones, mike placement, and electronic mixing and equalizing. As a result, almost all professional music is recorded by studio technicians rather than by production sound recordists.

However, production people do get involved in **playback**, the process of reproducing previously recorded vocal music while singers synchronize their simulated on-camera performance with the high-quality recording that they (or others) have made earlier, **Figure 14-8.** In playback, the camcorder will typically lay down a rough recording of the vocal lines sung by the performers on the set for later use as a reference track. In postproduction, the editor will match the prerecorded track to the playback version of it, then remove the rough production mixture from the finished track, leaving only the high-quality original.

Microphones

All sound recording must begin with a **microphone**, a device that translates the original noise, created by a pattern of moving air, into an electrical signal that closely imitates that pattern. In order to select and use microphones effectively, you need to know

Figure 14-8.
For vocals especially, performers often lip-synch previously recorded audio. The process is called "playback."

the design basics of the principal types. Those design characteristics include physical form, transmission method, and pickup pattern.

Microphone Transducers

The **transducer** in a microphone is the electromechanical system that converts sound energy into electrical energy. Of the several transducer designs developed over the years, the most common are *dynamic* and *condenser*.

Dynamic transducers

A dynamic microphone transducer is a taut, flat diaphragm like a drum skin that is vibrated by incoming sound waves. Dynamic microphones are useful because they are tough and uncomplicated and the signal they generate is strong enough

A dynamic transducer.

A dynamic microphone. (Sennheiser)

Physical Form

Physically, mikes are designed either to stand independently or to be worn by performers.

Independent mikes

These microphones are engineered to be held by the camera, by a boom or stand, or by the performer. Sometimes, independent mikes are suspended above the sound source, especially for recordings made in auditoriums.

User-worn mikes

Certain very small microphones are designed to be clipped onto the performer's clothing, **Figure 14-9.** Their advantage is that they do not have to be aimed or moved by a technician. Their disadvantage is that they are visible to the camera (unless specially concealed) and their cables or radio signals sometimes cause problems.

Transmission Method

Cable and radio transmission are the two methods by which microphones send their signals to the camcorder or standalone audio recorder.

Cabled mikes

Traditional microphones communicate via special cables. Because they are shielded against outside electrical interference, these cables provide the cleanest, most reliable signal. On the negative side, cables are difficult to conceal and to keep out of the way of technicians and wheeled equipment, and they require that the recorder be relatively close to the microphone.

---

that it needs no amplification. The hand-held mikes used in ENG (Electronic News Gathering) are often dynamic designs.

Dynamic mikes cannot always maintain a wide and even frequency response, and their sound is often described as "tight" or "less open" than that of the other common transducer type, the condenser.

Condenser transducers

A condenser transducer is a pair of electrically charged plates with air acting as an insulator between them. The distance between the two plates affects the voltage produced. One plate is rigidly fixed; the other is very sensitive to sound vibrations, which cause it to move toward and away from the fixed plate. The voltage fluctuations that result precisely imitate the sound waves that cause the flexible plate to vibrate.

Condenser microphones have wide, even frequency ranges and preserve high frequencies better than dynamic transducers. On the other hand, they are more delicate and the battery they require can fail in the middle of a recording task. Most condenser microphones need batteries in order to apply the electrical charge to the condenser plates and to drive a built-in preamplifier. The preamplifier is necessary because the signal strength of the output from the plates is quite low.

A condenser transducer.

Electrically charged plates

Sound waves

A stereo condenser microphone. (Sennheiser)

Figure 14-9.
A user-worn mike. (Sennheiser)

Wireless mikes

Wireless microphones, **Figure 14-10,** send their signals on specialized radio frequencies to receivers cabled to the audio recording system. Inexpensive wireless microphones are prone to interference from unwanted outside signals. High-quality professional types, however, capture sounds extremely accurately, transmit on frequencies free from most interference, and can be set to different frequencies, That way, several performers at once can transmit wireless signals to separate receivers (or channels on one receiver). These separate signals can be individually mixed and balanced for greater control.

Many wireless microphone/transmitter/ receiver systems run on 120 volt power, for use in auditoriums and studios. Battery powered units are available for use on location.

Figure 14-10.
A wireless microphone and transmitter. (Azden)

Level and Impedance

Level and *impedance* are electrical characteristics that affect the quality of recordings.

Level

Audio products from camcorders to VCRs to stereo receivers to computer sound cards have input and output jacks labeled "line" or "aux," "speaker," "headphones," "mike" or "mic," and sometimes other things. It is important to understand that each type of jack handles electrical signals of a particular strength, or "level."

In particular, line jacks carry high-level signals that average around one volt in strength. Microphone jacks, by contrast, carry low-level signals measured in millivolts. Microphones plugged into line level jacks will produce only feeble signals, so it is important to use only dedicated mike inputs.

Impedance

Impedance is resistance to the flow of electricity. Most inexpensive microphones are high-impedance types, while most professional units are low impedance. Low impedance translates into better signal transmission and better fidelity, especially in the high frequencies.

For best results, the microphones, cables, and equipment jacks should all be the same impedance. Cables fitted with XLR plugs almost always indicate a low-impedance system.

The impedance on these XLR camcorder jacks can be switched from high to low. (JVC)

To compensate for impedance differences in various system components, you can buy impedance-matching transformers.

Pickup Pattern

The most important characteristic of a microphone is its *pickup pattern:* the directions in which it is most sensitive to sound. In order to select one or more microphones for particular recording tasks, you need to understand their pickup patterns. For example:

- A sound effect like footsteps needs a mike with a narrow pickup pattern, to exclude unwanted background sound.
- A musical performance needs a broad but directional pattern to capture all the music but exclude coughs and shuffles in the audience.
- Newscasters' lapel mikes need omnidirectional pickup patterns to capture their voices, no matter which way they turn their heads.

These are the most popular of the many available microphone pickup designs.

Narrow pickup

So-called "shotgun" mikes (named for their long, thin barrels) are highly directional, with most of the pickup areas directly in front. See **Figure 14-11.** However, the secondary pickup areas of some shotgun

mikes will also capture sounds off to the sides; be sure to keep crew members at the camcorder quiet during takes. Shotgun mikes may be mounted on a camcorder, a boom, or a "fishpole." They are especially useful for distant sound sources, for recording in places with competing background noise, and for taping sound effects as cleanly as possible.

Broad, directional pickup

Most suspended, stand-mounted, and hand-held performer mikes have a fairly wide but still directional pickup pattern. This compromise pattern is less narrowly directional than shotgun pickup, but also less inclusive than an omnidirectional pattern. Because their pickup pattern is shaped more or less like a valentine heart, these are called *"cardioid"* microphones, **Figure 14-12.**

Figure 14-11.
The sensitivity pattern of a shotgun microphone.

A shotgun microphone (Sennheiser)

Figure 14-12.
The sensitivity pattern of a cardioid microphone.

Cutaway view of a cardioid microphone. (Sennheiser)

Microphone pickup patterns are actually much larger and more complex than the areas shown in Figures 14-11, 14-12, and 14-13.

Typically, a camcorder's built-in microphone is a compromise between a narrow shotgun and a broad cardioid pattern. Some camcorder mikes can be switched between wider and narrower pickup patterns.

Omnidirectional pickup

These microphones are sensitive in a spherical pattern stretching in all directions. The most common models, often called **lavalieres** or just "lavs," are worn directly on the body. In placing a lav on a shirt front, the goal is to position it high enough to get close to the performer's mouth but low enough to clear the "sound shadow" created by the chin. Because lavaliere mikes are balanced to compensate for their closeness to the wearer's chest, their relative insensitivity to lower sound frequencies makes them less suitable in some other applications.

In live television broadcasts, you will often see two lavalier mikes worn side-by-side. One is a backup mike in case the other fails in a situation where the performer must continue speaking uninterruptedly.

Stereo pickup

Stereo microphones have two separate pickup areas, each feeding its own audio channel. Stereo mikes can add presence and realism to almost any recording, and they are especially effective in studio and auditorium application, where the sound originates from a variety of directions. In studio situations, two mikes are often used, as shown in **Figure 14-13.** Camcorder stereo mikes use two pickups in a single housing.

Other Recording Equipment

To complete our survey of audio recording equipment, we can follow the path of the audio signal downstream from the mike on its microphone *support*, along a *cable* (or via

Figure 14-13.
Stereo recording using two monophonic mikes.

transmitter/receiver), through a production *mixer*, to its destination at a *recorder*.

Microphone Supports

Microphones can be mounted anywhere and supported by anything that will hold a clip or gaffer tape.

The first task of any support system is to isolate the microphone from bumps and vibrations that are transmitted as unwanted noises. For this reason, boom, fishpole, and some stand mikes are typically suspended within frameworks by arrangements of shock cords. Microphones mounted directly on the performer cannot be shockproofed, and must be positioned so that they do not pick up the rustle of clothing.

Booms

Mike **booms** are typically used in studios, where their weight and bulk are not inconvenient. Booms are useful because the operators do not have to hold the weight of the microphone and its support. From one place, they can follow a moving performer by pivoting the boom arm, telescoping it in and out, and rotating the mike to point in the right direction.

Fishpoles

Fishpole booms must be held, moved, and aimed manually, but they are far lighter and more compact than booms. For this

Using Wireless Microphones

Like all radio transmissions, the signals from wireless microphones are at the mercy of their environment. Electrical noise, other radio signals, and signals bounced around by the journey from transmitter to receiver — these and other problems can prevent you from obtaining quality audio recordings. Here are some tips for eliminating these problems.

- Always make the distance from transmitter to receiver as short as possible. If your equipment permits, place the receiver just outside the camera frame and then cable it back to the camera.

- Experiment with receiver position and receiver antenna. Radio mike signals are so sensitive to distance, direction, and reflection, that even small adjustments at the receiver end can improve quality dramatically.

- Have backup cabled mikes. Even the finest wireless mikes will not always work, so be ready to fall back on cabled lavalieres or a fishpole setup if necessary.

Finally, before recording audio in a location, scout it for problems, just as you would for video. Experiment with wireless miking to anticipate problems or, if all else fails, settle on an alternative solution using cabled mikes. Remember that production people may be tolerant of camera, lighting, and performance problems, but they (unfairly) grow impatient if the sound department holds up the shoot.

When the wireless receiver is placed near the camera, the distance to the transmitter may degrade quality.   To improve quality, conceal the receiver as near the transmitter as possible and cable it to the sound recorder.

Transmitter

Subject

Microphone

Receiver

Transmitter

Subject

Microphone

reason, fishpoles are preferred on many location shoots. See **Figure 14-14**.

Stands

Microphone stands are indispensable for recording narration, musical performance, and any other application in which the subject is off camera and remains in one place. Although short table stands are often used for voice recording, low floor stands with short horizontal booms permit more flexible mike positioning, and they typically accept shock mounts.

Cables

Microphone cables contain wires that are both electrically insulated and shielded from stray noise and even audible signals

Figure 14-14.
A fishpole boom in use. (Gitzo/Bogen)

that unshielded lines can pick up like radio antennas. For this reason, microphone connections should always be made with shielded cables manufactured expressly for that purpose. Cables should also be as short as possible, in order to minimize signal loss.

Though the plugs may match, never use a headphone extension cable for a microphone, as these lines are unshielded.

Line balance

Interference and signal loss are affected not only by the length of a microphone cable, but by its *"line balance"* as well. Cables with two electrical lines are unbalanced; those with three lines are balanced. See **Figure 14-15.**

Unbalanced cables are typically supplied with inexpensive microphones and fitted with phone- or mini-plug jacks. Though shielded from outside interference, unbalanced cables still suffer from this problem. They should be used for short runs only, usually less than 20 feet.

Balanced cables with three lines are quite secure from outside interference, and can be safely run for longer distances. Balanced and unbalanced lines are seldom identified, but you can usually tell them by their plugs. **Balanced lines** will have large XLR plugs, while **unbalanced lines** have phone plug connectors. A microphone fitted with an unbalanced line can be plugged to a balanced extension cable via a converter plug.

Connectors

Inexpensive microphone cables are typically fitted with phone plug connectors, either full-size or mini-plugs. Mono plugs have a single black band insulating the two connectors, while stereo plugs use a pair of insulators for their three connectors. See **Figure 14-16.**

Phone plugs, especially the mini-plug style, are unreliable because they easily lose their electrical connections and stop transmitting

Figure 14-16.
Mono and stereo mini-plugs.

the audio signal. This is doubly dangerous if the recordist is not monitoring the input through headphones. When a plug from an external mike is inserted into the camcorder's "audio in" jack, it automatically disables the unit's built-in mike. If the external plug becomes electrically disconnected but still remains in the camcorder jack, neither microphone will transmit an audio signal and the camcorder will capture no sound whatever.

Professional audio setups use XLR connectors that latch together for a reliable connection. You can obtain small, camera-mounted conversion units for some camcorders that allow you to use XLR plugs (with their balanced line cables) on camcorders fitted with mini-plug audio jacks.

The jacks for XLR plugs are labeled in Figure 14-17, and in the photo in the sidebar Level and Impedance.

Receivers

Wireless microphones incorporate radio transmitters that send the signals to matching receivers, **Figure 14-17.** The receivers, in turn, are cabled to the camcorder or separate audio recorder. Inexpensive transmitter/receiver systems use radio frequencies that can be subject to interference, while professional-grade models use much higher frequencies.

Figure 14-15.
Unbalanced and balanced audio cables.

Figure 14-17.
A receiver for a wireless microphone setup. (Azden)

Typically, high quality systems can transmit over longer distances with better signal quality and less interference.

Some receivers can accept signals from more than one microphone, each on its own separate frequency. Some types feature switchable frequencies. If one channel is degraded by interference, a different one can be selected.

Mixers and Equalizers

Whether your microphones are cabled or wireless, their signals must be blended for recording as a combined audio track.

Mixer

To do this, you use a production *mixer*, **Figure 14-18,** which is basically a volume control for each incoming signal and circuitry for combining them. A production mixer is useful for just one microphone too, adjusting the signal to the optimal strength for transmission to the recorder. Almost all professional productions use a production mixer.

Equalizer

An *equalizer* improves overall sound quality by adjusting the relative strengths of selected sound frequencies. In production sound recording, it is most commonly used to minimize undesirable sounds like the rumble of distant traffic or the wheeze of an air duct. An equalizer should not be overused. For example, reducing *all* the sound frequencies that contribute to traffic noise can distort actors' voices so much that they sound like cartoon characters.

Recorders

Production sound is recorded by the audio system built into the camcorder. Backgrounds, sound effects, voice, and music recordings can also be made by other sound recorders such as VCRs, digital audio recorders, and analog audiocassette recorders.

In TV studios, the audio/video recorders are typically separate from the cameras. In small operations, however, camcorders may be used as floor cameras.

Camcorder audio recording

In most cases, a camcorder is the best choice, even when the video part of the recording will not be used in the program. Camcorder audio recording offers many advantages:

- Because it is in the same format as the program material, it can be edited or transferred to computer without connecting special-purpose source decks.

- It offers extremely high quality sound. Analog stereo audio is almost as good as CD music audio; and Mini-DV audio can actually be *better*.

- Even if you will not use the picture recorded with the sound, it serves as a handy visual locator of audio clips, especially if you have identified them with written slates. See **Figure 14-19.**

- Because it is compact and battery-powered, a camcorder is easy to use in the field.

Figure 14-18.
A small production mixer. (Azden)

Figure 14-19.
During field recording, letter and record simple slates.

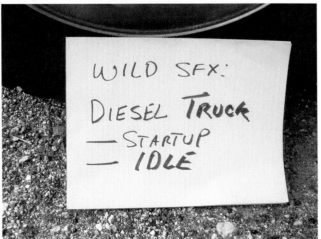

For most field recording applications, then, a stereo-quality camcorder will do the job as well as a special-purpose recorder.

VCR

In studio recording situations, for music, narration, and dialogue replacement, a desktop videocassette deck may be preferable to a camcorder. Its controls are larger and easier to use, its input jacks make it simple to add mixers and equalizers, and it may have manual level control. Manual control is extremely important, especially for recording isolated sounds.

Computer sound card

For studio audio recording, miking directly to the sound card in the editing computer offers all the advantages of a VCR, because the separate operation of inputting the audio from a source is eliminated. Computer audio cards are typically sold with sophisticated software for manual level control, equalization, and special effects like reverberation. Finally, the wave form display of most audio soft-

ware allows you to verify that recording levels are optimal for the system.

Audio recorder

A good digital audio recorder is useful if you do not want to use a camcorder. For simple effects such as automobile sounds, explosions, etc., you can also use an analog device like the audiocassette recorders found on portable radios.

Accessories

A professional sound recordist will carry a broad range of specialized accessories. Of these, the following are perhaps the most widely used.

Headphones

Headphones are essential for quality sound recording. Like the viewfinder for video, headphones let you preview what you are recording to check the quality (or simply to verify that sound is being properly recorded). In choosing headphones, select the full-ear type that blocks out extraneous sounds, **Figure 14-20.** Ideally, you want to hear nothing but the sound picked up by the mike.

Automatic Level Control

All consumer camcorders and VCR decks are fitted with automatic level controls: circuits that adjust volume automatically to compensate for different levels of incoming sound. In general, automatic level control works well. Problems arise, however, when a distinct sound is preceded by a long silence. If there is a near-silent period before a distinct noise, the automatic level control may turn the record volume up, in search of a signal. When a normal-level sound begins, the circuits cannot turn down the record level fast enough to prevent the start of that sound from distorting.

Automatic level control can fail to keep up with sudden volume changes.

Sound is distorted until auto level compensates

Recorded audio

Auto level compensates for increase

Volume set by auto level

Sudden increase in sound level

Sound level

Automatic level controls can also fail when the sound level rises or falls suddenly and dramatically. Here again, the circuits cannot anticipate the change and react fast enough to accommodate it. The solution is manual level control, a feature built into virtually all professional-level camcorders and decks. With manual control, the sound recordist can maintain a consistent level through quiet parts and anticipate sudden volume shifts by adjusting gain just before they happen.

Defeating automatic level control

When you cannot disable the automatic level control, you can sometimes work around it. If a loud noise occurs in the middle of a shot, use an external mike, hand-held or on a fishpole. That way, you can turn the mike away from the source of the loud sound, just before it happens. If you can, use a production mixer. By optimizing sound levels manually, before they reach the auto circuits, you can reduce unwanted variations. When recording voice for narration, follow each long pause with a voice slate. The slate, which will be removed in editing, gives the automatic system a sound on which to set a level, so that the narration is all recorded consistently.

Figure 14-20.
Full-ear headphones. (Sennheiser)

Windscreens

Wind noise is a common problem in exterior recording. A foam windscreen (sometimes called a sock or a doughnut) reduces wind noise by deflecting the air rushing past the microphone, **Figure 14-21.** A windscreen is also useful indoors for narration or dialogue recording, where performers' breath can create wind noise across an unprotected mike.

The built-in windscreens on (or in) the small mikes of miniature camcorders may not be visible. Some camcorders filter wind noise electronically.

Furniture pads

To prevent unwanted echoes and boomy-sounding audio, drape blankets at strategic points or deploy the furniture pads used by moving companies. You can obtain these pads inexpensively at do-it-yourself moving rental companies.

Plug and cable adapters

If you put together your own audio equipment, everything will be cabled and plugged compatibly. But if you must connect to other equipment, such as a public address system or an auditorium sound setup, you will need a variety of plug adapters.

Slate

When recording audio with a camcorder, use a simple tablet and marker to create identifying *slates.* Visible slates eliminate two major annoyances in audio editing. Unlike pictures, sounds cannot usually be scanned in fast-forward or reverse, so finding material can be time-consuming. Even at normal speed, some quite accurate, realistic sounds can be difficult to identify without visual clues. By visually identifying sound effects, slates will save a great deal of postproduction time and effort.

A complete slate should include the information shown in Figure 14-19. For simplicity, you can slate the production and date once, at the start of the session, then

Figure 14-21.
An inexpensive shotgun mike in a foam windscreen. (Azden)

A foam windscreen can be added to most hand-held mikes. (Sennheiser)

slate just the particular effect, recording the other information verbally.

Audio Recording Techniques

Production, background, effects, voice, and music tracks all require their own recording techniques.

Production Tracks

The audio recorded along with the video is the most important sound track. A good production track is distinguished by its quality, consistency, and freedom from unwanted noise.

Quality

The keys to good audio quality are distance and direction. Place the mike as close to the subject as you can, without getting it into the picture. Then, aim the mike directly at the sound source. If two people are talking, point the mike at each one when he or she is speaking. Mikes worn by the subject(s) take care of distance and direction automatically.

If you are using a fishpole boom, begin by deciding whether to place the microphone above or below the frame line. Then orient the mike on the fishpole as shown in **Figure 14-22.** That way, you can swing it back and forth between speakers by simply twisting the pole.

If you need to use the camcorder's built-in mike, place the camera as close to the subjects as practical.

Remember that the wide angle lens settings required at very short distances can distort subjects' features unpleasantly.

Consistency

The next task is to keep all the audio sounding alike. To do this, you need to confine the volume level within a relatively narrow range, so that soft passages are well-recorded and sudden loud parts do not sound distorted. If you have manual volume control, maintain sound levels by rehearsing the action and noting where softer or louder sounds occur. During the shooting, anticipate the volume changes by adjusting the sound level just a fraction of a second before they happen. If you have only automatic level control, monitor the sound during rehearsals and restage the action (and/or move the microphone) if possible, to minimize excessive volume changes.

In addition to consistent volume, you want to maintain the same audio character, so that the shots recorded from different setups sound alike. If you are using the camcorder's built-in mike, try to keep the camera roughly the same distance from the subjects in every shot, changing image size by zooming instead. With a fishpole mike, experiment with different angles and positions while listening to the effect.

For this reason, it is important for the boom operator as well as the recordist to wear headphones.

Figure 14-22.

Mike boom positioned beside the camera (boom operator omitted for clarity).

By twisting the boom, the operator can aim the mike at each subject in turn.

Freedom from noise

Outdoor production recording is a constant struggle to keep wind noise and background sounds out of the dialog track. Wind noise can often be tamed by a microphone screen. Background noise is more difficult. If possible, move the subjects so that noisy traffic or pedestrians or ocean waves are not behind them. This avoids aiming the microphone directly at the background noise. Watch out for reflective surfaces like masonry walls, which can bounce noises originating behind the camera back into the microphone, **Figure 14-23.** When practical, place the mike above the subjects, pointed downward. This will reduce its sensitivity to unwanted background sounds.

Figure 14-23.
Avoid placing the microphone where it will pick up reflected background sounds.

Recording Stage Performances

Recording plays, musicals, and concerts in auditoriums can be complicated by several factors. Audio quality is degraded by the distance between performers and your microphone. The width of the stage offers a sound field too broad for the pickup pattern of your mike. Audience noise is difficult to keep off the production track.

Unlike musicals, opera performances are often not miked by the theater. (Corel)

A typical auditorium sound setup for taping.

Tapping the source

If the performance is already miked by the auditorium's own sound system, the best solution may be to plug directly into it. Not only does this take advantage of microphones that are well placed for sound recording; it also eliminates sound from the auditorium loudspeakers.

If you do plug into the auditorium system, it will probably be to a line-level circuit, far too strong for the mike input on your camcorder. To match levels, you need to place a line-to-mike level converter in the signal path, or else cable the auditorium sound to the line level input on a VCR, as shown in the diagram.

Following the action

For a play or other performance where the sound sources move, a camcorder-mounted shotgun mike may offer the best reproduction. Assuming that its camcorder is constantly re-aimed to capture the most important action, the mike will be automatically reoriented with it.

Riding gain

Automatic gain control can be difficult to handle with the widely varying sound levels encountered in plays. During quiet moments, the volume circuits will increase the recording level to the point where audience shuffles and incidental stage noises may grow unnaturally loud. If you have a VCR with manual recording capability, feed picture and sound from the camcorder to a separate videotape recording in the deck. If your VCR lacks manual gain control, you can use an audio mixer between microphone and deck to smooth out extreme swings in level. For protection, you can record a second tape in the camcorder as well.

Recording on a VCR.

Background Tracks

The key to good background tracks is consistency—a uniform sound unmarred by distinctive noises that call attention to themselves. For example, background traffic sounds should not include horns, brakes screeching, or the footsteps of occasional pedestrians because audiences will pick them out of the background and think they are part of the program. Background tracks fall into two types: background noise and room tone.

Background noise

Traffic or restaurant chatter or ocean surf is fairly easy to record: simply position the mike where the noises sound realistic and record about five minutes worth of material. You want a long recording so that it can be laid under an entire sequence without obvious repetitions or edits.

It is possible to edit out unwanted parts if the background is fairly uniform. See Figure 14-24. Digital sound editing allows cross-fades between different pieces of background track.

Remember to record at a good strong volume. It is easy to decrease sound levels in editing but difficult to increase them without obvious quality loss.

Room tone

As explained previously, room tone is the characteristic sound quality of an environment that is audible (though usually unnoticed) even when there are no overt noises. It is only when an editor cuts pieces out of a production track that the resulting dead silence is obvious. By replacing the dead spots with pieces of room tone, the editor preserves the ambient sound of the environment. Here is the procedure for recording room tone:

● Have the actors, crew members, and equipment remain in place, with the people keeping still and quiet. This is necessary because room tone is so subtle that it is affected by the objects in the environment.

● Place the microphone in a position similar to those used in making the production recordings.

● Record three to five minutes of material. Remember: it does not matter if the near silence is interrupted by an occasional noise. Since room tone is typically used in short pieces, these noises are easily discarded.

Keep in mind that audio tracks can be reused as required. For this reason, it is not necessary to record every minute of background sound that you might possibly need.

Sound Effects

The keys to good sound effects are isolation and realism. To isolate effects from background noises, position the mike as close as possible to the sound source. Use a highly directional shotgun mike if possible. See **Figure 14-25.** If you record wild effects on videotape, voice-slate each take so that the effect is identified even when the camera is too close to the sound source to record a recognizable visual.

To obtain realistic sound effects, there is no substitute for listening carefully through good headphones and changing mike angle and distance until you are satisfied with the sound. As always, record at a good, strong volume. If the script calls for, say, a car driving off outside in the distance, the editor can reduce the volume and adjust the sound quality in postproduction, as needed.

Foley Effects

The same rules apply to the recording of Foley effects, which are synchronized to video playback. Prepare for recording by making a duplicate copy of the footage that needs sound effects so that you can record

Figure 14-24.
A factory will often provide fairly uniform background noise. (Western Recreational Vehicles)

Figure 14-25.
Because of the distance required, recording animal sound effects is especially difficult. (Corel)

Highly sensitive directional mikes are used for capturing nature sound effects. (Sennheiser)

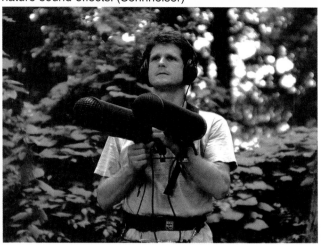

them on the copy. Later, it will be synchronized with the master video.

Voice recording

As in all recording, the goal in taping narration or other voiceover material is a clean, quality track. The keys to success are studio acoustics, microphone selection, and mike placement.

Studio acoustics

Voice tracks should be completely free of reverberation and background noise. If you are not recording in a sound studio, select an area with carpet, draperies, upholstered furniture, and other sound-absorbing materials. Using good quality headphones, listen to the "room tone" of the selected recording area for background noises and sounds like ventilation system hum. If necessary, change the mike orientation, sound absorption material, or even the location itself, to eliminate unwanted background sound.

Microphone selection

Use a cardioid mike, if possible, because its pickup pattern allows for some movement on the part of the performer.

Shotgun mikes with narrow pickup patterns are usually unsuitable for the close distances typical of studio mike placement.

Even inexpensive units will perform adequately; but a better-grade model adds a professional-sounding crispness that makes voice-over speech stand out.

Mike placement

Poorly-placed studio mikes create two problems. First, they cause *plosive* sounds like "puh," (as in "*p*oorly *p*laced") to overload the mike and "pop" on the sound track. Second, their stands can interfere with the scripts that are usually used in voice recording. To correct both problems at once, place the microphone at a slight angle to the performer. Positioning a table stand to one side makes room for a script. Placing a boom mike overhead is even better.

If you are recording two or more performers at the same time, it is preferable to provide two mikes, separated by as much space as the location allows, **Figure 14-26.** That way, neither mike will pick up the sounds of the other mike's performer. Use a production mixer to balance the levels between the two mikes.

Figure 14-26.
Each microphone picks up only one performer.

Mikes aimed at least 90 degrees apart

4-8 feet between performers

Managing Studio Voice Recording

In addition to placing the microphone and controlling record levels, you need to minimize script noises and identify parts of the recording for later editing.

Script rustle

To eliminate the noise of paper shuffling during narration recording, cover the table or music stand supporting the script with a scrap of carpeting. Place a blanket or rug on the floor beside the performer. Remove any staples or paper clips so that the script pages are loose. To use this setup, the narrator feathers the script pages as they rest on the carpet scrap. As each page is finished, it is picked up and dropped onto the carpet beside the reader.

Slating voice recordings

Normally, a narrator reads through a script in sequence, until making a mistake. When this happens, have the performer repeat the line immediately and then resume reading the next line. To document this repeat for the editor, have the narrator voice slate the retake (for example, "Line 21, take 2"). Place a vertical line (I) in the margin of your own script to stand for the first take. Add a line for each additional take (II, III, etc.). If, say, line 21 has three lines in the margin beside it, then the editor knows that it took three takes to get the line right and captures only the last one. Or, if you should decide that the second of the three takes was better, circling the second line will tell this to the editor.

Handling script pages silently.

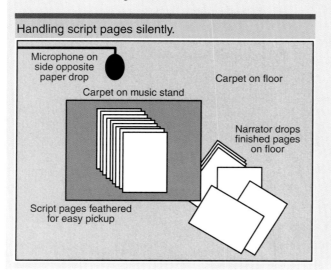

Dialogue Replacement

Dialogue replacement, **Figure 14-27,** is just a special form of voice recording, and all the suggestions presented earlier apply to this task as well. The major difference, of course, is the monitor, which is placed so that the performers can synchronize their dialogue with the lip movements on screen. Position the monitor so that the actors can easily look back and forth between their scripts and the screen.

Here is a simple procedure for replacing dialogue. Edit the original footage, including the poor quality dialogue; then make a duplicate tape of the completed edit. Record replacement dialogue on the duplicate, using the audio dub function. That way, the new audio track will not interfere with the video track being used for reference. Feed the original stereo dialogue to the actors through headphones, so that it will not be picked up by their microphones. When the dialogue has been re-recorded satisfactorily, sync the new dialogue track with the original footage.

You may find it easier to follow this procedure even if you are doing digital editing. It is sometimes easier to export an edited sequence to tape, do your looping in linear mode, and then digitize the completed track. Using a timeline, you can easily sync the new dialogue to the edited digital picture.

Music Recording

Professional music recording typically involves many microphones, each balanced and equalized by a large studio mixer and feeding a separate recording track. See **Figure 14-28**.

Production music recording is a simpler process. Taping a rock group, string quartet, or other small ensemble, you can obtain

Figure 14-27.
Scenes in noisy environments often require dialogue replacement.

Figure 14-28.
In studio music recording, instruments are often miked individually. (Sennheiser).

excellent results with a single well-placed microphone. As always, the keys to success are microphone selection and placement. For music recording, use a good quality stereo microphone of condenser design. Place the mike as close as possible to the group, while still keeping the performers inside the primary pickup pattern, **Figure 14-29.**

Camcorders with built-in stereo mikes are engineered to achieve separation automatically.

Without multiple microphones and recording channels, you can still equalize volume levels by moving the performers around so that the quieter instruments are nearest the mike and the louder ones are farthest away. Listen to the signal during

Figure 14-29.
Place the mike far enough away to pick up the whole group.

Too close

Proper placement

rehearsals and experiment until you achieve a good balance.

The Rewards of Audio Recording

If your primary interest is in the video side of production, you may begin with the idea that audio recording is simply a technical process that has to be learned in order to provide the professional sound track that you need. But as you get into the creative aspects of sound, you may well find that audio is a complex craft that can be rewarding in its own right.

Technical Terms

Audio: Sound as electronically recorded and reproduced.

Balanced line: A three-wire microphone cable designed to minimize electrical interference.

Boom: A studio microphone support consisting of a rolling pedestal and a horizontal arm.

Cardioid: A spatial pattern of microphone sensitivity, named for its resemblance to a Valentine heart.

Equalizer: A device for adjusting the relative strengths of different audio frequencies.

Fishpole: A location microphone support consisting of a hand-held telescoping arm.

Foley studio: An area set up for recording real-time sound effects synchronously with video playback.

Lavaliere: A very small microphone clipped to the subject's clothing, close to the mouth.

Looping: Replacing dialogue in real time by recording it synchronously with video playback.

Microphone (mike): A device that converts sound waves into electrical modulations, for recording.

Mixer: A device that balances the input strengths of signals from two or more sources, especially microphones.

Pickup pattern: The directions (in three dimensions) in which a microphone is most sensitive to sounds.

Playback: Previously recorded video and/or audio reproduced so that actors or technicians can add to or replace parts of it synchronously, in real time.

Slate: A written video and/or spoken audio identification of a component such as a shot, a line of narration, or a sound effect.

Transducer: The component of a microphone that converts changing air pressure ("sound") into an electrical signal ("audio").

Unbalanced line: A two-wire microphone cable subject to electrical interference, but less bulky and expensive, for use in amateur applications.

A field interview using wireless microphones. (Sennheiser)

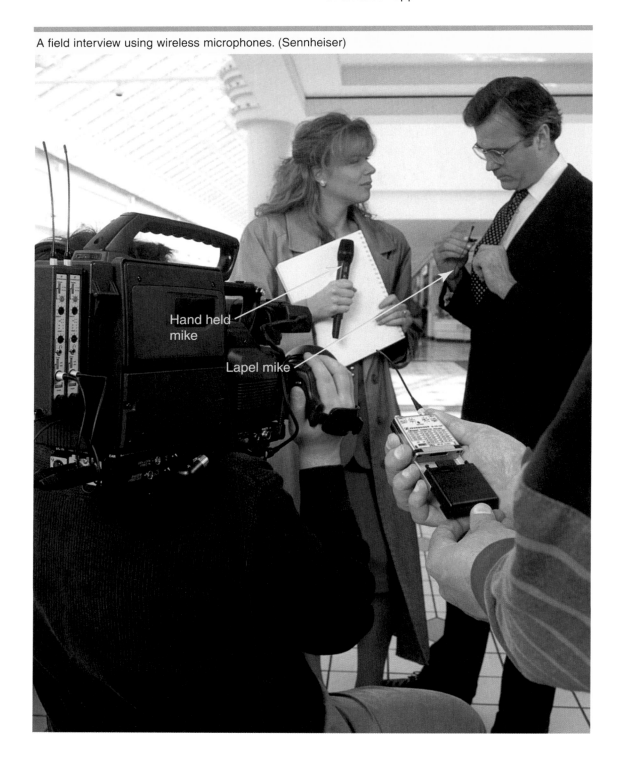

Hand held mike

Lapel mike

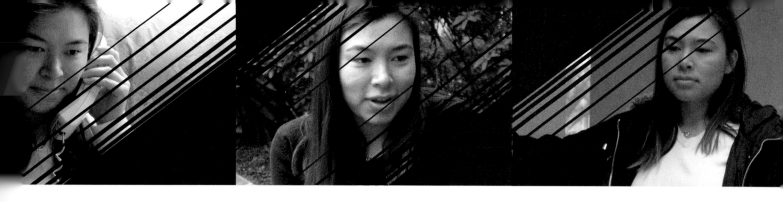

15 Directing for Content

Contents

About Directing for Content
Directing for Communication
Directing for Performance

Objectives

After studying this chapter, you will be able to:

❏ Deliver information on video completely and effectively.

❏ Communicate emotional effects to your audience.

❏ Guide on-screen talent in shaping their performances.

❏ Solve production problems arising from performance.

XLS: Car speeding through the night.

FS: The car.

FS: Charlie runs through gate.

POV: He sees the box.

CU: Reacts to box.

CU: The box.

227

About Directing for Content

When you direct a video, your job is to determine exactly what is shot and how the result looks and sounds. That makes you the final decision maker —the person in charge. Other people such as the writer, the videographer, and the editor make decisions in their own areas of responsibility. In addition, they often make recommendations that a wise director will consider with seriousness and respect. But even though production is a collaboration among many people, the final authority generally rests with the director.

In many professional situations, the director may share authority with the producer, the client, the financial backers, or other people.

Video directing requires the ability to juggle several different tasks at once, including:

- *Communication:* presenting the program content clearly to the audience.
- *Performance:* ensuring that the people in the video are believable and effective on screen.
- *Editing:* providing the raw materials from which the editor can construct a smoothly assembled program.
- *Camera:* choreographing the way in which the action is recorded.

This chapter is devoted to communication and performance. Chapter 16 covers editing and camera.

Since the realities of production demand constant adjustments and improvisations while shooting, the director must evaluate each new idea to see how it might affect these four tasks. In addition, a good director also imparts an overall style to the material, giving it a distinctive "look and feel." It has been said that a good director combines the talents of a painter, a dramatist, a diplomat, a psychiatrist, an accountant, and an air traffic controller. It is no wonder that it takes time and practice to master all the skills required for successful video directing.

Directing for Communication

Communicating with the audience means delivering information: selecting, organizing, shaping, and presenting it in a way that helps viewers absorb and respond to it. It is not enough to simply display information and expect the audience to pay attention to it. In directing, you must determine the way in which information is delivered by controlling *emphasis* and *effect*. Before you can shape information, however, you must see to it that the information actually gets into the program to begin with. That task is not as simple and obvious as it seems.

A Demonstration Sequence

In order to contrast different solutions to directing problems, we need to apply all of them to the same situation. Throughout the following discussion, we will draw most of our examples from the same source: a sequence about a burglary.

Why not just break the glass in the cabinet doors? Let us assume that the noise of the shattering glass would arouse the sleeping household; or perhaps the burglar is too nervous to think of this obvious solution.

A burglar … a locked cabinet full of valuables… a key to the locked cabinet.

Information

Perhaps the most common error that inexperienced directors make is to omit important information. For example, **Figure 15-1** shows how our burglary might be staged by an inexperienced director.

Where did the burglar find a key to the cabinet? The inexperienced director has not shown us. Though this omission is not critically important, it will bother the audience. To satisfy their curiosity, we need to include the information about the key, as you can see in **Figure 15-2.**

In the added shot, we see the burglar open the top desk drawer and remove a key from it. Now the missing piece of information has been included in the scene. The director's very first job, then, is to identify the information that the audience needs to know and ensure that all of it is included.

Emphasis

The added shot in Figure 15-2 is just another camera angle, with nothing special about it. Although we do see the discovery of the key, it is so unemphatically presented that we might very well miss it. To make sure that the audience gets the information, the director's second task is to emphasize it appropriately, as you can see from **Figure 15-3.** In this version, the audience sees the drawer being opened by the burglar and then the key inside, as her hand enters the shot and removes it. By giving the key its own closeup, the director adds emphasis to the information so that the audience will not overlook it.

In adding emphasis to information, you have several tools, including *image size, composition, camera angle,* and *shot length.*

Image size

The bigger the image, the more emphatic the information it contains. **Figure 15-4** shows two versions of the insert. Notice how the larger image presents the key more vividly.

Composition

You can call attention to the information you wish to emphasize by the way you organize the composition of the image. In

Figure 15-1.
The burglar discovers that the cabinet is locked...

and opens it with a key.

Figure 15-2.
The added shot explains the key.

Figure 15-3.

The insert emphasizes the key.

Figure 15-4.
The closer shot adds emphasis.

Figure 15-5, notice that in the first shot, the key is hard to separate visually from the other clutter in the drawer. In the better-composed second shot, the key has been placed and lit to draw the viewer's eye to it.

Camera angle

A powerful tool for emphasizing information is camera angle: the perspective from which the audience sees the information. In **Figure 15-6**, both images are inserts of the key in the drawer. The first is a so-called "objective" insert, meaning that the shot is from no particular point of view. The second is a "subjective" insert, showing the drawer as if the audience were looking at it through the burglar's eyes. Notice that the subjective camera angle is more emphatic than the objective (neutral) alternative.

Shot duration

You can control emphasis simply by how long you display a piece of information on the screen. If the audience sees only the single second during which the burglar's hand grabs the key, they may miss this information. But if they see the drawer opened to reveal a prominent key for a moment before the hand removes it, they have more time to notice and absorb the information.

Effect

In the previous examples, the insert shot of the key in the drawer is added purely to convey information. But a good director presents that information in a way that involves the audience emotionally. By utilizing camera angles, image sizes, shot lengths, lens

Figure 15-5.
The key is lost in the clutter.

The key is emphasized by the composition.

Figure 15-6.
An objective insert (shot from a neutral point of view).

A subjective insert (shot from the burglar's point of view).

Other Forms of Emphasis

Accomplished directors have used a wide variety of tricks to emphasize elements in their shots.

Brightness and Color

In classic Hollywood lighting of the pictorial realist style, the center of interest was almost always emphasized by brighter lighting—perhaps a hotter key light or an arrow of background light that served as a pointer. In Technicolor musicals, the stars typically wore costume colors that stood out from the overall color scheme.

Today, emphasis by light or color tends to be more subtle; but color especially, is still used to distinguish the most important element in a composition.

Though the third subject is small, his orange shirt attracts the viewer's attention.

Movement

Movement is an easy way to draw attention to a subject, especially when the rest of the frame is still. You can also reverse this procedure. In one of his many famous shots, Alfred Hitchcock showed a tennis match grandstand full of spectators whose heads swivelled left-right-left-right to follow a long volley on the court. Only the villain's head is not moving, because he is watching his prey rather than the match. Though he is small in the frame, the viewer's eye goes to him immediately.

Audio

Traditionally, audio had only a limited ability to emphasize a certain aspect of a shot. Today, however, most TV sets play stereo audio, and digital postproduction offers complete control over stereo imaging. This ability is especially useful for emphasizing important elements that are off-screen. The opening door, the car driving off in the distance, the incoming mortar shell—these sounds are greatly enhanced by stereo imaging.

Although audio emphasis is ultimately created in editing, the director must anticipate it in production. To use the example of the off-screen door, the director may want a performer to react to the sound, even though it is not heard on the set.

perspectives, camera movement, and other tools, the director creates *effects* that stimulate feelings. In short, a merely competent director communicates only information; a good director communicates both information and effects.

To see how effects can be created, say that the feeling you want for the burglary scene is suspense. Imagine that the burglar knows she has tripped the silent alarm and has only moments to get that cabinet open. But it is locked! Can the cabinet be opened and how long will it take? Your goal is to make the audience want to say, "Hurry, hurry!"

The two sequences of camera setups presented here show contrasting versions of the sequence. **Figure 15-7** includes the key only to convey the information that it exists.

Figure 15-7.

Finding the cabinet locked, the burglar opens the top desk drawer.

Her hand locates, then snatches the key.

She rams the key into the keyhole of the door.

Figure 15-8, however, breaks the action down into different camera angles and image sizes to emphasize the increasingly desperate search for that key. The resulting sequence adds the crucial effect of suspense.

As you study the second sequence, you will see that the suspense is developed by two principal techniques: image size and sequence length. These are the same directorial techniques that you use to emphasize information, only now they are employed to create emotional effect.

Image size

Notice that the camera stays close to its subjects: the burglar's face, her hands, the key. Generally, the bigger the image size, the more emotional impact it carries.

Sequence length

As you can see from the example, the information-only version requires just three shots, while the suspenseful alternative takes ten. By stretching the length of the sequence, the director increases the feeling of urgency.

Composition

Look again at the burglar's closeup, **Figure 15-9.**

In the first version, the camera is not level (that is, not parallel to the floor). This compositional effect (often called "dutch") imparts a sense of imbalance and insecurity. Compare the shot with a level version of the same angle (the second shot) to see how tilting the horizon unsettles the composition.

The term "dutch," an informal version of Deutsch ("German") was first applied to off-level angles because they were favored by European directors who brought the expressionistic style of German cinema to Hollywood in the 1920s and '30s.

Camera angle

Both image size and composition are created by camera placement; and camera angles, in general, can contribute to the overall emotional effect. In **Figure 15-10,** you

Figure 15-8.

The burglar sees that the door is locked.

She realizes that she must find the key.

She opens the lower desk drawers.

They are empty.

She is acutely aware that....

the motion sensor has picked her up.

The last drawer.

Her hand, offscreen, rummages the drawer.

Her hand snatches the key.

She jams the key into the keyhole.

Figure 15-9.
Composition with off-level background.   Composition with level background.

can see that high angles often convey a feeling of detachment, while low angles emphasize the power of the image (and the powerlessness of the viewer). Head-on angles feel formal and calm, while diagonal setups convey movement and energy.

In practice, image size, composition, and camera angles are all treated together, as aspects of the same thing.

Lens perspective

The "feel" of an image is strongly affected by the lens used to record it, **Figure 15-11.** Wide angle lenses exaggerate depth and motion toward or away from the camera. The effect they convey is dynamic and energetic. Telephoto lenses, by contrast, suppress depth and motion, keeping the viewer at a distance and conveying a sense of formality.

Camera movement

Camera movement can add significantly to the emotional cast of a scene. A stationary camera, panning and tilting from

one position, conveys a sense of detached observation. A moving camera, especially when dollying in and out, becomes part of the action. Moreover, a constantly moving camera imparts a feeling of restless energy.

Shot length

To create an effect, a director can control the length of a sequence by shooting it in a greater or smaller number of separate shots. In the same way, the individual shots themselves can be made shorter or longer, depending on the effect desired. In general, short shots with quick cuts convey a sense of dynamic energy, while lengthy shots feel calm and deliberate. That is why fights are typically constructed from many brief shots, while romantic scenes are often assembled from fewer but lengthier angles.

The Other Half of Content

Directing to communicate with your audience means managing information, emphasis, and effect. Together, these elements make up the content of your program. However, communicating content is only half the job.

Figure 15-10.

A high-angle shot feels more detached....   than a low-angle setup.   A formal, frontal angle is less dynamic than....   a strong diagonal composition.

Figure 15-11.
Wide angle lenses expand apparent depth...

while telephoto lenses compress it.

Unless you are making a specialized program like a nature documentary, that content is delivered largely by the people in your video —by the performers.

Directing for Performance

Everyone knows that directors work with actors, but few people understand what they really *do* with them. This section introduces the craft of drawing effective performances from the talent in your video programs, **Figure 15-12.**

"Talent" is the collective term for the people who appear in films and videos.

What follows is not an extensive treatment of the art of directing professional actors in fiction films. That would require a book in itself, and several are available.

Figure 15-12.
The "burglar" is, of course, a performer.

Instead, this section focuses on the craft of guiding people through all kinds of videos from stories to training programs to promotional pieces. Some of your performers may be professionals, but others may be amateurs like corporate spokespersons or workers demonstrating job skills or simply members of your family or community.

Actors and Performance

Directing performers like these means making them appear believable and effective on screen. To be believable, the performers should not appear to be acting, but simply living and behaving normally while the camera just happens to record them. Though a skilled actor is practicing a complex craft, the result looks simple and natural on screen because that craft is invisible to the audience.

To be effective, the performance must be more than simply believable. It must also engage viewers' attention and make an impression on them. Some professional actors achieve this by sheer force of personality, but most performers can do it if they get enough help from the director.

Many people think that performing means creating a character in a fictional program, and that is often the case. But the people who appear in nonfiction programs are also performing. As a director, you may be coaching a spokesperson for an organization, a person being interviewed on camera, a subject of a documentary program, or a person who demonstrates the skills or techniques being taught in a training video. Even the most seasoned professional actors will benefit from good direction because the director can show them where they fit in the program as a whole and how best to do their part in it.

Some professional directors feel that 90% of directing actors lies in casting exactly the right people for their roles and then getting out of the way and letting them work.

Outside of Hollywood-style production, most performers are not full-time professionals. Working with less seasoned talent, directors spend considerable time solving performance problems—problems like self consciousness, difficulty in speaking lines, ignorance of production techniques, and trouble expressing emotions. The most widespread problem with actors is a general insecurity: a fear that they look ridiculous, that they are inadequate, that they are failing.

Actors and Insecurity

Camera fright is a form of stage fright: a fear of subjecting yourself to public attention, of placing yourself under a spotlight for critical

---

Fixing Problems in Rehearsal

In working with nonprofessional actors, directors must deal with difficulties that come up again and again. Here are some of these common problems, with some suggestions for solving them in rehearsal.

Context

Videos consist of short individual shots that are often recorded out of order. This choppy, seemingly arbitrary production can leave performers confused about where they are and what they are supposed to be doing. An earlier chapter uses the example of two train station sequences that are shot back-to-back but are five years apart in story time. In another case, two screen lovers may be asked to enact their first meeting after playing many scenes in which they already have a romantic relationship.

To avoid problems with this shooting method, begin rehearsing each scene by explaining where it fits in the finished program and how it relates to scenes that the performers have already completed.

Memorizing

This chapter offers ways to help actors master their lines, but movement and activities can be hard to remember too, especially since they must often be repeated precisely from one setup to the next. (A performer's movement within the scene is called **blocking** and his or her activities are termed **business**.)

To control the amount of memorizing required of the actors, rehearse only a single sequence at a time. If the sequence is a long one, try to break it down further into *beats*, short subsections of perhaps two minutes of screen time.

To obtain consistent performances from one setup to the next, consider letting actors refresh their memories by watching playback of previous setups that cover the same material.

Expressing emotions

As noted elsewhere, amateurs can have problems in expressing emotions convincingly. Some tend to overact, others have trouble making transitions between different feelings, still others cannot handle complex, mixed reactions.

Rehearsal is the place to spot these problems and adjust accordingly. Step one is often to help the actor with the problem. If this does not work, you will want to plan a strategy for shooting around the difficulty. Develop solutions before you start shooting, whether this involves simplifying the performance requirements, breaking the recording into shorter shots, or thinking up cutaways to help edit out mistakes.

Tuning performances

In some cases, the quickest way to get the performance you require is by demonstration: you act out the role yourself to show how you want the blocking and business handled, and how you want the lines of dialogue to sound. Professional actors often object to being given these *line readings*, as they are called (though they seldom mind having their movements demonstrated); but nonprofessionals are often grateful for the help.

In modeling movement or speech for an actor, do just enough to get the idea across. If you go through the whole thing, you risk getting performances that are just mechanical imitations. (Charlie Chaplin, however, was famous for acting out every second of every role and then expecting his cast members to imitate him exactly.)

A 12-volt monitor allows playback on location.

inspection by the audience, **Figure 15-13.** Even professionals can suffer from it and almost all actors may occasionally feel ill at ease about performing.

Fortunately, camera fright is easier to combat than stage fright, because the performer is *not* actually appearing in public. With reluctant actors (in fact, with *all* actors) it helps to remind them that their mistakes are completely private and will never be seen by anyone except the cast and crew. Shooting multiple takes lets performers practice until they get it right. Assembling the program from separate shots allows the editor to cut out all the bad parts and show only the best. Finally, reassure the actors that your job is to make them look good on screen, and that is exactly what you are doing.

Helping Actors Overcome Self-consciousness

Self-consciousness is a painful awareness of face and body that makes the performer move stiffly and awkwardly. It also makes faces look tense and uncomfortable. There are several directorial tactics for reducing self-consciousness. First, allow plenty of time for rehearsal. The more familiar the performers are with the material, the more comfortable they feel about it. Often amateurs will perform more naturally if they think they are not being recorded, so it may help to disable the tally light on the camcorder (the button that glows red to indicate that the camera is recording). That way, you can tape rehearsals without alerting the performers.

Figure 15-13.
Amateur performers are often insecure.

If you cannot turn off the tally light, cover it with a small piece of opaque tape.

To reduce physical awkwardness, keep actor movements simple and natural. It helps to check with performers after each rehearsal to see if anything feels uncomfortable to them. If so, correct the problem. In the first shot of **Figure 15-14,** the performer does not know what to do with his hands. The chair provides a natural place to rest them.

Finally, the best way to make performers look natural is by having them do things that they do in real life, so that they do not have to learn new skills. For instance, if you are making a training program on how to operate a fork lift, use an actual fork lift operator as your on-camera demonstrator.

Figure 15-14.
Simply standing still can be difficult for amateur performers.

You can often use a prop to anchor them.

Helping Actors with Lines

All performers can have trouble memorizing speeches and amateurs have the additional problem of stiffness.

We have all seen local commercials in which the owner of a small business stands woodenly in front of the camera and intones something like "So-Come-On-Down-To-Billy-Bob's-House-Of-Barbecues-And-Fireplaces..."

If the performer cannot read aloud convincingly, the easiest solution is to allow him or her to improvise. For example, the director might say something like, "Okay, now tell the folks to come visit your store and be sure to say the whole name." Allowed to say his own words in his own way, the performer/client will probably sound more natural.

If the problem is remembering lines, you can minimize it by avoiding long speeches and breaking conversations down into several brief shots. Remind performers that it does not matter if they make a mistake or how many times they make it. In the finished program, only the correct version will appear.

Finally, be prepared to use cue cards so that performers can read their lines instead of memorizing them, **Figure 15-15.** Place the cue cards off-camera but in positions such that the performers' eyes appear to be looking in the right direction.

Do not transcribe all the lines to cue cards before shooting. Instead, have sheets of cardboard and broad markers available at the shoot and make cards only when performers are having real difficulties. Otherwise, your

Figure 15-15.
A hand-lettered cue card.

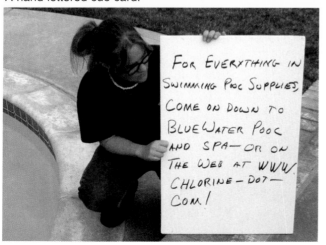

Improvised Teleprompters

For reading lengthy texts on camera, professionals use Teleprompters: special displays that scroll the copy. Commercial models can be expensive, but you can achieve the same results with a personal computer.

The system is more flexible on a laptop model because the computer screen is easier to position off-camera where the actor can read it comfortably. With a little ingenuity, however, you can also use the monitor of a desktop computer.

Preparing the text

The best applications for teleprompting are slide show programs such as Corel Presentations and Microsoft PowerPoint, because they can display slides full-screen, without surrounding menus. Also, slide programs are specifically designed to display text in large sizes.

If a slide program is not available, you can use a word processor by hiding all unnecessary workbars and menus, setting the copy in a large type size, and setting the viewing width so that the text fills the computer screen side-to-side:

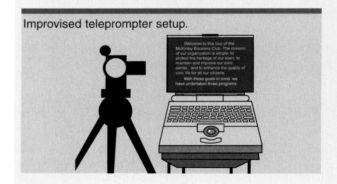

Improvised teleprompter setup.

The first step is to key (or import) the text into the program and format it in convenient sections. Set the type face in a simple font like Arial or Swiss, at a very large size (try 32, 36, or 48 points).

Unlike true teleprompters, slide programs cannot scroll text continuously. Instead, they display one full page at a time. For this reason, inexperienced readers can be confused by rapidly

talent will expect cue cards for every scene and refuse to memorize their lines.

With a speech or lengthy remarks by an on-camera spokesperson, you will, of course, need to prepare cue cards in advance.

A word processor display used as a teleprompting device.

A slide program work screen.

changing text pages. To solve the problem, repeat the last sentence of each outgoing page at the top of the incoming page. On both pages, set the repeated text in a contrasting color. This makes it easy for the reader to follow continuing copy from one slide to the next.

Setting up the system

Position the computer screen facing the performer, and as close to the camera lens as possible. To conceal the fact that the person is looking to one side of the lens, use a telephoto

First slide, with text to be repeated in white.

setting and place the camera as far away as practical. (The setup must be close enough for the performer to read the computer display.)

To minimize the angle between the lens and the display screen, set the camera as far from the performer as practical.

Too close to the camera, the subject is obviously looking to one side.

Farther from the camera, the subject's look is not obvious.

Using the system

To use the program as a set of cue cards, have the continuity supervisor follow the dialogue, advancing the slides to change the virtual "cards."

Helping Actors with Production Techniques

Many times, amateur performers have problems because they do not understand the technical requirements of the video medium. Here are some of their most common mistakes, along with suggested remedies.

Hitting marks

Often a performer is asked to move through a shot and then stop at a predetermined spot (usually because that spot is specially lit for the performer and the camera is set to create a good composition there). Some amateurs have trouble stopping at the

Figure 15-16.
Chalk marks show the performer where to walk and stop.

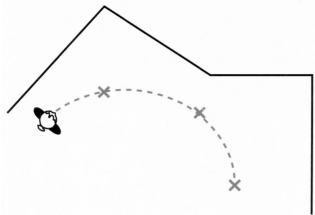

right place, or can do so only by searching obviously for their marks on the floor, **Figure 15-16.**

The simplest solution is to avoid the problem entirely. For example, instead of having the actor move into frame and then stop, have the actor stand off-screen while the camera moves to frame him or her.

Looking at the camera

It is natural for amateurs to look directly into the camera lens, especially after they think they have finished a shot. Their look asks, "Is the shot over?" or "Was that okay?" This can be a problem if you need extra footage at the end of the shot. Explain diplomatically that the shot was not usable because the actor looked at the camera; then retake the shot. If the actor cannot soon learn to avoid looking at the camera, this is a sure sign that you will encounter other problems and you had better replace this performer sooner rather than later.

Matching action

Once you explain the importance of doing (and saying) everything identically in each angle on a scene, most amateur actors will try to do this. To help them out, keep good continuity notes so that you can remind them of details before every shot. Use an on-set monitor to play back their previous angles so that they can see exactly what they said and did.

Overall, the best solution to technical problems with amateur actors is to remove the problems rather ask the performers to solve them. It is unlikely that you can turn your talent into professionals during a single shoot.

Helping Actors Express Emotions

Professional actors are skilled at adjusting the intensity of their performances to suit the director. Amateur performers often lack this ability.

This section applies mainly to fiction movies, since nonfiction programs seldom require performers to simulate feelings.

Overacting is often easy to correct. Simply show the offenders some closeups of their work on a monitor and they will realize that they need to rein themselves in. With persistent overactors, you may want to pull the camera back from them because the smaller the image, the less intense it appears to the audience. Be aware, however, that this technique has other consequences. If the wider shot of one actor is intercut with closer angles on another, the actor with the larger image may well dominate the scene.

With amateurs, a bigger problem is complex acting involving combinations of emotions. For example, if you say to an amateur performer, "You're delighted that your no-good brother-in-law is leaving, but unhappy that your mother-in-law's staying," the actor may well be unable to show these two opposite emotions at the same time and the result will be a failure, **Figure 15-17.**

To solve the problem, rework the scene so that the actor can react separately to the good news and the bad news. When the transition between emotions happens off screen, the actor has to play only one in each shot, **Figure 15-18.**

Since you shoot the wife's happy and unhappy closeups as separate shots, the performer can take all the time she needs between setups to change from happiness to anger.

Enhancing a Subject's Authority

Low angles tend to make a person seem more powerful, more commanding. High angles have the opposite effect. When shooting an executive or a spokesperson for a corporate video, make certain that the camera is at least slightly below the subject's eye level, **Figure 15-19.**

Content and Form

In discussing the director's responsibilities for controlling communication and shaping performance, we have covered the

Figure 15-17.
HUSBAND: My brother's leaving tomorrow, but Mom's staying six more weeks.

WIFE: (dismayed) What!?

Figure 15-18.
HUSBAND: My brother's leaving tomorrow.

HUSBAND: But Mom's staying six more weeks.

WIFE: What!!?

Figure 15-19.
A low angle conveys a feeling of authority.

Setting the camera just below eye-level conveys the effect more subtly.

subject of directing for content. But that is only one-half of a video director's responsibilities. The other half is the technical side: directing for editing, staging action for the screen, and moving the camera. Those topics appear in the following chapter.

Technical Terms

Beat: A short unit of action in a program, often, though not always, corresponding to a scene.

Blocking: A performer's movement within a shot. It must be rehearsed and memorized so the actor hits the correct spots with respect to camera and lighting, and so the movements can be repeated exactly for other angles on the same action.

Business: Activities performed during a shot, such as writing a letter or filling a vase with flowers.

Dutch: Referring to an off-level camera. To "put dutch on a shot" is to purposely tilt the composition.

Line reading: A vocal interpretation of a line that includes its speed, emphases, and intonations. In simple terms, "You came back!" is one reading of a line, and "You came *back*?" is a different reading.

Lines: Scripted speech to be spoken by performers.

Marks: Places within the shot where the performer is to pause, stop, turn, etc. These spots are identified by marks made of tape or chalk lines.

Objective insert: A detail of the action presented from a neutral point of view.

Subjective insert: A detail of the action presented from a character's point of view.

Tally light: A small light on a camera that glows to show that the unit is recording.

Teleprompter: A machine that displays text progressively as a performer reads it on-camera.

Working with actors is one-half of a director's job.

16 Directing for Form

Contents

About Directing for Form
Covering the Action
Maintaining Continuity
Managing Screen Direction
Staging for the Screen
Moving the Camera

Objectives

After studying this chapter, you will be able to:

❑ Deliver footage that can be edited smoothly and flexibly.

❑ Create a three-dimensional world on the two-dimensional screen.

❑ Choreograph effective camera movement.

About Directing for Form

Complementing Chapter 15 on directing for content (communication and performance), this chapter covers directing for form. Mastering the techniques of video form requires some technical knowledge because of the special nature of the medium. Every program consists of hundreds of very short pieces (shots) that are often recorded out of order. When rearranged by the editor, these pieces must fit together seamlessly, even though each is made quite independently of the others. Also, because space and time on the two-dimensional screen follow their own special rules, action must be carefully staged to appear as if it is happening in the real world.

The two-dimensional world on the screen is discussed in Chapters 3 and 4.

For these reasons, a video director needs a thorough understanding of the formal aspects of the craft, beginning with the fundamental principle that absolutely everything recorded, both visually and aurally, is nothing more than raw material for future editing.

Covering the Action

As you direct a production, you need to remember that you are not making a video program, but only its separate component parts. The actual program will be assembled from your shots at a later time by the video editor. What you are doing is providing the building blocks, the component materials from which the editor will construct the final program.

For clarity, we will treat the editor and director as two different people, though directors often edit their own programs.

To help ensure a successful result, the components you supply must provide the editor with everything that is needed, in a form that the editor can use. The process of shooting the material to anticipate the editor's requirements is called *directing to edit*. To begin with, directing to edit means providing coverage of the action so that the editor has enough material to work with.

Coverage

Coverage means more than just taping all the action. It also means ensuring that the action is recorded in multiple shots that repeat all or at least part of the content. Good coverage typically requires *repetition, overlap, variety, protection*, and *cutaways*.

Repetition

Repetition involves recording the same action more than once by shooting it from more than one point of view. For instance, as shown in **Figure 16-1**, you might record the entire scene from three different camera setups: a two-shot, a closeup favoring one actor, and another closeup favoring the second actor.

Multiple angles allow the editor to cut between one shot and another at any time to improve performance, adjust timing, and control style.

A Demonstration Sequence

The discussion of coverage uses a simple sequence of a couple picnicking on a wooded bluff above the ocean. The basic actions in the sequence are summarized in the following illustrations.

In actuality, this short sequence might be covered by just three or four setups; but for demonstration purposes, we will use many more angles than usual.

The couple picnicking.

He takes a drink of soda.

He points out a storm over the ocean.

She doubts that it will reach them.

Figure 16-1.

| A neutral two-shot covers entire sequence. | Her closeup repeats entire sequence. | His closeup also repeats entire action. |

Overlap

Overlapping means beginning a new piece of action by repeating the last part of the preceding action. Even when you do not re-record the entire action in each of several setups, it is usually important to overlap action from shot to shot. This is illustrated in **Figure 16-2.**

By overlapping action, you allow the editor leeway in setting the edit point between the two shots. Even if you think you already know exactly where you want the edit to be, protect yourself and the editor by providing extra footage.

In addition to overlapping parts of the action, you should begin recording at least five to ten seconds before any action begins and continue shooting for the same length of time afterward as well.

Variety and protection

To offer the editor a broad range of options, you should provide coverage from a variety of angles. Varying angles helps make invisible edits and it also tends to hide small mismatches between different takes (recordings) of the same action, **Figure 16-3**.

Sometimes mismatches or other mistakes are too large to hide, so the editor cannot use the shots in which they appear. That is another reason for covering the same action from different angles. In fact, if you are not sure about something in a shot, obtain an extra shot from another angle.

Such an alternative setup is sometimes referred to, literally, as a "protection shot."

Cutaways

Cutaways are shots that show information other than the main action. Typical cutaways, **Figure 16-4,** include:

- *Inserts*: closeups of details.
- *Reaction shots*: the responses of actors other than the one who is currently the center of interest.

Figure 16-2.

| He picks up his soda at the end of the first shot. | He picks up his soda at the start of the second shot, drinks, then puts it down again at the end. |

Figure 16-3.
His action is covered in three different styles of closeup.

● *Color shots*: shots that show expressive details of the environment in which the scene is unfolding.

Nowadays, using a shot for color alone is considered somewhat old-fashioned. It is better to relate color cutaways to the main action.

In addition to delivering extra information, cutaways are extremely useful for interrupting other shots so that they can be invisibly shortened or so that other changes can be made. For example, suppose that the two-shot of the couple includes more dialogue than necessary, **Figure 16-5.**

The trouble is that the basket is already packed. Discovering this potential problem, the director adds a cutaway shot of the ocean. By inserting this cutaway into the closeup, **Figure 16-6,** the editor can snip out the line about packing without leaving a hole in the original shot.

Of course, a reaction shot of the woman could be used instead.

Maintaining Continuity

Continuity is the complex process of ensuring that all the small pieces of a video (the shots and the details recorded in them) add up to a smooth, consistent whole. A program with good continuity appears to be a single *continuous* presentation that has no mismatches in information, action, or screen direction.

On larger productions, the script supervisor keeps track of these elements, but the director still needs to be keenly aware of continuity. The script supervisor's job is not to create and maintain continuity, but only to

Figure 16-5.
HE: I don't like the looks of that squall coming in. I'll start packing the picnic basket. You'd better finish your soda.

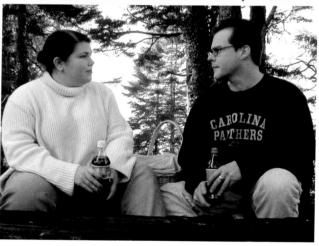

Figure 16-4.
Cutaways. A—*Insert* of the soda being set down.

B—*Reaction shot* of her while he talks offscreen.

C—*Color shot* of the ocean view. (Sue Stinson)

A

B

C

Figure 16-6.
HE: I don't like the looks of that squall coming in.

You'd better finish your soda.

monitor it. Achieving good continuity is the director's job. In smaller productions, script supervision may be only a part-time responsibility of a production manager or an assistant. In such a situation, the director is the only person who can ensure consistency.

Continuity of Information

In shots that include duplicate or overlapping action, the details should all be the same. For example, dialogue should be identical. Do not allow an actor to say "Hello!" in the two-shot and "Yo!" in his closeup. Though an editor can cut mistakes and trim pauses (if given enough coverage), it helps if the actor's lines are consistent from shot to shot.

Physical details should match. If the actor is holding a glass in the two-shot, then in the closeup, he or she should continue to hold the glass, it should be in the same hand, and the liquid in the glass should remain at the same level.

This may seem obvious, but remember that shots appearing back-to-back in the program may be recorded days or even weeks apart. For example, an actor may park a car in one location and then enter a building

hours later and miles away, **Figure 16-7.** Between the two shooting sessions, the clothing carried on hangers has changed.

Continuity of Action

You also need to ensure that action is repeated accurately from one shot to the next. In our demonstration picnic, for instance, the man puts down his soda bottle, points off screen, and talks about a squall over the ocean.

Now suppose the editor wants to use a wider shot of his warning about the squall. The problem is that, in the performer's first shot, he says the line *after* he puts down the bottle. But when he repeats the action for his next angle, he points offscreen with his soda while he says the line and never puts the bottle down, **Figure 16-8.**

The problem arises because the next shot starts with the bottle already on the bench, **Figure 16-9.** If the editor cuts from the closeup to the two-shot, the bottle will jump from the man's hand to the bench.

But since the alert director has shot an insert of the bottle being set down on the bench, **Figure 16-10,** the editor can use it to cover the mistake.

Figure 16-7.
Since the first shot shows the light shirt on the outside…

the same shirt must be outside in the next shot.

Styles of Coverage

Although most directors have their own working methods, general approaches to ensuring full coverage fall into three broad types: *classical*, *contemporary*, and *personal*.

Classical coverage

In Hollywood before about 1960, it was standard practice to record a scene like this:

Notice several things about this classical approach to coverage. Starting with a wide view, it gradually moves closer and closer to the characters. The complete scene is recorded at least five times, offering the editor a wide choice of shots. Finally, the pairs of over-the-shoulder two-shots and closeups are symmetrical, in that they are almost mirror-images of one another.

Classical coverage. A— Establishing shot B— Master shot. C— Over the shoulder CU of her.
D— Over the shoulder CU of him. E— CU of her. F— CU of him.

1. *Establishing shot,* **A.** Usually a wide shot including much of the location (restaurant, bedroom, campfire, etc.) to orient the audience and establish the positions of the performers.
2. *Master shot,* **B.** Usually somewhat closer than the establishing shot, but still including all the principal performers and all the action and dialogue.
3. *Over-the-shoulder two-shot* favoring one character, **C.** This angle moves closer but still holds more than one person,
4. *Over-the-shoulder two-shot* favoring the other character, **D.** This angle is the reverse of the other one,
5. *Closeup of one character,* **E.** Closer now, and only one person on screen.
6. *Closeup of the other character,* **F.** The reverse of its predecessor.

Keep in mind that this example demonstrates classical coverage in its fullest and most conventional form. In actuality, many Hollywood directors omitted some of these angles and covered only parts of the action from each of the angles that they did use. Some directors, like John Ford and Alfred Hitchcock, shot very little extra material, to force editors to cut the film the way the director envisioned it. Others, like George Stevens, often shot many more angles than they could use, to allow themselves the greatest possible freedom in editing.

Contemporary coverage

Today, the establishing and master shots are sometimes omitted, or at least combined. In these wide shots, the actors may begin the scenes with the opening lines, then jump directly to the closing ones, knowing that the remainder will be captured by other camera setups. The following photos present

Contemporary coverage.

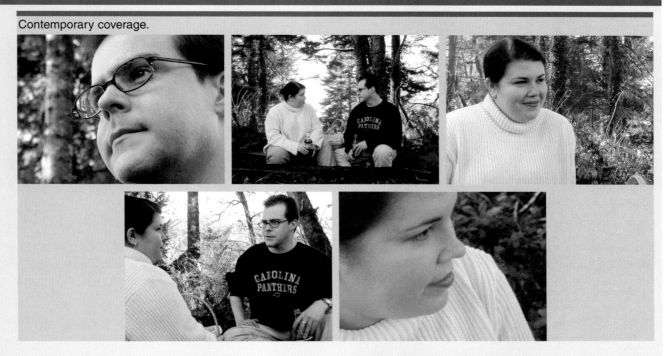

an approximation of the same scene shot in contemporary style. Notice that the angles are not symmetrically opposed and that the coverage tends toward tighter angles for the small video screen.

Personal coverage

In the personal style typical of commercials and music videos, each part of the action is treated separately and composed without much regard to a formal plan. (Notice that screen direction is reversed in the third and fifth shots.)

Even with the most personal style, however, an astute director will give the editor options by shooting at least some material from multiple angles and by overlapping action from shot to shot.

Personal-style coverage will often not show a formal pattern. (Sue Stinson)

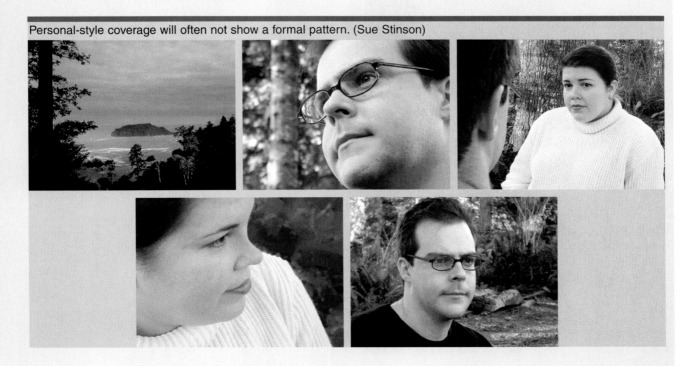

Figure 16-8.
He sets down the bottle before he says his line.

He gestures with the bottle as he says the line.

Figure 16-9.
The bottle is already down when the next shot begins.

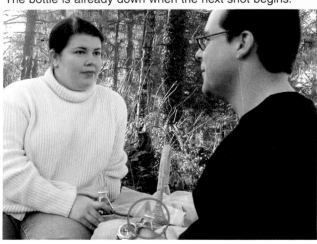

Now we have seen the cutaway of the bottle used for two different reasons: first to cover the omission of the line about the squall and then to conceal the action mismatch between two other shots.

Continuity of Direction

The third and final consistency is continuity of direction. It is called **screen direction** because actors' looks and movements are measured by reference to the borders of the screen. Although direction is just one of three principal types of continuity (along with information and action), it is such a large, complex, and important subject that it deserves a more extensive discussion.

Managing Screen Direction

Screen direction is the concept that people and objects on *screen* should usually point in a consistent *direction*. This means that they should aim more or less at the same edge of the frame (usually left or right) from one shot to the next, until either the sequence (scene or continuous action) ends, or the director indicates a purposeful change in screen direction. **Figure 16-11** illustrates a mistake in screen direction.

In **Figure 16-12**, the screen direction is consistent.

Figure 16-10.
HE: I don't like the looks of that squall coming in.

You'd better finish up your soda.

Figure 16-11.
A two-shot establishes the screen direction. The woman on the left looks to the right in her closeup, but the second woman also looks screen right, when she should look left.

Figure 16-12.
Now the second woman's closeup matches her direction in the two-shot.

The Importance of Consistent Direction

It is important to maintain screen direction for two reasons. First, whenever you present a new subject, your viewers respond by establishing their basic point of view: where they "are" in relation to the scene. They do this automatically and without thinking about it.

As long as people and objects on screen continue to face approximately the same direction, viewers do not have to make the subconscious effort to reorient themselves. But if someone suddenly switches screen direction, viewers are forced to mentally relocate themselves to match. In Figure 16-11, for example, the viewpoint suddenly jumps to the opposite side of the bench. Though viewers can easily figure out that the second woman has not really moved, the brief effort required to do so diverts their attention from the content of the program and reminds them that it is only a video, rather than reality.

Another reason for maintaining screen direction is to enhance the illusion that an action is unfolding continuously in real time,

instead of in numerous separate shots. Finally, assigning different screen directions to different actions allows you to alternate between them without confusing the audience.

Keep in mind that screen direction is only a convention, and that it can be successfully broken when you have a specific need to do so.

The Power of the Frame

Screen direction can be confusing because you must establish and maintain it in the real world, where you are shooting your program. But screen direction is not determined by events in the actual world. *It exists only in relation to the frame around the image.* To see how this works, study Figure 16-14, in which a subject walks around three sides of a house.

Notice that in the real world, the subject walks in three different directions: south, then east, then north (as shown in the composite image, **Figure 16-13**).

In the video world, however, she never changes direction, always moving from screen-left to screen-right. See **Figure 16-14.**

Figure 16-13.
In the real world, the subject walks in three different directions.

But if the sequence includes an angle from the point of view of the man on the front stoop, the screen direction must be temporarily reversed, as shown in **Figure 16-15,** even though the subject follows exactly the same route in the real world.

In short, screen direction has nothing to do with the action itself and everything to do with the viewpoint of the camera.

There are three types of screen direction: look, movement, and convention.

● *Look* means that actors remaining in one place face in the same direction from shot to shot.
● *Movement* means that moving actors and objects like vehicles always go across the screen in more or less the same direction, from shot to shot.
● *Convention* means that subjects face and/or move either toward the left or toward the right in accordance with the conventions established by maps.
We will examine each type, in turn.

Screen Direction: Look

When two people are speaking to each another, good screen direction calls for one person to face one side of the screen and the other person to face the opposite side. **Figure 16-16** illustrates correct screen direction looks.

Note that screen direction does not have to be exactly identical from shot to shot, as long as the subject is oriented more-or-less toward the same screen edge. Note, too, that the subject is positioned toward the screen edge opposite the direction of the person's look.

Figure 16-14.
In all camera setups, the screen direction remains left to right.

Figure 16-15.
Basic left-right screen direction.

Shot from the man's point of view reverses screen direction.

The basic screen direction resumes.

Figure 16-16.
From almost full front to 3/4 rear, all these angles maintain the same screen direction.

Screen direction is often preserved even when the subjects are not together. In a telephone sequence, for example, it is customary for one caller to face screen right and the other screen left. As you cut back and forth between the two, the opposing screen directions reinforce the idea that the two people are talking to each other, **Figure 16-17.**

It is also common to divide the screen with a partial wipe and show both callers at once, **Figure 16-18.**

You can also use screen direction to indicate that subjects are *not* related. For example, suppose you show a disk jockey offering prizes for the first person who calls in. The following shots show two different callers responding, as in **Figure 16-19.**

Notice that this split screen contains exactly the same shots as the previous example. But because the callers are facing in opposite directions, it is clear that they are not talking to each other.

Screen Direction: Movement

When movement of a subject continues through several shots, the screen direction should be essentially the same in every shot, **Figure 16-20.**

Frequently, you will need to manage the screen directions of more than one subject at a time. In doing so, you help the audience remember who is who in a sequence. You can also use screen direction to show what type of action you are presenting.

Figure 16-18.
Split-screen conversation between two subjects.

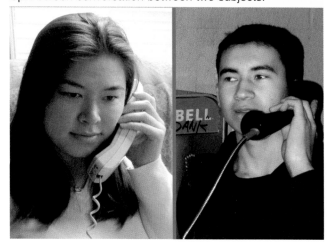

Figure 16-17.
Opposing screen directions...

of subjects speaking to each other.

Figure 16-19.
A split screen showing two different phone conversations.

Parallel movement

When two subjects start at the same point and head for a common destination, you keep the screen directions of both subjects the same, **Figure 16-21.**

Opposing movement

When subjects are moving simultaneously, but toward different destinations, their screen directions are opposite, **Figure 16-22.**

Divergence

You can also use opposing screen directions to indicate that two people are starting from the same point and heading for different destinations.

Figure 16-20.
Shot-to-shot screen direction maintained.

Figure 16-21.
When one subject is following another, their screen directions are the same.

Figure 16-22.
When subjects are headed for different destinations, their screen directions are opposite.

Random movement

You can use screen direction to indicate that a succession of shots is not a continuous action. To do this, you purposely vary screen direction so it shows no pattern at all. **Figure 16-23** shows the subject headed in different directions, as if to present an anthology of her activities.

It helps, of course that the backgrounds and costumes are different, as well.

Screen Direction: Convention

Finally, some screen directions are set by convention. As noted in the sidebar, *Scenes in Automobiles*, a car traveling from New York to California is established as moving from right to left because on a map, convention places New York to the right of California. See **Figure 16-24**.

For the same reason, a person watching a sunset will often face screen left because left is the "west" side of the screen.

Figure 16-24.
Convention dictates some screen directions: a car traveling westward should move from right to left.

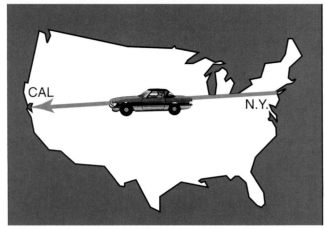

Figure 16-23.
A complete lack of consistent screen direction says clearly that the shots are not continuous.

Scenes in Automobiles

Shots made inside automobiles follow special screen direction conventions because movie makers have no choice. If you shoot the driver from the passenger side, the performer will face screen right. The passenger, shot from the driver's point of view, will face screen left.

If you establish that a car is headed from New York to California, convention dictates that it travel from screen right ("east") to screen left ("west"). By the conventions of normal screen direction, that would make the driver and the passenger travel in opposite screen directions and the driver would be moving in the opposite screen direction from the car. However, since viewers have ridden in cars, they recognize the passenger's viewpoint of the driver, and are able to ignore the apparent violations of screen direction.

Controlling Screen Direction

To create and maintain a screen direction, use the concept of the **action line**, an imaginary line drawn to divide the camera from the subject(s). To see how this works, study the camera ground plan in **Figure 16-25**, for the walk around the cottage presented earlier. The action line is represented as an arc between the subjects and camera setups A, B, and C.

As long as subjects and camera remain on opposite sides of the action line, the screen direction will remain consistent, **Figure 16-26**.

But if the camera crosses the action line, screen direction will be reversed. From camera setups D and E, the subject reverses screen direction, **Figure 16-27**.

Of course, there are situations in which you *want* to reverse screen direction. As noted earlier, the man watching from the front stoop of the house would see the walker from the other side of the action line. For this reason, a shot from his point of view would correctly reverse screen direction, **Figure 16-28**.

Changing Screen Direction

It is neither possible nor desirable to continue a screen direction indefinitely. When a sequence ends, the next sequence

Figure 16-25.
Ground plan showing camera setups and the action line.

Figure 16-26.
Consistent screen direction:
Shot A.

Shot B.

Shot C.

Figure 16-27.
Reversed screen directions.
Shot D.

Shot E.

Figure 16-28.

| Setup A sets the screen direction. | Setup B establishes the man looking. | Setup E represents his point of view. | Setup C resumes the original screen direction. |

will naturally start with its own new screen direction; but it may also be necessary to change direction within a single sequence. When you need to do this, you have four options.

On-screen change

One way is to show your subject changing direction in the middle of a shot, **Figure 16-29.** That establishes a new screen direction.

Neutral direction

A second way to soften a change in screen direction is by using a neutral screen direction (either toward or away from the camera), as you can see from **Figure 16-30.**

Figure 16-29.
The audience watches as the subject reverses screen direction.

Cutaway buffer

You can conceal a direction change by inserting a cutaway shot of something else between shots with different screen directions, **Figure 16-31.**

Empty frame

Finally, you can have the subject change direction while off the screen entirely. In the first shot, the subject leaves the frame. The camera holds on the empty screen for a moment, then we cut to a second shot in which the subject is moving in a different screen direction, **Figure 16-32.** This technique works equally well in reverse: cutting to an empty second shot, which the subject then enters.

For the smoothest possible transition, use both techniques at once: have the subject exit shot one, hold the empty shot, cut to empty shot two, have the subject enter the shot.

Continuity of action and direction are also the responsibility of the editor, and we will consider these topics further in Chapter 18, Editing Principles.

Staging for the Screen

Maintaining screen direction is just one part of a larger task: staging action for the screen. It has been said that half a director's

Figure 16-30.
A neutral screen direction softens the change from one direction to another.

Figure 16-31.

| The subject walks screen-left to screen-right. | Cutaway shot. | Subject has reversed screen direction. |

Figure 16-32

| The subject leaves the frame. | The empty frame holds a moment | then the subject is seen moving in the opposite screen direction. |

job is to put the camera in exactly the right place at the right time with the right lens pointed in the right direction—in short, to select the ideal camera setup for each shot. What is the most effective setup for each shot and how does the director know it? Partly by instinct—an artist's gift—and partly by practice.

Some would say that there is no such thing as an "ideal" or "right" camera angle. They argue that the "right" angle is whichever one works.

The craft of staging action for the camera is grounded in four basic principles concerning the special world on the screen:

1. The actual world is nothing more than raw material for the creation of the screen world.

2. The only unchangeable part of the screen world is the frame around it.

3. The dimension of depth in the screen world is controlled by the director.

4. The window on the screen world is small and the view is somewhat indistinct.

The world on the screen is discussed more fully in Chapters 3 and 4.

In short, the director does not record the real world, but creates an artificial world on a small, two-dimensional screen that is surrounded by a frame. No matter what you are shooting, your selection of camera angles should be guided by these four principles.

Creating a Screen Geography

1. The actual world is nothing more than raw material for the creation of the screen world. Whether you are shooting in a tiny room, on a large soundstage, or on location in an endless landscape, your actual surroundings are nothing more than raw material that you use to create screen images. In the real world, you can see where everything is and how it relates to everything else, but the audience watching the world on the screen cannot do that without your help. So your first job is to create a screen world geography that shows viewers where the action is taking place.

Depending on your needs, you may wish to show the whole environment, or you may want to reveal only enough of the locale to let your audience know where they are. Since **Figure 16-33A** was shot at an actual farmer's market, it can include a considerable amount of real-world space. But since the stall in **Figure 16-33B** is actually a small set erected on a quiet street, we see only enough to tell us what we are looking at.

If needed, you can combine two or more separate real-world places into a single screen environment. For example, the graveyard in **Figure 16-34** is actually many miles away from the church.

As these examples suggest, you create a screen world environment by controlling what you show (and how much of it) and how you combine multiple real-world environments into single screen locales.

Working within the Frame

2. The only unchangeable part of the screen world is the frame around it. The frame is by far the most powerful tool that a video director has to work with. It can hide anything that you do not want viewers to see. For example, **Figure 16-35B** seems to be the gloved hand of the burglar shown in **Figure 16-35A**. But as **Figure 16-35C** reveals, the sequence's inserts were actually shot with a different performer. The frame around shot B, with the gloved hand, hides the deception by framing off the second actor.

Figure 16-33.
Creating screen geography. A— On location at an actual farmer's market. B— Closer view of a vendor's stall.

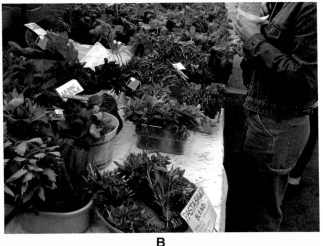

A

B

Figure 16-34.
By establishing the church in the first shot, the editor makes the graveyard shot seem to be in the same location. (Sue Stinson)

Figure 16-35.
The power of the frame to conceal. A—This shot is from the main burglar sequence. B—Inserts of the burglar's hand...
C—were shot later with a different performer.

A   B   C

By hiding the edges of sets or unwanted details of locations, the frame can also suggest that the world displayed on the screen continues indefinitely beyond the borders of the image, **Figure 16-36**. This, of course, is what makes the farmer's market stall set seem convincing.

3. The dimension of depth in the screen world is controlled by the director. We have repeatedly emphasized that depth in the world of the screen is only an illusion. Controlling this illusory third dimension is an important part of staging for the screen. Sometimes, you may wish to suppress the feeling of depth; but more often, you are trying to enhance it.

Enhancing depth

To strengthen the feeling of three-dimensional space, a director can use several strategies:

- Stage the action to move toward and away from the camera, rather than from side to side. That way, your subjects appear to move through the depth of the scene.

- Set up shots so that the camera looks diagonally at walls, roads, and other surfaces with parallel edges.
- Look for multiple planes parallel to the camera.
- Stage movement against stationary backgrounds, for contrast.
- Use wide-angle lenses. In conjunction with action staged to flow toward or away from the camera, wide lenses exaggerate apparent depth and enhance the sense of dynamic movement, **Figure 16-37**.

Suppressing depth

There are times when you want to reduce apparent depth instead of enlarging it; when you want to turn the action into a design painted on the flat surface of the screen, **Figure 16-38**. To do this, you reverse all the previous suggestions for enhancing depth: keep action parallel to the camera, avoid diagonals and converging lines, and omit foreground objects that would reveal the scale of the action. Above all, use telephoto

Figure 16-36.
Once the actual farmer's market has been established...

the close shots of the set seem to be part of it.

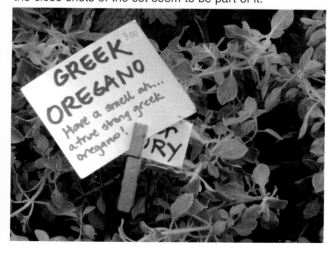

Figure 16-37.
To increase the sense of depth, the second image was taken closer to the sign, using a wider angle lens.

 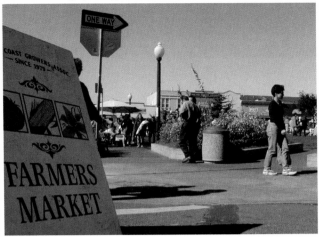

lens settings — the longer the better. They suppress the sense of apparent depth and emphasize that what the viewer is really looking at is a video painting with the screen as its canvas.

Scaling for the Video Screen

4. The window on the screen world is small and the view is somewhat indistinct. In staging action for the camera remember that video is a low-resolution medium that cannot capture fine details. Even digital and digital/high definition TV images are able to resolve less detail than 35 mm film images. Video is also intended for small screens, most of which are 36 inches or less, measured diagonally. (Video projection systems merely enlarge the images without improving them.)

Figure 16-38.
The telephoto lens squeezes the houses into a design on the picture plane.

There are strategies for combating the effects of low resolution and small screen size. To compensate for low resolution, work close to your subjects in order to make details more visible. To offset the loss of dynamic impact on a small screen, use lenses and stage action to emphasize depth. See **Figure 16-39**.

Remember that video's smaller scale does not always make it the "inferior" medium. Well-handled by a director who understands it, video has an intimate quality that welcomes viewers and makes them feel comfortable. This intimacy and comfort is part of the reason for the enormous psychological power of TV.

Moving the Camera

In considering staging for the screen, we have assumed that the camera remains essentially in one place for each shot. In actual video directing, that is often not the case, because the camera is almost always in motion to one extent or another. Sometimes the movement is as obvious as a dramatic crane shot that swoops down from high above the action. At other times, the movement may be confined to subtle panning and tilting. But even when the camera appears to be still, the operator is usually making small adjustments to keep the shot well-composed. (This technique is often called **correcting.**)

To make these continuous small corrections, a good camera operator never locks the movement controls on a tripod, even if the shot is supposed to be a fixed one.

Figure 16-39.

As soon as you have set the scene,

work close to your subjects.

Use wide angle lenses to enhance impact.

Camera movement is one of the director's most powerful and versatile tools. Used well, it can greatly enhance your programs. Used badly, it can consume valuable production time and resources while contributing little or nothing.

Moving shots, especially shots using a dolly, crane, or stabilizer, can be expensive and time-consuming to set up, rehearse, and execute.

Types of Camera Movement

There are several different types of camera movement, and each type creates a distinctive visual effect.

Rotation

With rotation, the camera support (tripod or dolly) remains in one place while the camera is pivoted on it, **Figure 16-40.** Horizontal rotation is called *panning* and vertical rotation is *tilting.*

Dollying

Dollying shifts both the camera and its support from one spot to another during the shot. Dollying in and out moves the camera into the action, while dollying laterally moves

the camera beside the action. Moving the camera up or down in an arc is called *booming*, while raising or lowering it on its central column is termed *pedestaling*. See **Figure 16-41.**

Except for "pan" and "tilt," there are no standard terms for camera movement. You will see "truck," "track," and "dolly" used for horizontal movement and "boom," "crane," and "pedestal" applied to vertical shifts.

Zooming

The term *zooming* refers to changing the lens focal length during the shot to show a wider angle with smaller subjects or a narrower angle with larger ones. Because a zoom out reveals more of the scene, it somewhat resembles a dolly out, and the opposite is true of a zoom in. But a zoom is not a true movement. Because zooms do not involve changing the position of the camera, they do not shift the

Figure 16-41.
Booming and dollying.

Figure 16-40.
Panning and tilting.

Pan

Tilt

point of view of the lens. Instead, they merely reduce or enlarge the same image, **Figure 16-42.**

The distinctions between rotations, moves, and zooms is not merely theoretical, because each type of movement produces a different visual effect. In professional production, dollying is often preferred to zooming, though zoom lenses are, of course, indispensable for real-time coverage of news and sports.

Composite movement

Though types of movement can be separated for discussion purposes, real-world videography typically mixes several types at once. For example, a crane designed for dollying back and forth and booming up and down is also fitted with a pan head so that the camcorder can rotate as well as change position. Mount a zoom lens on the camera supported by this system and you can combine all types of movement at once. Steadicams and remote-controlled jib arm booms also combine zooming with all forms of camera movement.

Today, directors tend to think less in terms of panning, tilting, and dollying. Instead, they simply want the camera to flow freely with the action. For clarity, we will continue to organize camera moves into separate types (rotate, dolly, and zoom), but keep in mind

Figure 16-42.
Zooming in progressively enlarges the center of the original image to fill the frame. (Sue Stinson)

that real-world videography is moving toward a fully integrated form of composite motion.

Reasons for Moving the Camera

Why move the camera at all? Why not compose the action in a succession of fixed shots and then edit them together? That approach is simpler, faster, and cheaper. There are several good reasons for camera movement. Though some people use it just because "it feels right for this shot," thoughtful directors understand what a moving camera can do and why they want to use it.

Traveling shots take extra time to set up and rehearse; they also tend to require more takes because they are more difficult to execute properly.

Moving to follow action

The most obvious reason for moving the camera is to follow action that is also in motion. For example, to keep a walking subject in a full shot, the camera has to dolly along beside her, **Figure 16-43.**

Moving to reveal information

Because the audience cannot see anything that is outside the frame, moving that frame, by moving the camera, delivers new information. For example, **Figure 16-44** shows two successive shots revealing that what looks like a statue is actually alive.

As an alternative, imagine that the camera frames the lower robes of the "statue" and then slowly tilts up to reveal the living eyes in its white face, **Figure 16-45.**

Although both approaches deliver the same information, the slow revelation by the moving camera is subtler and perhaps more effective.

In this example, the movement is a rotation: the camera tilts up to reveal the human eyes in the "statue's" face. When the movement is a dolly or crane shot, the new information may be about spatial relationships, which the camera reveals by rolling through the acting area.

A Typical Composite Movement

Here is a single shot that includes several different camera movements. As a truck pulls off a forest road and into a campground, the camera:

1. Dollies to the right to hold the truck in frame.
2. Dollies forward while booming downward.
3. Makes a right angle and continues forward and downward to the side of the truck.
4. Booms down to a low angle shot.
5. Dollies back to hold the subject as she gets out of the truck.
6. Pans with her as she walks away.

Notice how the foreground tree acts as a fixed reference that helps enhance the feeling of forward and downward movement.

The truck and camera movements. A—As the truck appears, the camera dollies right. B—At the end of the dolly, the tree appears. C— The camera dollies and booms down. D— The dolly/boom continues. E—The foreground tree enhances the sense of movement. F—The truck stops as the dolly/boom down continues... G—and ends framing the driver. H— The camera dollies right to hold the driver...I—and booms down to a worm's-eye angle. J— The camera dollies back while panning to hold the subject.

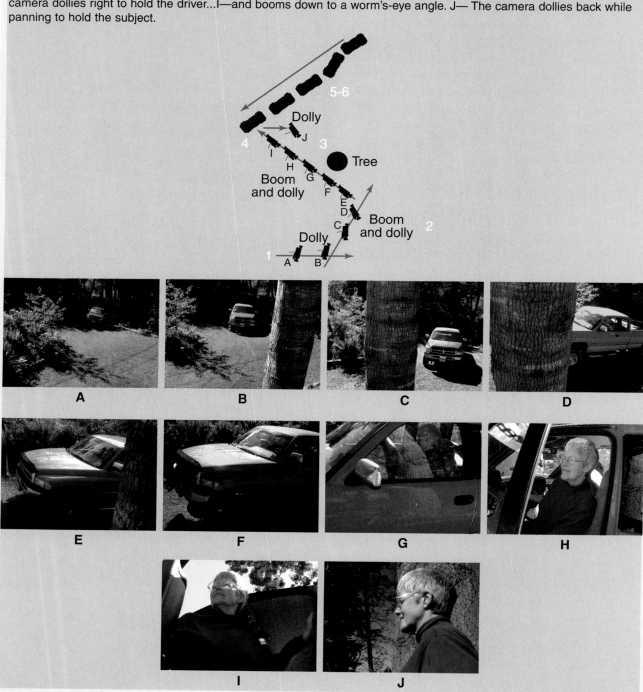

Figure 16-43.
By dollying along with a moving subject, the camera maintains the same perspective.

Figure 16-44.
Shot 1 establishes the "statue." (Sue Stinson)

Shot 2 shows her moving.

 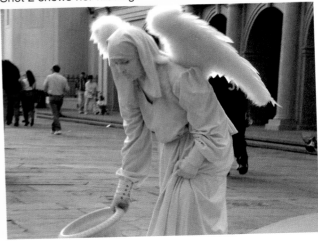

Figure 16-45.
The beginning of the tilt.

The end of the tilt.

Moving to emphasize depth

By dollying into or out of the action, the camera strengthens the feeling of a third dimension in the scene.

Moving to involve the viewer

Since the camera functions as the viewer's "eyes," it carries them with it into the center of the action, involving them kinetically in the story.

Moving to increase energy

By its very nature, movement is more dynamic than stillness. A good director knows when to keep the camera still and let the action move across and through it, and when to move with the action so that the background changes behind it.

Moving to enhance continuity

Above all, a moving shot strengthens the feeling that events are unfolding right before the audience's eyes. No matter how smoothly separate shots are cut together, they are still unconsciously perceived as assembled pieces. A continuous moving shot, however, feels like "the real thing."

Improvised Dollies

Almost any moving (or movable) object can be pressed into service as a camera dolly. Here are some suggestions.

Chairs

A thrift-shop wheelchair makes an excellent dolly because it is light, collapsible, and fitted with very large wheels. With larger cameras, the system is limited to low angles because the operator shoots sitting down. With an external LCD screen, however, you can hold the camera above your head for a more normal height.

Office chairs also make smooth-rolling dollies, especially on the hard, even floors of commercial buildings. The sound recorded during moving shots may not be usable, however, because the small wheels are noisy.

For this shot, the videographer was pulled along in a child's wagon!

People movers

When possible, take advantage of systems that do your moving for you. Airport beltways allow the camera to keep pace with subjects moving along side. Escalators are naturals for improvised crane shots. You may wish to follow a subject on the escalator, or else shoot down on a subject walking on a lower floor.

Some hotels, casinos, and even parking structures have glass-sided elevators that allow dramatic booming up or down. It is difficult to conceal the camera's

An available-light moving shot in a mall.

means of transport, however, because the passing floors interrupt the view.

Vehicles

Vehicles make good camera platforms. Big-budget productions use camera cars and trucks, as well as special suction-cup camera mounts; but you can obtain excellent shots out car windows by framing shots in an external viewfinder and using your arms as shock absorbers. To reduce vibrations that shake the image, make sure that the camcorder does not touch any part of the car.

The camera car dollies with the motorcyclist. (Sue Stinson)

Hand-held crane shots

Camera stabilizers permit hand-held moving shots that closely imitate the movements of large and expensive studio cranes.

For example, the previously described moving shot of a truck entering a campground was actually made using the steps of a forest cabin.

Remember: in the screen world, if it is not in the frame, it does not exist!

The "crane shot" was made with a hand-held camcorder.

Techniques for Moving the Camera

Like other aspects of directing and camera work, good camera moves are carefully planned and executed. The audience may be unaware of a well-designed move and yet unconsciously pleased and satisfied by it.

In professional productions, responsibility for camera moves may be shared among the director, the videographer, the camera operator, and often the chief of the dolly crew.

In planning camera movements, you need to consider composition, motivation, and speed.

Composition

A moving shot consists of three parts: before, during, and after the actual motion. Of these, the start and finish are especially important. In composing them, remember that both the beginning and ending frames should be pleasing compositions. When practical, the ending composition should be the stronger of the two. By following these suggestions, you give viewers a satisfying feeling of a beginning, middle, and end—of progress to a completion.

Motivation

Earlier, we identified a number of reasons (motivations) for moving the camera. Here, we use the word motivation in a special sense: the visible justification for making the move. The most common justification is subject movement. When performers walk across the screen and the camera starts moving to keep them in the frame, the audience takes that motion for granted. When the camera dollies forward to get into the center of the action, the viewer instinctively understands and accepts the move. The audience will often accept a move that lacks clear motivation, but the best moves justify themselves to the viewer.

Speed

A well-executed camera move accelerates and decelerates like a car that goes from 0 to 60 and then slows to a stop again. (Obviously, this does not apply to moves intended to parallel moving subjects.)

Finally, keep in mind that the best camera moves are unnoticed by the audience. They may be aware that their viewing position has changed, but they do not notice all the video craft required to change it.

The exceptions occur in programs like commercials and music videos, where dynamic camera moves are used purely for dramatic effect.

A reminder

This chapter has concentrated on the "cinematic" part of the video director's job: the design and execution of images and shots that succeed individually while providing suitable material for editing. As you think about these visual aspects of directing, remember the other half of the job, covered in Chapter 15: directing to communicate with the audience and to draw effective performances from the cast. Directing at the professional level requires all these skills, all operating together.

Technical Terms

Action line: An imaginary line separating camera and subject. Keeping the camera on its side of the line maintains screen direction.

Booming: Moving the entire camera up or down through a vertical arc (also *craning*).

Color shot: A view of the scene, or a detail of it, not directly part of the action.

Correcting: Making small continuous framing adjustments to maintain a good composition.

Cutaway: A shot other than, but related to, the main action.

Dollying: Moving the entire camera horizontally (also *trucking* and *tracking*).

Insert: A close shot of a detail of the action, often shot after the wider angles, for later *insertion* by the editor.

Panning: Pivoting the camera horizontally in place.

Pedestaling: Moving the camera up or down on its central support.

Protection shot: A shot taken to help fix potential problems with other shots.

Screen direction: The subjects' orientation (usually left or right) with respect to the borders of the screen.

Tilting: Pivoting the camera vertically in place.

Zooming: Changing the lens' angle of view to fill the frame with a smaller area (zooming in) or a larger area (zooming out). The effect is to apparently reduce or expand the size of subjects in the frame.

The Steadicam

Today, perhaps a majority of moving shots are made with a Steadicam, the industry standard in camera stabilizing systems. (Glidecam and other designs are also available.)

(Steadicam/Tiffen)

In this photo, Melanie Motiska, a professional Steadicam operator, demonstrates a large model designed for heavy weights like the Panaflex camera mounted on it. Steadicams are also available for video cameras ranging from HD broadcast units down to very small Mini-DV camcorders.

17 Editing Operations

Contents

About Editing Operations
The Craft of Editing
Organizing
Assembling
Enhancing
Synthesizing
Archiving

Objectives

After studying this chapter, you will be able to:

❏ Describe the craft of editing.
❏ Demonstrate the fundamental operations of editing.

About Editing Operations

Editing is the task of taking the materials recorded during production and transforming them into a finished audiovisual program. Like videography, simple editing can be performed by a beginner with almost no instruction; while at the professional level, editing is a rich and satisfying art that requires mastery of the many tasks, skills, and techniques of video postproduction. These tasks and techniques are the subject of this chapter.

The word editing is used interchangeably with "cutting," because movie editing, where the art developed, involves physically cutting pieces of film.

The Craft of Editing

Since this is the first of four chapters on editing, we should begin with an overview of the craft. At its simplest, video editing means placing one shot after another to create an organization that makes sense while it presents information or a story. At the next level of complexity, editing achieves that organization and presentation invisibly. The audience perceives the program as a simple continuous flow, without noticing that it is carefully built up, one piece at a time, of many separate units of picture and sound. At its most sophisticated, editing does more than organize information and present it invisibly. It does those jobs with *style*, with an emotional character that touches viewers' feelings as well as their minds.

A two-hour program may be a mosaic of many hundreds of individual pieces of video and audio.

Every one of a video's many pieces appears in the program as the result of an editorial decision. The editor has determined to use that particular element at that particular point and for that length of time. Multiply this three-part decision by the hundreds or thousands of elements in a professional program, and you can imagine how much artistic control is in the hands of the video editor.

To illustrate the number of choices required for even the simplest edit, look at **Figure 17-1**, which shows the raw materials for a typical sequence.

Should the editor begin with an establishing shot, then move to a two-shot, as in **Figure 17-2**?

Perhaps the first shot should establish Subject A before revealing the whole scene, as in **Figure 17-3**.

Which choice is right? Either one, depending on the program's needs at that point. In fact, there are 20 different ways to

Figure 17-1.

Master shot

Two-shot favoring A.

Two-shot favoring B.

Closeup A.

Closeup B.

Figure 17-2.
Master shot.

Two-shot favoring A.

Figure 17-3.
Closeup A.

Master shot.

select the first two shots in this sequence. How do you decide, then? Ultimately, you do it by an instinct for the right thing at the right time. At its highest level, editing is an art that cannot be fully described.

Like all arts, however, it is created through craft. The craft of editing consists of the *operations* of postproduction and the *principles* that guide them. The editing operations discussed in this chapter are the things that you do to create a program. Editing principles (covered in Chapter 18) are your *reasons* for doing those things. If you master these editing operations and principles you will command the craft, and once you have mastered the craft you are ready to practice the art.

Video editing is part of a creative process that includes writing and directing. Since editors are dependent on their directors for competent footage, we will occasionally look back at the director's job of recording appropriate raw material for editing.

In editing as in directing, many people evolve through three stages:

- Beginners often record material without planning the shooting and without modifying the raw footage. The result is called "home movies."

- Experienced amateurs record material from selected viewpoints and cut out the mistakes and repetitions in the footage.

- Professionals create and record material in short, well-planned pieces and assemble programs by selecting and sequencing those pieces.

To put it another way, amateur video editing tends to be *subtractive*, while professional editing is *additive*. In order to understand the essential nature of true editing, you need to understand the fundamental difference between the subtractive and additive approaches.

Subtractive Editing

Subtractive editing means removing elements from a shooting session by copying the tape while omitting the unwanted parts. Editing subtractively resembles the way you might organize a folder of still photos for mounting in an album: first, you discard the obvious mistakes; then you remove duplicate or near-duplicate shots. Removing the obvious mistakes improves the look of the album page and cutting duplicate shots makes it more interesting. For the same reasons, videos created by subtractive editing are at least less boring than raw, unedited footage.

The problem is that a video is not an album of pictures that happen to move, but a presentation of actions and/or ideas with a beginning, middle, and end — in short, with a continuity. Since video shots are not always recorded in their intended sequence, showing them in their original order can deprive them of some of their meaning and much of their effect.

Additive Editing

Even when a video records real events like a vacation or family party, its component shots can often be taken out of shooting order and rearranged to make better sense or tell a more coherent story. Used in this way, shots become self-contained building blocks that can be selected and placed in any order to construct a program from the ground up. This is additive editing, **Figure 17-4.**

With **additive editing,** a video program starts as an absolute blank, like a canvas before an artist puts paint on it or a foundation slab before a house is constructed. On that empty tape (or blank computer timeline) the editor places pictures, sounds, graphics, titles, and effects one piece at a time, building up a structure from nothing until it becomes a complete program.

In fabricating your program, you are limited only by the availability of material. You can ignore shots that you think unnecessary, arrange shots in whatever order you choose, repeat shots or pieces of them, and include material that was not originally shot for the program. In short, you can do anything you

Figure 17-4.
Like this empty timeline, an additive editing project begins with a perfect blank. (Adobe)

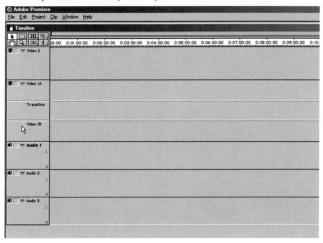

like, as long as you remember that you are not improving an existing program that was created in the camcorder. Instead, you are creating a *new* program, completely from scratch.

Without the key concept of additive editing, you can only make photo albums that move. But if you understand the basic idea that editing means creating something quite new, then you can master the five phases of postproduction.

Editing Phases

Here are the five major editing phases.

Organizing. First, the video shots, sound components, and other raw materials are catalogued and filed so that each separate piece can be located for use.

Assembling. The pieces of the program are chosen and copied onto an edit master in the proper order.

In computer-based nonlinear editing applications, the "edit master" may be a timeline metaphor on a computer screen, and the final assembling may not take place until the program is finished.

Enhancing. The selected picture and sound elements are modified, where necessary, to improve their quality or adjust their effect.

Synthesizing. The separate layers of material (for instance, live action and graphic visuals, plus production sound, sound effects, and music) are blended together and

Subtractive and Additive Editing

Here are sequences from two videos shot when the famous Budweiser Clydesdales visited the town of McKinley. Both programs were constructed from essentially the same raw footage.

Subtractive editing

The first program was edited subtractively. Although two near-duplicate shots have been cut, the remaining footage is presented in the order shot. Notice that the effect is repetitive, and arbitrary changes of screen direction give the program a choppy look.

Editing subtractively means cutting bad or repetitive shots.

Additive editing

The second video was created by additive editing. This opening sequence was built shot by shot to introduce the team, identify their sponsor, and establish the locale. Notice that screen direction is changed by cutting in a head-on shot of two horses before reversing the orientation of the team in the final shots.

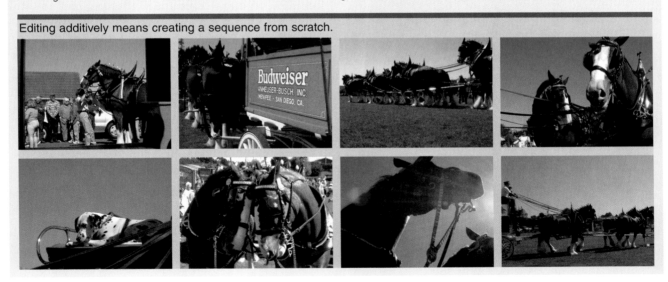

Editing additively means creating a sequence from scratch.

the shots and sequences are linked by transitions to create a single, seamless program.

Archiving. Finally, the finished video is stored on tape or disk, **Figure 17-5**.

In traditional linear editing, the archival "master tape" is built, shot-by-shot, as a result of the assembly process.

We will look at each operation in detail. Though we must examine them one at a time, keep in mind that a video editor typically works on several of these operations at once. Remember too that "video" is the general term for electronic motion pictures, so that the phrase "video postproduction" covers sound as well as image editing.

Figure 17-5.
Digital storage is preferable for archiving programs.

Figure 17-6.
Slate information is often written with a felt marker.

Prod. McKinley Boosters		
Date 10/01	Roll 06	
Dir. Adams	Cam. Jones	
Scene **27**	Shot **A**	Take **3**

Organizing

All video projects begin with a great deal of picture and sound material, and this material commonly suffers from several problems. Every shot is somewhere on a tape that may be an hour or more in length. The only way to reach a shot is by rolling its tape down to the place where that shot may be found. The fastest way to roll through a tape does not play visible picture or audible sound; so you cannot identify material by inspection as it goes by. When you do reach the right section of a tape, you often find various angles and takes of a shot that look quite similar. In short, materials to be edited can be time-consuming to locate and difficult to identify. For these reasons, it is useful to organize them systematically before you start to use them.

Organizing audiovisual materials involves *identifying*, *describing*, *locating*, and *managing* them.

Identifying

In most professional productions, shots are identified by a **slate** recorded at the start of each take and noted in a master copy of the script, **Figure 17-6.**

When a shot cannot be slated before it starts, an "end slate" is photographed afterward, with the slate held upside down to signal that it goes with the preceding shot instead of the following one.

Professional slates generally show the program title, director, and videographer — information that remains the same from shot to shot. The tape cassette in the camera is also identified, typically by a simple number. The individual shots are usually identified by code in which the scene is numbered, the shot is given a letter, and the take is numbered. (A *shot* is an uninterrupted length of audio/video footage from camera start to camera stop. A *take* is one attempt to record a shot, an attempt that is often repeated until the director is satisfied.) In this coding system, "27 A 3" translates, "scene 27, shot A, take 3." As you can see, a slate labels each program element, no matter how small, so that it can be catalogued and tracked.

In professional news, sports, and documentary programs, as well as in most amateur videos, shot-by-shot slates are not generally recorded during production. Instead, the editor identifies each shot in postproduction. Even when applied by the editor, the production slating system of sequence/shot/take ("27 A 3") is highly effective because it describes the piece of material as well as naming it. If you adopt a simpler slating system, the minimum identification should include the tape and a shot number. In this case, "2-27" indicates the 27th individual piece of footage (whether a shot or one take of a shot) on roll 2.

Describing

Typically, a shot description includes several items.

Angle: The image size and camera position, as "neutral angle medium shot" (or in brief form, "Neutral MS")."

Content: What the shot depicts, as "Tammy takes sip of coffee."

Slating by Timecode

Since digital camcorders display timecode in the viewfinder, it is easy to make a slate log by noting the starting address of each take. Typically, the person handling continuity keeps a database on a laptop computer, filling in the information shot-by-shot. The timecode is read off by the camera operator or transcribed from a reference monitor.

Keep in mind, however, that timecode contains no information whatever about shot content. Classic slating, by contrast, identifies the scene, setup, and take of each separate piece of material. For this reason, timecode information is a useful addition to, but not a good substitute for, a descriptive slating system.

All digital camcorder viewfinders can display timecode.

00:21:37:22

Quality: NG for no good, OK for acceptable, or perhaps B for best.

Notes: It is often helpful to add notes about the shot, such as "she smiles in this take only."

Spending the time to describe every program component before starting to edit can save far more time later in locating shots.

Locating

Other aids in finding shots are tape roll number, counter number, timecode address, and filename.

Roll number. If you are working with more than one cassette, you need to know which materials are on which roll.

Counter number. The control track on a videotape allows a playback VCR to display elapsed hours, minutes, and seconds, **Figure 17-7.** If you rewind the tape and zero the counter before logging your shots, you can obtain a position locator for each one.

Techniques for providing accurate counter addresses are covered in the chapter on linear editing.

Timecode address. All digital and some analog recording formats label every single frame of video with a unique code, based on the time elapsed from the first coded frame on the tape, **Figure 17-8.** Thus, a *timecode address* of 01:23:16:12 labels the twelfth frame of the sixteenth second of the 23rd minute of the second hour on the tape. (The first hour would read "00.")

Figure 17-7.
Counter numbers, displayed here on a monitor, show hours, minutes, and seconds, but not frames.

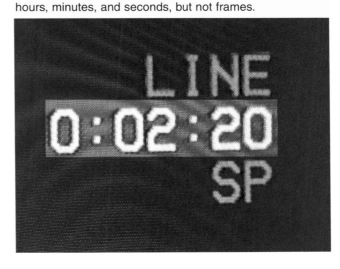

Figure 17-8.
Timecode addresses are arbitrary, because the initial recording can begin anywhere on a tape.

0	0	0	0
hours	minutes	seconds	frames

00:00:00:00

1	23	16	12
hours	minutes	seconds	frames

01:23:16:12

In some recording formats that use 60 minute tapes, the videographer can set the timecode to start at any hour, to match the number of the cassette. That way, tape number 3 can start with the timecode 03:00:00:01. This system builds the tape number right into each timecode address.

Filename. In digital editing, shot identification is often made while importing the program materials from tape to computer. As each shot is stored on a hard drive, it is given a unique *filename.* Though it is tempting to devise descriptive filenames (like "Tammy coffee") it is much better to file shots by slate number (like "27 A 3"). Names that seemed descriptive when first applied can grow very difficult to interpret days or weeks later. A slate number, however, refers you directly to the complete shot description in the shot list or database.

Some computer operating systems are not really designed to handle long filenames, even if their programs can do so by work-around methods. In these situations, long filenames can cause problems.

Managing

For any program that utilizes more than perhaps 25 pieces of raw footage, all the shot identification, description, and location information can be logged in a database like the simple model shown in **Figure 17-9.**

By working with a database, you can organize and search your program materials in any way you need. To create an inventory of each source tape, design a report form that sorts first by roll number and then by timecode address. To collect all the shots needed for a sequence, sort by sequence (or by slate number, if it begins with the sequence). If, for example, you are digitizing only selected takes for nonlinear editing, sort by tape roll and then use a database filter to display only the takes you wish to transfer.

Professional editing software has database features built in, so you can often log footage automatically as you import it to your computer. Most software, however, does not log every shot on a tape, but only the ones selected for transfer. Since you will often need to return to your source tapes for footage that you did not originally capture, it helps to have a full log of untransferred footage, too.

Admittedly, the identifying, describing, locating, and managing of your material is not a very exciting process; and you may be tempted to skimp on it or even omit it. But after you have spent a tedious hour in a frustrating search for a shot that you know exists but cannot locate, you will appreciate the importance of systematically organizing your editing components.

When you have organized your raw footage, you are ready to work with it. You start by assembling the pieces of your program.

Assembling

Even when it is well organized, unedited video footage is still just a collection of separate shots, takes, and pieces of audio. At its simplest level, editing means putting together these pieces of raw material to create a finished program. This assembly operation includes *selecting, sequencing, timing,* and *transferring* each individual shot.

For simplicity, we will treat each step individually, as if you selected all the shots in a sequence at once, then put all of them in order at once, and so forth. In actual practice, you are more likely to select, sequence, and time each shot in order before proceeding to the next shot.

In nonlinear compiling and archiving, you are able to work with all shots at once. A key difference between linear and nonlinear editing is that the nonlinear method permits you to work and rework materials anywhere in your program.

Figure 17-9.
A simple shot log database.

Raw Footage

The discussion that follows refers to the shots in a single sequence that shows the pouring and offering of a drink. (The three images in each shot represent the beginning, middle, and end of the shot content).

SLATE: 15 A 1: Two-shot favoring Frank (Take 1).

SLATE: 15 A 2: Two-shot favoring Frank (Take 2).

SLATE: 15 B 1:Two-shot favoring Jack.

SLATE: 15 C 2: Zoom in to closeup of Jack.

SLATE: 15 D 1: Birdseye insert.

SLATE: 15 E 1:High-angle insert.

Selecting

Since all professional projects start with far more footage than will appear in the finished program, the editor begins by picking the shots to be included and selecting the best take of each. The sidebar *Raw Footage* shows all the unedited shots in a demonstration sequence. This simple action of pouring and offering a drink has been covered by five separate shots:

- *Slate 15 A 1* and *Slate 15 A 2.* A two-shot favoring Frank, the pourer (Takes 1 and 2).
- *Slate 15 B 1.* A reverse two-shot favoring Jack.
- *Slate 15 C 1.* A medium shot of Jack that zooms to a closeup.
- *Slate 15 D 1.* An extremely high ("birdseye") insert of the drink being poured.

- *Slate 15 E 1.* A somewhat lower alternative insert of the drink being poured.

In reviewing this raw material, the editor notes several things:

- *Shots A, B,* and *C* all cover the entire action, so any one of them alone could deliver all the information in the sequence.
- Frank's two-shot offers two slightly different takes to choose from.
- Jack is covered in two completely different angles.
- The pouring insert has been shot in two different versions.

Accordingly, the first task is to decide which shots to use. In this case, the editor chooses *Shots 15 A 1, 15 B 1,* and *15 E 1.* See **Figures 17-10, 11,** and **12.**

Figure 17-10.
Shot 15 A Take 1 covers the action more completely.

Figure 17-11.
Shot 15 B balances the two-shot of 15 A, and is technically better than 15 C.

Figure 17-12.
Shot 15 E is a less-extreme angle than 15 D, and it covers more of the action.

Sequencing

With the preferred shots and takes chosen, the next task is to put them in order. On the camera tape, the insert of the pitcher and cup follows the other shots, **Figure 17-13.**

Now the editor makes the decision to move the insert to its proper place in the action, **Figure 17-14.**

Timing

In our example, the action is repeated three times, so the next task is to time each shot by assigning it just one part of the action and discarding the overlapping parts. Each shot is trimmed to its usable section by setting its in-point (start point) and out-point (end point).

Transferring

When you have selected and timed each shot, the final step in assembling the sequence is to transfer it. How you do this depends on which of two basic editing methods you are using:

Linear editing. If you are working in traditional mode, you transfer the program as you copy the selected portion of each shot, in order, to your assembly tape, as shown in **Figure 17-15.**

Nonlinear editing. If you are working on a computer, you create a virtual version of the program by transferring your selection to the timeline, **Figure 17-16.**

With either system, you inspect your work, make any changes that might be needed, and then repeat the whole process with the next sequence.

Enhancing

When you have assembled your images and sounds, you can enhance them to better suit the requirements of the program. Enhancing raw editing materials can mean *improving* them, *conforming* them, and/or *redesigning* them.

Figure 17-15.
Transferring footage in linear editing.

Figure 17-13.
The inserts were originally taped after the main shots.

Figure 17-14.
The insert is moved to its proper place in the action.

Figure 17-16.
Transferring footage in nonlinear editing.

Improving

Even in high-level professional production, some footage may not measure up to the quality standards of the program.

Video. A shot may have luminance and chrominance problems that make it too dark or too light or degraded by an unwanted color cast, **Figure 17-17.** Its white balance may be off, due to a mistake or to a camera movement from, say, a window-lit subject to a scene lit by incandescent lighting. Contrast is often a problem, especially in outdoor locations. Finally, framing may need improvement to recompose a shot or eliminate a visible microphone, **Figure 17-18.** With even simple color processors, you can improve many of these problems; with digital manipulation you can often fix all of them completely.

Audio. Audio problems include incorrect volume levels, as well as poor sound equalization, presence, and mike-to-subject distance. Sophisticated audio processors are available for linear editing; and with computer-based digital sound editing, you can make substantial enhancements.

Figure 17-17.
A—Original footage too dark.

B—Exposure corrected digitally. (Sue Stinson)

A

B

Figure 17-18.
A—Microphone in upper right part of frame.

B— Mike removed by digital cropping.

A

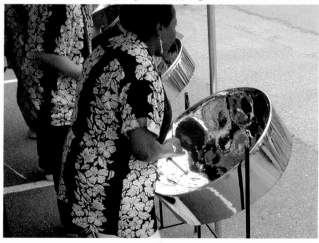

B

Even the simple software included with Mac or Windows operating systems or with computer sound cards can make respectable improvements in sound quality.

Conforming

Even when various components are all equally acceptable for quality, they may not always match. Frequently, you need to adjust video and audio to iron out differences between one piece and the next.

Video. Often, white balance is not consistent from shot to shot, especially when different setups are shot at different times of day, or even on separate days, **Figure 17-19**. When intercutting these shots, you tweak the color balance to conform their look.

Audio. Since every new camera angle demands a different microphone position, equalizing characteristics like distance, presence, and background noise is a constant chore.

Redesigning

Digital processing allows you to change picture and sound character as well as quality. Sometimes this involves computer-generated sounds and images; but more often it involves processing raw footage for editing.

Video. On the video side, you can adjust overall color to provide a sunset glow, create a nostalgic sepia monotone, or create a black and white program. You can apply slow- or fast-motion effects, or strobe. You can transform the image with mosaic and paint effects, and apply any of the dozens or even hundreds of image filters available for use in computer-based editing.

Audio. In the sound department, you can alter material to create any effect you choose.

Today, with digital nonlinear editing the new standard, even for amateur production, image and sound enhancement is so widespread that many editors process most of their shots and audio clips as a matter of routine.

Synthesizing

Synthesizing means fusing separate elements together to create a single, new product — in the editor's case, a video program.

To understand synthesizing, it helps to think of programs the way many computer editing applications represent them: as multilayered timelines, **Figure 17-20**.

A *timeline* is like a very long matrix, with the program's shots represented in order on

Figure 17-20.
Computer editing applications represent programs as multilayered timelines. (Adobe)

Figure 17-19.
Late afternoon light can change color temperature between one setup and the next.

Speeding or Slowing Action

Digital processing allows you to change the speed of a shot, not only to create obvious fast or slow motion, but also to make subtle adjustments. You can usually alter speed as much as 10 percent without making the shift noticeable (though you need to try different modifications and judge the results on a case-by-case basis).

The simplest reason for changing speed is to adjust the length of a shot for timing purposes, usually to fit an available slot in the program.

Slowing an action slightly can also lend it added significance by giving it greater visual weight. Be aware, however, that even high-quality digital processing can make slow motion effects look slightly jerky.

Also, in many nonlinear editing programs, small speed changes can produce unwanted visual artifacts, so be sure to render and screen the

Any shot can be stretched to fill the required time.

Shot too short to fit its slot

Shot expanded by slowing its speed

results to verify that these have not crept into the altered footage.

a horizontal axis. The program begins on the left and the timeline scrolls leftward as you move along it to the end, which appears on the right. The timeline is several levels high, usually with separate lines for two or more video streams, transitions, titles, and filters. The audio component may appear as a dozen or more separate tracks of production sound, background, effects, and music.

Integrating material horizontally, from moment to moment through the length of the program, may be called connecting; while blending the many levels of picture and sound may be thought of as layering.

Connecting

Creating a seamless horizontal flow from start to finish requires connecting shots to form sequences, sequences to form sections, and sections to form whole programs.

In short videos, the entire program may be a single section. Also, in fiction programs, sections are often called "acts," like the acts in theatrical dramas.

Typically, you select shots and choose their in- and out-points to make invisible edits, so that each sequence seems to the audience like a single presentation rather than a collection of individual pieces.

You connect sequences with transitions like fades, dissolves, wipes, and digital effects. The decisions you make in selecting

and timing the transitions between sequences will determine the coherence of the program as a whole.

Layering

Where connecting joins elements end-to-end, layering melds them from top to bottom. Even a simple program may involve working with several visual layers at once, including:

Composites. Pieces of different images may be combined into a single picture through color matting or other digital techniques.

Superimpositions. Two or more images may be layered so that all are visible at once.

In compositing, pieces of one image completely replace pieces of another. In superimposing, each is displayed in its entirety, but at partial intensity, so that both pictures are visible at the same time.

Multiple images. The screen may be divided into separate areas to display either one or more small images in a larger one ("picture-in-picture") or to create a mosaic of images. See **Figure 17-21.**

Titles. Titles are often layered over live action, or even vice versa, **Figure 17-22.**

Audio layering is often even more elaborate. Usually, the visual track presents only one image at a time, but a sophisticated audio track is almost always a mix of many elements, including dialogue, background effects, synched sound effects, and music.

Figure 17-21.
Multiple images. A—Picture-in-picture. B—Mosaic.

A

B

Figure 17-22.
Two versions of the same title.

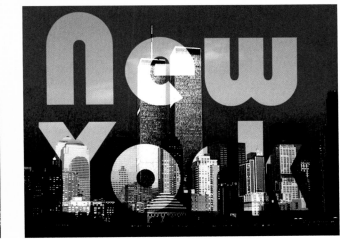

To permit more precise control, these components are usually divided into subcomponents. Often, the dialogue will include separate tracks for each speaker. Sound effects tracks may number two, four, or even more to permit multiple overlapping effects. Music may be distributed among multiple tracks to allow cross-fading between sections and stereo imaging.

Historically, video has been limited in its ability to synthesize program material out of multiple streams of picture and sound, but the development of digital nonlinear postproduction has offered editors almost limitless possibilities in integrating program components.

Archiving

The final task in editing a program is storing it in its finished form, so that it can be presented, duplicated, and preserved. The concept of archiving belongs exclusively to computer-based nonlinear editing. It does not apply to traditional linear editing, for two reasons. Because you record the final version of a linear project one shot at a time, you create a permanent master copy as you edit, instead of as a separate editing step. Also, archiving means making a permanent record. But since the signal on analog format videotape cannot be copied without quality loss, a truly permanent master is impossible to create in this medium.

In digital format, archiving is the essential last step in the postproduction process. Archiving involves the two steps of *rendering* and *storing*.

Rendering

In **rendering** a finished program, a computer takes the low-quality editing version that you have assembled and uses it as a blueprint for automatically creating a high-quality version. To save hard-drive space and editing time, some digital editing applications work with low resolution images and crudely rendered effects and titles. The resulting "work print" contains all the instructions necessary to make a duplicate that is exactly the same, except that the images, sounds, and effects are all full quality. Rendering is the process of creating this finished-quality copy, **Figure 17-23.**

Other editing software, designed to run on fast computers with large memories, can render programs in real time, as each subcomponent is completed.

Storing

The rendered version of a digital program is automatically stored on a hard drive; but that storage is only temporary. Digital video requires so much space that programs can quickly fill even very large arrays of hard drives.

On systems with smaller drive capacities, high-quality videos must be edited and archived in short sections. After each one is completed, the storage medium is cleared of its working elements and the next program section is loaded in.

To overcome this problem, the rendered program is exported for permanent storage on a high-capacity medium like tape or disk. Because of the long potential life of the program signal, the program is truly archived.

No medium is absolutely permanent. Digital tape signals fade like their analog cousins and disks are eventually degraded by handling. But as long as a complete signal can be read from a digital tape or disk, a perfect duplicate can be made. For this reason, well-maintained digital video libraries are indeed archives.

Operations and Principles

In this chapter on video editing operations, we have reviewed the fundamental editing procedures that are common to all programs. The next step is to see why we carry out these operations—what we are trying to achieve in editing. That is the subject of Chapter 18, *Editing Principles.*

Technical Terms

Additive editing: Creating a program from raw footage by starting with nothing and adding selected components.

Compositing: A digital editing process in which elements of one image replace elements of another image to create a combination of both.

Editing: Creating a video program from production footage and other raw materials.

Filename: The identification of an editing element as it is stored in a computer. Filenames may or may not be identical to timecode addresses or slate numbers.

Rendering: Creating a full-quality version of material previously edited in a lower quality form.

Slate: The identification assigned a take before shooting it.

Subtractive editing: Creating a program by removing redundant or poor-quality material from the original footage and leaving the remainder essentially as it was shot.

Timecode address: The unique identifying code number assigned to each frame (image) of video. Timecode is expressed in hours, minutes, seconds, and frames, counted from the point at which timecode recording is started.

Timeline: The graphic representation of a program as a matrix of video, audio, and computer-generated elements.

Figure 17-23.
In rendering your completed project, you can specify its video and audio parameters.

18 Editing Principles

CONTENTS
About Editing Principles
Continuity
Performance
Emphasis
Pace

Objectives

After studying this chapter, you will be able to:

- ❑ Connect shots with edits invisible to the audience.
- ❑ Adjust and improve actors' performances.
- ❑ Direct viewers' attention within a program.
- ❑ Present program materials at an appropriate pace.
- ❑ Elicit emotional responses from audiences.

About Editing Principles

Editing principles determine the qualities that you want in your finished programs. In effect, editing *operations* (covered in Chapter 17) are what you do; editing *principles* are what you want to achieve by doing it. Important editing principles include:

- *Continuity:* the information or story should be presented in a coherent order that the audience can follow.

- *Performance*: the people in the program should appear believable, and they should create the intended effect on the audience.

- *Emphasis:* information should be presented with an impact proportional to its importance, and the audience's attention should be directed to the most important aspects of the program.

- *Pace:* the program should flow briskly enough to maintain interest, but deliberately enough so that viewers can absorb the content.

While performance, emphasis, and pace are very important, the principle of continuity is absolutely essential: without it, your program cannot communicate adequately.

Continuity

Video is usually a linear form of communication. When telling a story, explaining an idea, teaching a skill, or presenting a person or place, you take the viewer through one thing after another, in a predetermined order from start to finish. The principle that governs the order of presentation is **continuity**; the art of organizing and sequencing program content so that it makes sense to the audience.

We are concerned here with the "classical" continuity popularized by Hollywood and now more or less standard. There are, however, other forms of visual narrative.

Methods of Organization

Continuity can be achieved through different methods of organization, depending on the type of program. These methods include *narrative*, *argument*, *association,* and *subjective*.

Narrative

Stories are usually organized in chronological order. Documentaries and training programs — especially about events, tasks, or processes — are also chronological. The program illustrated in **Figure 18-1**, for instance, shows the building of an Alpenlite fifth-wheel trailer from chassis to finished RV.

Argument

Programs intended to persuade viewers are typically organized by logical argument. For example, an argument for recycling is expressed in **Figure 18-2**.

Association

Programs (or program segments) intended to convey an impression of people, places, or events may be organized by association,

Figure 18-1.
Documentaries often use a narrative sequence. (Western Recreational Vehicles)

Figure 18-2.

We produce a lot of trash.

Discarded trash degrades the environment.

A degraded environment harms wildlife.

Disposing of trash is difficult.

We should recycle trash instead of disposing of it.

Recycled paper saves a lot of trees

with similar things grouped together. At the Humboldt County Kinetic Sculpture Race, for example, one sequence might associate the attempts, by several different extravagant vehicles, to climb the notorious "slippery slimy slope." See **Figure 18-3.**

Subjective

The most elusive form of thematic continuity is purely subjective: like a poet or a painter, the editor presents content in a structure that viewers can feel, even if they cannot clearly explain it. Subjective continuity

Figure 18-3.

Kinetic Sculpture Race vehicles must be human-powered.

is not illustrated here because it is impossible to suggest on the printed page.

In all its forms, continuity is evident at several levels of organization: the individual *shot*, the *sequence* made up of shots, and the *program* made up of sequences. In addition, longer programs are often divided into *acts*.

Shot-to-shot Continuity

You establish basic continuity at the shot level by putting shots in order. Returning to an example introduced in Chapter 16, **Figure 18-4** shows three shots in the order they were recorded on the camera tape.

Since the insert of pouring the drink is out of order, the editor establishes correct continuity by placing it between the pair of two-shots. See **Figure 18-5**.

Matching action

When inserting the closeup between the main shots, the editor has to match the movement in order to preserve the illusion that the audience is watching a single continuous view rather than three independent shots. In matching action, the editor often has three different options:

- *Start or end off screen.* The easiest method is to make the transition off screen, where the audience cannot tell whether or not the action matches. **Figure 18-6** shows the sequence starting closer on Frank, the pourer. Because the camera frames off the pitcher, viewers cannot see where it is when the insert begins.

- *Cut during a pause.* In **Figure 18-7,** the wide shot continues until the static moment when water is flowing into the cup, before the closeup begins. Matching is relatively easy because movement is minimal in both shots.

- *Cut during the movement.* Though this is the most difficult option, it is often the most effective, because the seemingly continuous motion helps sell the illusion that there is a single, uninterrupted view. See **Figure 18-8.**

Except in special circumstances, matching action is usually done with every shot in a continuous sequence.

It is not always necessary or even desirable to match action exactly, as we will see.

Figure 18-4.
The insert was originally shot out of order.

Figure 18-5.
The editor moves the insert to its proper place.

Figure 18-6.

Because the pitcher is not in the first shot...

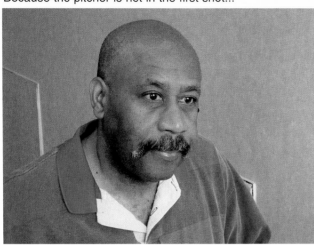

...its movement need not be perfectly matched.

Figure 18-7.

At the end of the first shot, the pitcher has already been tipped...

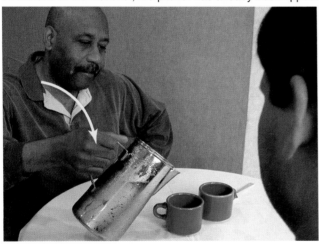

...so the insert begins after the movement has stopped.

Figure 18-8.

The pitcher is descending as...

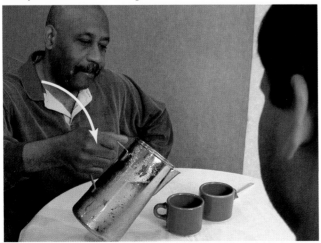

...the editor cuts to the insert.

Scenes and Sequences

The words *sequence* and *scene* can cause confusion because they are sometimes used interchangeably. Strictly speaking, though, sequences and scenes are not the same. A **scene** is a single action or process. A **sequence** is a single unit of fiction or nonfiction content. (The word "scene" itself can causes confusion because in stage plays, the word is used where movies use "sequence." Also, some discussions of films use "scene" as a synonym for "shot.")

A scene

A scene usually has the following characteristics: it consists of a small number of individual shots (typically fewer than ten) , the shots all cover (or at least relate to) one short piece of a larger action, and — though the shots may be made from different camera setups — they are all in a single area of the set or location.

An example

To demonstrate the difference between scene and sequence, imagine a short training program titled, *How to Make Your Own Firewood.*

The sequences. This process consists of three major parts; cutting down a tree, cutting the felled tree into firewood, and building a wood pile. In the edited training video, these parts will become separate sequences.

The scenes. The first sequence, *cutting down a tree,* breaks down into individual scenes: preparing the chain saw, selecting the tree, and felling the tree. Each scene covers a small part of the action that unfolds continuously in a single place and at a single time.

The shots. The first of these scenes, *preparing the chain saw,* is made up, in turn, of several individual shots.

Filling the fuel tank.

Adding chain oil.

Setting the choke.

Checking chain tension.

A sequence

A sequence often consists of several separate scenes, all of them related so that they build a continuous action; a sequence will often (but not always) end with a transition (like a dissolve or wipe) to the new sequence that follows.

Production vs editing

Another difference is that scenes are units of organization used during production, while sequences are created during the process of editing.

Note that camera slates carry scene numbers rather than sequence numbers. (Sequences are not identified by number or letter.) So, "27A3" on a slate identifies the third take of shot A in *scene 27.*

Maintaining screen direction

In addition to seeming uninterrupted, continuing action needs to maintain a consistent screen direction. If the director has done a good job, the raw shots in a sequence will have their screen direction already established.

Screen direction is covered in Chapter 16, Directing for Form.

If there are inconsistencies, you will often want to remove them. To do this, you have three available methods:

- *Use only correct shots.* If you can cover all the action adequately without the incorrectly oriented shots, simply omit them from the sequence.
- *Insert cutaways.* If you must use an incorrect screen direction, precede it with a shot that does not show the action. **Figure 18-9** shows two mismatched shots.

By cutting away from the movement, you soften the fact that, when you return to it, the screen direction has changed. See **Figure 18-10.**

- *Flop the shot.* If you lack material for a cutaway, you can sometimes reverse the shot. With digital processing, it is simple to correct screen direction by reversing the left/right orientation of an image, **Figure 18-11.** Of course, reversing the shot will not work if details in it reveal that it is backward.

Editors often use the term "flopping" for reversing an image because in film this was accomplished by turning a strip of film over and copying it through its transparent backing. Today, the process is usually digital and is often called "flipping" instead.

Intentional mismatches

In narrative and other linear types of continuity, matching action and direction is usually important. But in **associative continuity**, when shots are linked only by theme (as they are in the kinetic sculpture

Figure 18-9.
In the second shot, the screen direction is reversed (and the cup is in the wrong hand).

 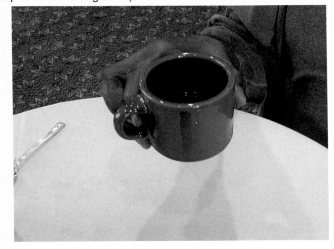

Figure 18-10.

The cutaway to the other subject...   softens the mismatched screen direction.

Figure 18-11.
Reversing the closeup of the cup.

race example), there is no need to match action or screen direction. In fact, it is often better to juxtapose shots with clearly different actions and directions, to emphasize their independence.

Sequence Continuity

Sequence continuity is the organization of all the shots in a sequence.

What is a sequence? Though there is no precise definition, a sequence may be thought of as an assembly of shots organized to present a single action, process, or idea.

For a fuller discussion of scenes and sequences, see the sidebar, One Action, Three Sequences. The continuity of a sequence may be linear, associative, or subjective.

Linear sequences

The majority of sequences employ **linear continuity,** with the shots lined up in temporal order for stories and training programs, and in logical order for editorial presentations.

In creating a linear sequence, the challenge is to decide how much detail to include. That is:

● How many sub-steps in the action do you need to select for showing?

● How much of each step should be shown?

The answers to these questions depend on the purpose of the sequence.

Timing each shot is addressed in the discussion of emphasis, later in this chapter.

Since the editorial decision process is easier to illustrate than to explain, consult the sidebar, *One Action, Three Sequences* for a demonstration.

Associative sequences

Sequences organized by theme can be more difficult to arrange because they lack the built-in constraints of chronological order. For this reason, it is helpful to discover some other organizing principle in the raw footage and use it to govern the sequence. The possibilities depend entirely on the material you have to work with, so here are some examples from a documentary about the weekly McKinley farmer's market:

● *Color*. Sequence the shots to begin with muted colors and gradually work up to bright, dramatic hues, **Figure 18-12.**

● *Subject*. Often, you can find several shots related by the fact that they contain similar subject matter — in this case, hats. See **Figure 18-13.**

● *Size*. An alternative approach is to begin with small subjects that grow in size as the sequence progresses, **Figure 18-14.**

As you can see, there is no "logical" reason to group shots by size or color or any other characteristic. The point is to give the audience a feeling, however unconscious, of coherence and order. Without consciously thinking about it, viewers generally want to feel that there is a purpose behind the program they are watching. A well-ordered sequence conveys that sense of purpose.

Subjective sequences

In specialized programs like certain music videos or very personal expressions, sequences may have no organizing principle other than the editor's purely subjective preferences. Though this is a perfectly legitimate approach to creating sequences, it can be difficult to handle because there are no organizational guidelines. The only test is,

Figure 18-12.
Shots associated by color.

does the result succeed — that is, does the intended audience find satisfaction in watching it and listening to it? If viewers sense an underlying coherence in a sequence, however obscure, they feel reassured that they are not just watching random footage.

Program Continuity

We have noted that the basic building block of a video is the individual shot; a number of shots that are related, ordered, and matched is a sequence. Sequences, in turn, are organized into complete programs.

This three-level organization, shot/sequence/program, is often enough for short works. Longer videos usually play better when the sequences are first combined into larger groups which, collectively, make up the program as a whole.

These larger groups of sequences have different names in different program types. The scripts of feature films and TV shows are typically

Figure 18-13.
Shots associated by subject matter.

Figure 18-14.
Shots associated by size.

(Sue Stinson)

organized into acts. Long nonfiction programs like documentaries, infomercials, and training videos are also constructed in multisequence groups that are referred to simply as parts or sections. Like individual shots in a sequence, these larger groups are also organized to create a coherent, effective continuity of presentation.

Parallel sequences

Often, separate sequences are presented concurrently, in alternating pieces. This technique is known as **parallel cutting** or cross cutting. Classic parallel cutting is as old as the movies:

● Our Heroine is tied to the railroad tracks. CUT TO:

● Our Hero racing to the rescue. CUT TO:

● The train rushing toward her. CUT TO...

...and so-on. In Chapter 4, *Video Time,* parallel cutting is illustrated by the shots repeated as **Figure 18-15.**

For simplicity, this example consists of single shots. However, each segment may actually consist of a short scene, say three or four shots of his struggle to climb up over the railing, then several more of her racing up flights of stairs to reach him, and so forth. Also, complex actions may involve intercutting three different sequences, or even more, at once.

To choose a more complex example, the conclusion of *Star Wars Episode I* intercuts

four separate actions as the princess, the boy, the Jedi knights, and the alien army lead separate attacks at the same time on their common enemy. Each visit to each of these actions consists of a full sequence made of many individual shots.

Acts

As noted previously, the sequences In longer programs are often grouped into larger units called acts. An **act** is a major division that is traditionally opened with a fade-in effect and closed with a fade-out.

In commercial television, act breaks are also punctuated by commercials.

In programs that are not constrained by TV time requirements, act divisions are flexible. Typically, an act will end for one or more reasons:

● The preceding group of sequences creates a cumulative effect on the audience (like the suspenseful effect of an elaborate robbery or escape).

● The audience needs a moment to relax and/or absorb the information in the previous group of sequences.

● The material that will follow is different in style or tone.

● The material that will follow is different in content, whether a distinctly new part of a story or a major subject change in an informational program.

Figure 18-15.
Two sequences presented through parallel cutting.

Transitions

The conventions of traditional continuity separate sequences and acts by transitions. A dissolve signals a change from one sequence to the next. A fade-out/fade-in marks the transition between acts. Today, however, it is common practice to speed up the pace by joining sequences with direct cuts. Act breaks, however, are usually still signaled by fades or dissolves, **Figure 18-16.**

With the availability of digital effects (DVEs), new transitions are beginning to acquire standardized meanings. A slow wipe, especially a horizontal one, can replace a fade-out/fade-in, creating a major pause without fully closing and reopening the program. (Of course, this alternative will not work if the program must stop for a commercial.)

Star Wars Episode I is also notable for using soft-edged horizontal wipes for transitions.

Special DVEs like flips, fly-ins, or hundreds of other choices, can signal a change in the program without indicating whether the audience should consider it minor (like a dissolve) or major (like a pair of fades).

Choosing and timing transitions is a subjective process that depends greatly on the taste of the editor.

Sound and Continuity

In this discussion of continuity, we have repeatedly mentioned audio. Of all the tools for creating continuity at the shot, sequence, and program levels, sound is by far the most powerful. Audio can be flexible, subtle,

Figure 18-16.
A fade-out. (Sue Stinson)

One Action; Three Sequences

Here is a single action edited into three very different sequences.

The action covers the process of connecting a travel trailer to its tow vehicle and driving off with it. The three sequences show how this action might be presented in three very different types of video program:

- *Instructional.* This is a training program on how to operate a trailer.

- *Promotional.* This video is designed to sell potential buyers on the delights of trailer travel and recreation. The objective is to show how easy it is to manage a fifth-wheel trailer (the kind that overlaps the pickup truck that tows it).

- *Dramatic.* This is the story of a woman who sets out to see the world on her own.

Instructional version

In this version, the objective is to show the steps in hitching up as clearly as possible. The shots detail mechanical and electrical hookup procedures.

Operating the jacks.

Hitching the trailer.

Latching the hitch.

Attaching the safety cable.

Plugging in the electrical cable.

Hand position for backing the rig.

evocative, easy to work with, and very inexpensive. For a more comprehensive treatment of audio's expressive capabilities, see Chapter 7, *Video Sound*.

Performance

After continuity, the next major editing principle involves performance, since almost all video programs involve people. Though you cannot transform an awkward amateur into an award winner, you can often rescue a poor performance, improve an adequate one, and fine-tune even an accomplished job of screen acting. Editing performance involves four major tasks:

- *Selecting* the best parts of the best shots.

- *Adjusting* the timing of dialogue and action to create sequences that move effectively.

Promotional version

The purpose of this version is to suggest that hitching up is a quick and easy process.

| Simply hitch the truck and trailer | ...and operate the electric switches | ...to retract the support jacks automatically | ...and drive away. |

Dramatic version

The goal of this version is suspense: can she succeed in the tricky business of mating truck and trailer?

The bystanders add suspense to the sequence.

- *Enhancing* the content by underlining, shading, or even changing the actors' original meanings.

- *Directing* viewers to the most important aspects of the performances.

To understand how these four processes shape performance, imagine a sequence in which Bob is desperate to buy a car and Bill is reluctant to lend him the down payment, **Figure 18-17.**

Selecting the Best Performance

Typically, each moment of an actor's performance is recorded more than once. The same action is usually shot from two or more different camera setups, and each shot may be repeated to provide multiple takes. Since no two shots are exactly identical, your first task is to select the best ones for your purposes.

The selection task is easy if one entire shot is better than the others, but this is not always the case. Sometimes, the best

Figure 18-17.
Bill and Bob at the used car lot.

Figure 18-18.
BOB (Take 1): Please lend me *that* money. I need the *money*, and I need it now!

performance is in separate pieces that are distributed among several setups and multiple takes of each one. When this happens, your task is to cement the best sections together with joints that are invisible to the audience. To demonstrate, imagine that an actor misreads a line, as in **Figure 18-18.**

The problem is that the actor was supposed to say, "I need the *cash*," in order to avoid repeating the word *money.* To correct the error, the director shot a second take, **Figure 18-19.**

In Take 2, the actor misread the *other* half of the speech, saying "the" money instead of "that" money. To make the entire speech read correctly, you need to join the first line in Take 1 to the second line in Take 2. If you butted two takes of the same angle together, the result would be an unacceptable jump cut, **Figure 18-20.**

Figure 18-19.
BOB (Take 2): Please lend me *the* money. I need the *cash*, and I need it now!

Figure 18-20.
Butting two similar shots results in a jump cut.

To avoid this problem, you have three options:

● Cut to a different angle of the performer.

● Cut to another actor in the scene.

● Provide an insert or a cutaway buffer shot between the two halves of the line.

Which option you choose depends on the materials available.

Changing angles

If the director has covered the actor from more then one angle, you can try for a matched cut, as in **Figure 18-21.**

Changing performers

If you lack another angle of the performer, you can sometimes substitute another actor in the scene, letting the performer's offscreen voice carry over the shot, as in **Figure 18-22.**

Using buffer shots

Another way to hide the join is by adding a **buffer shot**, an image of something completely different. There are two types of buffer shots: inserts and cutaways. An **insert** is a small detail of the action that excludes the actor, **Figure 18-23.**

A **cutaway** is an image outside the action, **Figure 18-24.**

All of these methods of selecting pieces of a performance require cutting from the first shot to another angle of the same performer, a shot of a different performer, or an insert or cutaway. These same techniques are also employed to adjust actors' performances and to control the pacing of sequences.

Controlling Performance Pace

With judicious editing, you can change the pace of an actor's performance or even

Figure 18-21.
BOB (Take 1): Please lend me that money.

BOB: (Take 2) I need the cash and I need it now!

Figure 18-22.
BOB (Take 1): Please lend me that money.

BOB (Voice over, from Take 2): I need the cash..

BOB (Take 1, cont.) ...and I need it now!

Figure 18-23.

BOB (Take 1): Please lend me that money.

BOB (Voice over, from Take 2): I need the cash..

BOB (Take 1, cont.) ...and I need it now!

Figure 18-24.

BOB (Take 1): Please lend me that money.

BOB (Voice over, from Take 2): I need the cash..

BOB (Take 1, cont.) ...and I need it now!

the speed of a whole sequence. Usually the goal is to shorten it.

You can do this if the available footage includes individual shots of each performer and/or over-the-shoulder two shots in which one actor's mouth is invisible to the camera.

Some actors tend to pause before and during their lines or business (actions) to make their responses appear more deeply felt; but these pauses slow down the sequence. If you can cut away from the pause, you can often shorten or omit it and speed up the scene. The techniques are the same as the ones demonstrated above.

In other situations, you may want to stretch a scene out rather than tighten it up. To do this, you could leave in the performers' pauses; but too much of this device can seem artificial. To lengthen a sequence more naturally, try adding performers' reaction shots or cutaways or both. As you can see from **Figure 18-25**, lengthening the sequence heightens the suspense: will Bill lend Bob the money or not?

Enhancing or Adding Meanings

Figure 18-25 uses Bill's reaction shots to build suspense. Notice that they also make him seem reluctant to lend the money. We can imply all kinds of performer feelings by the way we time the edits.

To use a different example, we can make Bob seem as reluctant to ask for a loan as Bill is to give it, **Figure 18-26.** By repeating the word "please" and inserting significant pauses, we seem to drag the request out of the borrower.

Now, suppose the director did not shoot Bill's reaction, but we do have that insert of his hand holding the money. By timing that insert, we can make the hand act for us. In **Figure 18-27,** Bob has no problem with giving up his cash.

In **Figure 18-28,** however, he is reluctant to part with his cash.

As a general rule, showing pauses *ahead of* actors' reactions makes them appear to be thinking. Since viewers know what is taking place in the sequence, they will generally supply the thoughts.

Figure 18-25.

BOB (Take 1): Please lend me that money.

BOB (Voice over, from Take 2): I need the cash..

BOB (Take 1, cont.) ...and I need it now!

Figure 18-26.

(A long pause as Bob looks at Bill.)

BOB: Please...

BOB (after another pause): Please lend me that money.

Figure 18-27.

BOB: Please lend me that money.

(Bill's hand thrusts the cash forward at once)

Figure 18-28.

BOB: Please lend me that money.

After a long hesitation...

Bill's hand thrusts the cash forward.

Conferring Importance

In fiction programs especially, one performer may be more important, dramatically, than other players in a sequence. You can increase a performer's prominence by selecting image size, assigning screen time, and giving him or her the critical moments in the scene.

Selecting image size

In many cases, sequences will be covered by more than one camera angle, for example, a medium (waist) shot and a closeup (head) shot. From the standpoint of viewer psychology, the bigger the image, the more impact it has; you can make key players more important by intercutting closer angles of them with wider shots of others. **Figure 18-29** makes Bill bigger and, therefore, more important.

Apportioning screen time

A second way to enhance a character's importance is by giving him or her more time on-screen. For example, in Figure 18-29, Bob has two shots to Bill's one. To strengthen Bill's status as the more important character, we could reverse the shot ratio, as in **Figure 18-30.**

By giving Bill most of the screen time, we make him the focus of the sequence, even though he does not say a word.

Figure 18-29

BOB: Please lend me that money.

BOB (Offscreen): I need the cash.

BOB: I need it right now!

Figure 18-30.

BOB: Please lend me that money.

BOB: (offscreen): I need the cash.

BOB: (offscreen): I need it right now!!

Giving the moment

In addition to image size and screen time, performers also gain importance from *when* they are on screen. Showing a character at a critical point may be called *giving him or her the moment*. **Figure 18-31** focuses our attention on Bob's emotions at getting his loan.

On the other hand, if Bill is the more important character, you can give the moment to him instead by putting him on screen as he makes up his mind, **Figure 18-32.**

Of the three methods of conferring importance on a performance, giving the screen to an actor at critical moments is perhaps the most powerful.

Emphasis

After continuity and performance, the next editing principle concerns emphasis. We have already seen how editors emphasize one aspect of video programs: actor performance. As a matter of fact, *all* aspects of movies are shaped by editorial emphasis. You emphasize something by making it more prominent, so that the audience pays more attention to it. In the hands of a skilled editor, controlling emphasis can be a sophisticated process; but the basic techniques are quite straight-

forward. Simply put, you highlight selected material by managing:

- *Content.* What you show.
- *Angle*: How you show it.
- *Timing*: How long you show it.
- *Shot order.* When you show it.
- *Reinforcement.* How you call attention to it with additional material.

In this discussion, we will assume that the director has supplied the editor with complete coverage of the sequence.

To illustrate these techniques for adding editorial emphasis, we will return to the sequence about hitching up a trailer. The essentials of the sequence are reviewed in **Figure 18-33.**

With the footage available, we can create several quite different sequences, simply by controlling the editorial emphasis. We do this by managing *content, angle, timing, shot order,* and *punctuation.*

Content

To illustrate controlling content, imagine that we decide we want to emphasize the support of the female bystander, while downplaying

---

Figure 18-31.
BOB: I need the cash. I need it right now!.

(His expression turns to delight as he looks down at...

Bill's hand holding the money out.)

Figure 18-32.
BOB: I need the cash.

BOB (offscreen): I need it right now!.

(BILL smiles, giving in, and looks down at...

his hand holding out the money.)

The Art of Montage

A **montage** is a quick succession of sounds and images designed to condense a lot of material into a brief amount of screen time. For example, a montage dramatizing a winning baseball season might be communicated in a rapid-fire succession of shots showing hitters, scoreboards, umpires signaling "safe!" and so on, intercut with repeated newspaper headlines announcing team wins, pages flying off a desk calendar, and shots of the team bus traveling to one game after another.

Dramatic effect

Most montages are not absolutely necessary for conveying information. After all, the content of a baseball montage could be fully communicated by a single insert of a newspaper headline, such as this one:

The essential information could be conveyed in a single shot.

The real purpose of a montage is drama: developing a sense of momentum and excitement from the kaleidoscope of images. By showing highlights of a story, a montage preserves the feeling of narrative, in highly condensed form.

Styles

The simplest montages are linear, with one quick shot after another filling the screen. More complex versions may display multiple images in several forms:

- Superimposed double or even triple exposures.
- Screen divided into several separate images.
- Changing background images composited behind a foreground character.

Superimposition and split screen are not usually employed together because the result might be too confusing to follow.

The role of sound

Sound is very important in montages for several reasons:

- Because audiences can process audio information very quickly, sound can be several layers deep.
- Compared to video, audio is easy and inexpensive (laying in the sound of a steam train is much easier than videotaping a real engine).
- Music, especially, can communicate nostalgia and many other feelings.

As a general strategy, you may wish to keep the visuals relatively simple, while mixing a complex and evocative composite sound track.

An example

Here is an example of a simple montage. For demonstration purposes, it progresses through only six stages, and contains just six elements. A real montage might run longer and contain many more layers of information. Our montage dramatizes the rise of the brilliant actor Laurence O'Livery from a callow youth to a revered icon of the theater. The montage contains six kinds of information:

1. A succession of theater programs that show O'Livery's rise from extra to superstar.

2. Calendar years changing constantly, to show the passage of time.

3. Titles of the plays our hero appears in.

4. Lines spoken by the great O'Livery,

5. Evocative music of each period.

6. Sound effects of applause.

1945 The Faceless Crowd

Solicitor	Craig Sassoon
Landlady	Walla Warfield
First Policeman	Jason Quigley
Second Policeman	Harlan Stander

The Crowd
Angela Aames, William Bassett, Charles Dark, Melissa Evans, George Grimes, Cedric Haddon, Mary Jones, Gwyneth Kalem, **Laurence O'Livery**, Michael Porter, Daryl Ransom, Gale Starr, Herschel Tannen, Gregory Wilson.

Lyceum Theatre Programme/The Faceless Crowd

ACTION: Flipping calendar pages show the years advancing.
VOICEOVER: Crowd noise
EFFECTS: Scattered applause
MUSIC: Big band

1950 Smedley Soldiers On

	with
Lady Landsdwone	Bernice Duprey
Lord Landsdowne	Guy Bainbridge
Rev. Cheadle	Jack Crammell
A. Hobo	Launce Gobbo
Parlor Maid	Fanny Pryce
Butler	**Laurence O'Livery**

Presented by arrangement with his Majesty's Theatre, Hammersmith. Grateful acknowledgement is made to the estate of Lord Wolverhampton for provision of the suits of armour appearing in Act II.

Kinghtsbridge Theatre Programme

ACTION: Flipping calendar pages show the years advancing.
VOICEOVER: You rang, Sir?
EFFECTS: Polite applause
MUSIC: Pop song.

1955 Weekend at Windemere

The Theatre Company, Ltd.
presents
Edward Maybridge and Vanessa Prawn
in
Weekend at Windemere
with
Cedrec Cubbins, George Brandt
and Laurence O'Livery as Freddie

ACTION: Flipping calendar pages show the years advancing.
VOICEOVER: Anyone for tennis?
EFFECTS: Strong applause
MUSIC: Do-wop pop song.

1960 A Love for the Ages

Selwyn and Selwyn
presents
A Love for the Ages
by
Hamish Korngold
starring
Laurency O'Livery   Angela Bredhan
with
Percy Adline
Maurice Rample

ACTION: Flipping calendar pages show the years advancing.
VOICEOVER: I love you, my darling!
EFFECTS: Very loud applause
MUSIC: Beach Boys song

1970 Hamlet

The Imperial Shakespeare Company
presents
Laurence O'Livery
in
*Hamlet
Prince of Denmark*
by
William Shakespeare

ACTION: Flipping calendar pages show the years advancing.
VOICEOVER: To be or not to be...
EFFECTS: Thunderous applause
MUSIC: Paul Simon song

1985 The Tempest

presents the
Laurence O'Livery
production of
The Tempest
starring
Laurence O'Livery
by
William Shakespeare

ACTION: Flipping calendar pages show the years advancing.
VOICEOVER: We are such stuff as dreams are made on...
EFFECTS: Distant, filtered applause
MUSIC: New Age/Celtic instrumental.

Notice how inexpensive this montage is to create. There is not a single shot of an actual play in progress.

Montage and video

Though popular up through the 1950s, montages almost disappeared for a few decades, partly because they went out of fashion and partly because the film laboratory work required was very expensive. But with digital editing, most software can create complex and effective montages for just the price of the editor's time.

Figure 18-33.
Hitching the trailer.

the skepticism of the male. The result might resemble **Figure 18-34**.

We have emphasized the response of the female bystander by replacing a piece of content: the original two-shot is now a closeup of her reaction.

Angle

To emphasize the difficulty of the process, we can use our control of camera angles. Up to now, shots of the trailer and truck hitch components mating have been made from neutral angles. By showing this action from the driver's point of view, we show how hard it is to line up the hitch, **Figure 18-35**.

Timing

The sequence still lacks suspense, because it all seems too cut-and-dried. By lengthening the first half of the sequence, **Figure 18-36,** we can build suspense before showing the successful hitch.

By adjusting content, camera angle, and timing, we have edited a tight, suspenseful sequence.

Now, suppose we decide to change the story slightly by showing that the woman never doubts her ability to hitch up the trailer. Since we have no footage that specifically shows this, we will make the change by simply altering the shot order.

Figure 18-34.
The female bystander gets an extra closeup.

Figure 18-35.
Her worried closeup emphasizes the difficulty.

Figure 18-36.
Adding shots helps build suspense.

Shot order

In most programs, events happen in chronological order. That means that the sooner something appears, the earlier it is in story time. Though we have no footage designed specifically to reveal the woman's inner confidence, we do have a shot of her reacting to the success of her efforts.

To make her seem confident from the start, all we need to do is move her reaction closer to the beginning of the sequence, **Figure 18-37.**

By showing her grin *before* she hitches the trailer, we inform viewers that she is confident of success.

Figure 18-37.
Changing shot order.

She grins *before* the two halves mate.

Reinforcement

Up to this point we have controlled emphasis by *selecting, timing,* and *positioning* shots. To add the final touch to our sequence, we can use editorial reinforcement. Reinforcement can take visual form. For example, we could have the hitch components mate in slow motion, to lengthen and emphasize the success of the operation. To enhance the effect, we can add further reinforcement with sound, **Figure 18-38.**

As the hitch halves mate in slow motion, we lay in the low, reverberating *clang* of a great iron door slamming shut. Though this effect is not realistic, it will be accepted by viewers because it is subjectively "right" for the feeling of the image.

Pace

After continuity, performance, and emphasis, the last major editing principle involves pace. Pace is the sense of progress, of forward movement, that the audience gets from a program. "Pace" is not identical to "speed," although speed is one of its main determiners. In fact, a very fast-moving program can still feel boring if it lacks the other two components of pace: variety and rhythm.

Of course, if the content is boring, it cannot be made interesting by adjusting its pace.

Delivering Content

The easiest way to evaluate the pace of a program is by seeing how well it delivers its content to the audience. If viewers miss important details, the pace is too fast. If content points are belabored after the viewers have already absorbed them, the pace is too slow. If viewers feel that they are getting the material while moving briskly forward, then the pace is about right.

Editing *pace* should not be confused with content *density*. How rapidly a subject is presented also depends on how much detail is included. See **Figure 18-39.** Suppose, for example, that you finish a how-to video on

Figure 18-38.
Reinforcing with sound.

Figure 18-39.
Good cooking programs deliver their content at a carefully measured pace.

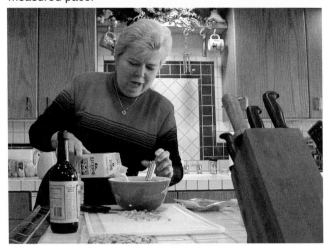

creating a dinner party with a cherry pie dessert. Depending on your needs, you could detail every step in baking the pie, or cover only the highlights of that process, or just show the finished pie being served.

Since content density is a function primarily of scripting, it lies outside a discussion of editing. Here, we are concerned with the pacing of the material that the editor is given to work with, whatever its density may be.

Because pacing is judged by the response of the viewers, you will want to consider your target audience in establishing a pace for a program. An elementary school class, a stockholders' meeting, and a classic car club respond to video programs in quite different ways.

The concept of the target audience is covered in Chapter 8, Program Development.

Content delivery is also determined by the type of program. Often, fiction programs are paced energetically so that audiences can follow the story but not catch all the enriching details on the first viewing. (The *Star Wars* episodes and the best Disney animated features are good examples.)

At the other extreme, training programs are paced quite deliberately to ensure that viewers absorb all the essential information. In the final analysis, evaluations of pace must be based on personal taste and experience. In effect, if it *feels* right, it *is* right. Though

variety and rhythm contribute to the sense of pace, the most important determiner is speed.

Speed

Speed may be expressed as the average length, in seconds, of the shots in a sequence. See **Figure 18-40.** Though there are no fixed rules about appropriate speed, here is a rough guide:

● One-half second per shot (120/minute) is quite fast.

● One second per shot (60/minute) is fast.

● Two-three seconds per shot (30-20/minute) is brisk.

● Four-six seconds per shot (15-10/minute) is moderate.

● Ten-fifteen seconds per shot (6-4/minute) is slow.

In nonfiction videos, shots typically average between three and ten seconds apiece. It should be emphasized that these figures are not rules, but only examples.

It is possible to have 30 single-frame shots per second of NTSC video (1,800 per minute) and this ultra-high-speed cutting can be used quite effectively, in short bursts. At the other extreme, some documentary programs include shots lasting a minute or more.

In the movie Rope, Alfred Hitchcock made an entire film out of shots lasting several minutes apiece.

The average speed of the shots in a sequence typically depends on the nature of

Figure 18-40.
Typical shot durations.

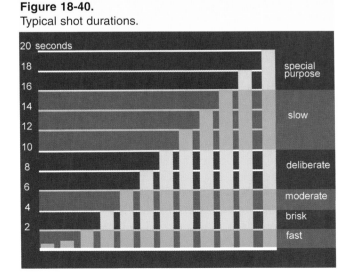

the subject matter. For instance, a fight or car chase will typically be cut together from very short shots. A business meeting or dinner conversation might consist of moderately long takes, and a languorous love scene might be built from individual pieces many seconds long. Alternatively, you can time your shots *against* the subject matter, presenting a chase in long, deliberate pieces to build suspense or cutting a love scene quickly to mirror its emotional intensity.

Variety

Read these sentences. They are similar. They are the same length. They are short. They are boring.

Shots are like sentences: even short ones grow boring if they are too similar, and long ones can become agonizing if they go on and on without relief. The solution to the problem is variety: mixing shots of varying lengths to avoid falling into repetitive patterns. In most programs, good editors achieve variety instinctively, that is, they do not consciously think, *"The two preceding shots are six and eight seconds long, respectively, so I will follow them with a short shot in order to achieve variety."* Instead, they rely on their feel for the rhythm of the sequence, while keeping the general goal of variety in mind as they work. In doing so, even experienced editors operate by a sort of successive approximation:

● Building a trial sequence.

● Evaluating the effect.

● Fine-tuning it if it seems to be working, *or*

● Discarding it and start over if it is not working.

The easiest way to achieve variety in shot lengths is by reviewing your work as you go and adjusting shot timing until you like the effect. When this style of cutting is successful, the result is like a path made of irregular flagstones: though it has no visible pattern, it feels like a coherent design.

Rhythm

But, sometimes, an editor wants a sequence to resemble a patterned brick walk instead of an informal path. Sometimes you want to time your shots to develop a clear and repetitive rhythm. See **Figure 18-41**.

Figure 18-41.
A sequence of rhythmic edits is like a patterned brick walkway.

Rhythm for contrast

Instead of varying shot length continually, you may want to group several long, slow shots, punctuate them with a group of very brief shots, then resume the pattern of lengthy shots. This is the classic western gunfight rhythm: slow cutting while the adversaries stalk each other; a hail of gunfire handled in very quick shots; then another slow passage of cat-and-mouse stalking.

Rhythm for drive

Another classic editing rhythm might be called "marching the prisoner." Imagine that, flanked by Imperial Troopers, our Hero is escorted from the battle cruiser's landing bay to the command center of the Admiral, deep within the giant mother ship. To achieve this sequence, the director has had the actors march through five different sets at exactly the same pace. Using the rhythmic footsteps of the troopers, the editor cuts four out of five shots to exactly the same length:

1. Landing bay: TROMP! TROMP! TROMP! TROMP!

2. Curved corridor: TROMP! TROMP! TROMP! TROMP!

3. Straight corridor: TROMP! TROMP! TROMP! TROMP!

4. Antechamber: TROMP! TROMP! TROMP! TROMP!

5. Command room where the Admiral is waiting: TROMP! TROMP! TROMP! TROMP! TROMP! TROMP! TROMP!

Notice the rhythm of the final shot, which contains three additional steps. The extra paces contribute a sense of closure to the sequence. Also, it consists of an odd number of steps (7), where the other shots contain even numbers (4 each). For psychological reasons that are not perfectly understood, a sequence often feels more powerful when it concludes on an odd number.

The two most common English verse forms are iambic pentameter with five beats per line:

> *Shall I compare thee to a Summer's day?*
> *Thou art more lovely and more temperate.*

and ballad measure with seven beats per line:

> *It looked extremely rocky for the*
>   *Mudville nine that day.*
> *The score stood four to two with but*
>   *one inning left to play.*

Rhythm for comedy

Comedy often relies on surprise, on the unexpected. Since rhythmic cutting sets up the expectation that it will be continued, an editor can help a joke by building rhythmically to the payoff and then suddenly breaking the pattern. For example, suppose that the storm trooper marching sequence was shot by a comic director like Mel Brooks. The edited result might resemble this:

1. TROMP! TROMP! TROMP! TROMP! Landing bay

2. TROMP! TROMP! TROMP! TROMP! Curved corridor

3. TROMP! TROMP! TROMP! TROMP! Straight corridor

4. TROMP! TROMP! TROMP... Whoa! Somehow, they are back in the landing bay.

Here, the editor sets up a strong, repetitive rhythm and then deliberately breaks it in order to reinforce the climax of the joke. If you study classic movie comedy, from Charlie Chaplin to the present, you will see how dependent it is on rhythmic editing.

Rhythm for montage

The sidebar called *The Art of Montage* explains how multiple images and sounds can be presented to dramatize events over time. Because montages are constructed in repetitive patterns, they are usually edited to strict rhythms set by musical underscoring. Occasionally, however, a montage may be purposely built without any discernible rhythm. For example, imagine a football game. If the story calls for one side to march triumphantly over the other, this might be expressed in a classic rhythmic montage. But if the game is fought to a messy, brutal scoreless tie, then the montage might be as formless and confusing as the game itself.

Cutting to music

Rhythmic cutting is widely used in matching visuals to music. The is usually done for music videos, and for sequences in other programs in which shots are linked by association rather than by chronological order. For instance, a succession of views of the Italian countryside might be edited to the lyrical rhythms of Vivaldi's *The Four Seasons*. A montage of New York City going about its complex daily business, **Figure 18-42,** could be cut to the rhythm of a modern jazz composition.

At its best, editing picture to music is like dancing: though you follow the basic beat, you do not match the music exactly, phrase for phrase and measure for measure. Instead, you maintain an organic collaboration between picture and sound. Handled this way, cutting to music can be the most satisfying kind of rhythmic editing.

The End Result

In this discussion of editing principles, we have considered continuity, performance, emphasis, and pace. There is more to the

Figure 18-42.
A New York street.

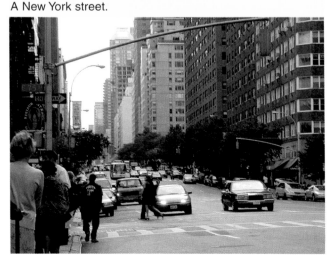

craft of editing, especially in subtle matters of tone, mood, and style. We have not addressed these matters directly because as an editor, you cannot do so either. Tone, mood, and style are not guiding principles but ultimate goals: they are what you will achieve through the way in which you handle *continuity, performance, emphasis,* and *pace.*

Technical Terms

Act: A major division of a program, typically ten or more minutes long, and divided from other acts by fade-out/fade-in transitions.

Associative continuity: A sequence of shots related by similarity of content.

Buffer shot: A shot placed between two others to conceal differences between them.

Continuity: The illusion that a video program is a single continuous piece.

Cutaway: A shot other than, but related to, the main action.

Insert: A closeup detail of the action.

Linear Continuity: A sequence of shots organized chronologically and/or logically.

Montage: A brief, multilayer passage of video and audio elements designed to present a large amount of information in highly condensed form.

Parallel cutting: Presenting two or more sequences at once by showing parts of one, then another, then the first again (or a third) and so-on.

Scene: A brief content component, usually recorded in several shots.

Sequence: A coherent assembly of shots.

Shot: A single recording, from camera start to stop.

Subjective continuity: A sequence organized according to the feelings of the director/editor, rather than by chronological or other objective criteria.

Another associative continuity sequence from the farmer's market.

19 Linear Editing

CONTENTS

About Linear Editing
A Linear Editing Setup
Editing Picture and Track
Transitions, Effects, and Titles

Objectives

After studying this chapter, you will be able to:

- ❑ Describe the difference between linear and nonlinear editing.
- ❑ Select and connect editing hardware components.
- ❑ Perform basic editing operations with picture and sound.
- ❑ Add digital visuals such as transitions and titles.

About Linear Editing

Linear editing is the name given to traditional tape-based video postproduction, to distinguish it from the "nonlinear" style of editing that uses materials stored in a computer. Tape-based editing is linear because you cannot jump instantly to any point in a videotape. To reach a desired spot from any starting place, you must roll through every shot between those two points. On complex projects with multiple source tapes, finding raw footage can be time-consuming.

Like the source tapes, the assembly tape containing the project being edited is also linear. To create it, you must begin by recording the opening shot in the program and then record all the rest of the shots in chronological order.

Two exceptions to this rule are the video insert and audio dub functions, which can add new material in the middle of previously edited footage.

In linear editing, you must perform all operations simultaneously. This means, for example, that you cannot add a dissolve later to a previously edited cut between shots. You cannot superimpose a title over a previously transferred shot. Everything you do to a piece of material must be performed simultaneously, as you transfer it to the assembly tape.

Linear editing, then, is s*equential*: you must assemble each shot in strict chronological order, and it is *concurrent*: you must create all the parts of the finished shot at the same time.

You can premix certain kinds of audio tracks before feeding the result to the assembly track.

Why Linear Editing?

In most postproduction today, computer-based nonlinear editing has replaced the traditional tape-based linear approach because of nonlinear editing's speed, versatility, and output quality. For simpler projects and casual video shooters, however, tape-based editing still has certain advantages.

For one thing, it requires no special equipment. Although you could buy elaborate linear hardware, you can perform simple editing tasks very effectively with just a camcorder and a consumer VCR. This makes it cost-effective for the person who edits only occasionally. Also, linear editing is relatively simple, so you can master the basics in half an hour. Finally, linear editing lets you experiment with postproduction before deciding whether or not to invest money and learning time in a full-fledged nonlinear system.

A Linear Editing Setup

Before you can edit videos, you must assemble and connect the components of an editing system. We will start with a very simple setup and then explain how additional pieces can improve convenience and enlarge your editing capabilities.

Essential Editing Components

The most basic editing setup consists of three pieces: a camcorder, a VCR, and a TV set, **Figure 19-1**. The camcorder functions as the source deck, in which you play back the original footage. The VCR is the record deck on which you assemble your edited program. You watch what you are doing on the TV set.

The VCR on which you are building your finished program is usually called the assembly deck.

Adding an Editing VCR

If you decide to add dedicated editing equipment to a basic setup, the first investment should probably be an editing-quality VCR. Edit quality VCRs have flying erase heads, which allow perfect cuts from shot-to-shot without the rainbowlike patterns that sometimes mar edits

Figure 19-1.
A simple editing setup.

on simple VCRs. Flying erase heads also permit you to replace previously transferred video, audio, or both with other material. This function is essential for more advanced editing, as we will see.

Adding an Editing Monitor

You can edit quite capably with just one monitor (or TV set), due to the way in which the assembly deck VCR displays footage. The signal sent to the TV set depends on the mode in which the assembly VCR is operating, **Figure 19-2:**

- STOP, RECORD, or RECORD/PAUSE modes display the signal passed through from the source VCR (or camcorder), so you can see your original footage.

- PLAY or PAUSE modes display the signal already recorded on the assembly tape.

Nevertheless, you may want to provide your source deck with a monitor of its own. When working with only one monitor, it can be hard to remember quickly whether the image on the screen is from the source deck or the assembly deck. For this reason, a second monitor connected directly to the source camera is a convenience, **Figure 19-3.**

Figure 19-3.
A source monitor always displays the source image.

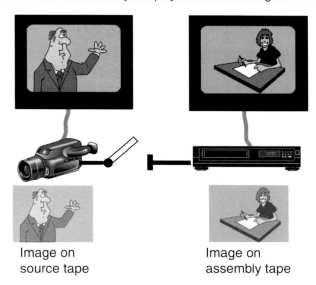

Image on source tape   Image on assembly tape

In summary then, here are the simplest, least expensive setups for linear editing:

- Camera to home VCR, with TV set.
- Camera to editing VCR, with TV set.
- Camera to editing VCR, with TV set and separate source video monitor.

Figure 19-2.
Image display with different VCR modes. A—STOP, RECORD, or RECORD/PAUSE modes. B—PLAY or PAUSE modes.

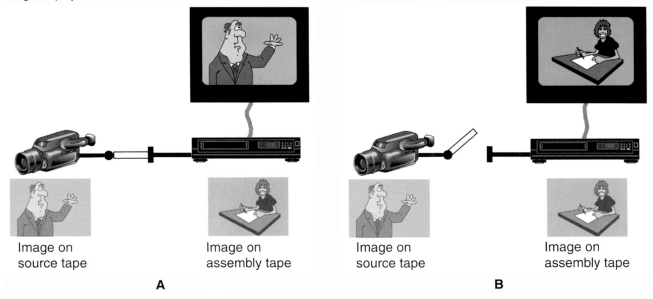

Image on source tape   Image on assembly tape

Image on source tape   Image on assembly tape

A   B

Analog vs Digital; Linear vs Nonlinear

Throughout these chapters on editing, you will see the term *analog* contrasted with *digital* and *linear* contrasted with *nonlinear*. It is important to understand that these two different pairs of opposing terms have no connection to each other.

Analog vs digital

The terms analog and digital refer to the way in which the video and audio signals are encoded.

Analog signals are recorded as subtle variations in the voltage of the electrical signal. Graphed, they resemble the accompanying diagram. Analog recording closely reproduces the continuous voltage fluctuations created by the imaging circuits and the microphone.

The varying voltage of an analog signal.

Analog video signal

Signal recorded on tape

Digital recording does not copy the fluctuating voltage of the signal. Instead, it inspects (samples) that signal at intervals, notes its strength at each point, and expresses both values in the ones and zeros of binary notation. It is these graph coordinates that constitute digital recording, rather than the original signal. Because the samples are taken so frequently (many thousands of times each second), the resulting numerical values accurately represent the original voltage patterns.

In summary, an analog recording copies the original signal directly, while a digital recording represents it as a series of numbers instead. In general, digital recording is preferred to analog because the resulting files can be copied endlessly (like all computer files) with 100 percent accuracy. By contrast, copies of copies of analog recordings (like Xerographic copies) deteriorate in quality from one **generation** to the next.

Linear vs nonlinear

The terms linear and nonlinear refer to the way in which you can gain access to your materials.

Linear materials are recorded on tape, so you cannot jump instantly to any part of the record. Instead, you must roll through the tape to the desired point. Linear recording systems include:

● Analog audio tape

● Digital audiotape (DAT)

● Analog video tape (VHS, 8mm, etc.)

● Digital video tape (Mini-DV, Digital 8, etc.)

Nonlinear materials are recorded so that you can quickly access your material, wherever it is stored. Nonlinear recording systems include:

● Print materials (books, magazines, newspapers)

● Computer files (on hard drives, DVDs, CD-ROMs, floppy disks)

● CD audio disks

Digital recording. A—The varying voltage of an audio/video signal. B—The signal strength is sampled at intervals… C—and recorded as ones (signal on) and zeros (signal off).

A   **B**   **C**

- Analog video disks (laser disks)
- Digital video disks (DVD).

Notice that both analog and digital recording systems exist in both linear and nonlinear formats:

	Analog recording	Digital recording
Linear access	VHS, 8mm	Mini-DV tape
Nonlinear access	Laser disk, vinyl LP	DVD, CD, hard drive

Noncomputerized vs computerized

It is inaccurate to say that nonlinear video is computerized while linear video is not. Computers have long played important roles in traditional linear editing. Edit controllers and switcher/DVE generators contain small, specialized computers. In professional postproduction, computers have been used for decades to create and store edit decision lists (EDLs) to help automate final program assembly.

Temporary vs permanent

Finally, it is not true that digital video is permanent, while traditional analog video decays and fades away. The fact is that *any* signal recorded on magnetic tape or disk will deteriorate over time, regardless of whether it is analog or digital.

Unlike analog recordings, however, digital recordings can be copied and recopied without appreciable quality loss (**generation loss**). In practical terms, this means that digital video is *potentially* permanent, as long as fresh copies are made at suitable intervals.

Optically scanned disks, whether analog or digital, are not subject to signal decay because they are not magnetic recording media. However, the disks themselves are not truly permanent, because they are vulnerable to scratches and other physical injuries.

Adding a Switcher/DVE Generator

A digital switcher, **Figure 19-4,** accepts and switches video and audio input from two VCRs, and usually from additional sources like microphones and CD players.

A switcher is essential for making transitions like dissolves between shots, and for mixing audio sources. All digital switchers include digital video effects (DVEs) for transitions like wipes, flips, and fly-ins, and for special visual effects like mosaic, strobe, and compositing.

Figure 19-4.
A digital switcher. (Videonics)

Setting up an Editing System

If your editing system is nothing more than your camcorder, home VCR, and TV set, there is practically no setup. Simply cable from the camcorder's video and audio outputs to the comparable inputs on your VCR, **Figure 19-5.** The VCR is already cabled to display audio and video on the TV set.

Figure 19-5.
Better VCRs include audio/video inputs on the front of the deck, for convenience in attaching a camcorder.

Flying Heads

Heads are tiny electromagnets that record, play, or erase video signals. **Fixed heads** remain still while the tape rolls past them. **Flying heads** are mounted on a rapidly spinning ("flying") drum. All video record heads revolve on this drum, but some audio record and video/audio erase heads are fixed.

The flying heads on a VCR drum.

Because the tape moves past the spinning drum at an angle, the flying heads record the signal in a series of diagonal bars. This is called "helical scan" recording.

The diagonal stripes represent the video track.

Fixed heads, however, record (or erase) in a continuous linear pattern.

Most home VCRs are equipped only with fixed erase heads. Every time you press the record button on your VCR, you also activate the fixed erase head, which cleans any previously recorded signal off the tape before it reaches the record heads. Because the fixed erase head does not operate in a helical pattern, it always leaves partially erased track bars.

A fixed erase head destroys parts of several track passes.

These partially erased signals create wavy lines and rainbow patterns between shots. Also, because the fixed erase head is in front of the record head, it erases material that is not replaced when the re-recording stops.

Flying erase heads solve this problem because they erase in the same helical pattern as the record heads. Editing decks are equipped with both fixed and flying erase heads. When you engage the VIDEO INSERT or AUDIO DUB controls on an editing deck, the flying erase heads operate instead of the fixed erase head, and you can drop replacement video and/or audio into the middle of previously recorded material.

Flying erase heads conform to the recording pattern.

For all but the simplest projects, however, it will pay to create a setup specifically for editing. Doing this means arranging the hardware and cabling components together.

Arranging the hardware

Since people in most western cultures read and work from left to right, you may want to position your components this way, with the camcorder to the left and the assembly VCR to the right. If you are working with a TV set, it is probably not worth moving, but if you have small monitors, place each one directly on top of its VCR. If the VCR is a camcorder, position its monitor behind it instead.

Inexpensive Monitors

Monitors are television display units that lack channel tuners and RF (antenna lead) inputs. Typically, they produce higher-quality pictures than all but the most expensive TV sets, and they include sophisticated setup controls for adjusting their displays. All professional editing installations use monitors.

Small (13-inch) TV sets are often a good alternative to professional monitors because they typically cost far less. And though their picture is not studio quality, it is quite good enough for evaluating raw footage on the source VCR. Also, many home VCRs have only one set of composite (and sometimes S-connector) outputs. On the other hand, all of them include RF outputs, so you can connect them to the RF input on a TV set without tying up any editing connections. (RF jacks and plugs are the standard connectors used with TV antenna or cable leads.)

Recycling old hardware

Because of the RF connection, any surplus TV set, black and white or color, will work adequately as a source deck monitor. You can even use old computer monitors, if they have the "RGB" inputs

RF connections allow you to connect a TV set to your source VCR or camcorder.

that were common in the early generations of Apple and IBM desktop models. (RGB computer monitors lack RF inputs, however, so they require a second line-level output on the VCR.)

The key point is that a source monitor does not require quality high enough to evaluate image sharpness or color, because the same image is displayed on the assembly deck monitor.

Cabling the components

Linking equipment is relatively simple if you follow a few standard procedures:

- Always cable from a video or audio "out" plug on the source to an "in" plug on the destination. Remember that all plugs (except 1394 digital models) work in one direction only. The most common reasons for not transmitting picture or sound are failure to plug from "out" to "in" and inserting jacks in the wrong plugs.

- Always use Y/C (S-video) connectors, **Figure 19-6,** for video when available, for better picture quality.

- RCA plugs and jacks are color coded: yellow for composite video, white for left stereo audio, and red for right stereo audio. If you are connecting to a mono assembly deck, use the yellow jack for composite video and the white jack for audio (it carries both the left stereo and the monaural tracks).

In this discussion, a port on a piece of hardware is called a "jack" and a pin on the end of a cable is called a "plug."

Color coding on hardware jacks is meaningful (for example, a yellow jack *always*

Figure 19-6.
Most hardware offers both composite video jacks (yellow) and Y/C video, also called S-video. (Videonics)

means composite video) but color codes on cable plugs are purely for convenience. Any plug will work in any jack. To help trace connections, though, it is good procedure to match plug colors to those of the jack you insert them into. If you are using TV sets, connect them to their decks via RF connectors. If your connections are not working properly, start troubleshooting at the last component and check plugging and switch settings, working upstream toward the signal source.

Connecting other hardware

If you have a switcher/DVE generator, it is placed downstream of the source deck(s). Often this setup will involve a second source deck and monitor, to permit transitions between shots (A/B roll editing).

Since additional editing components degrade the signal slightly as it passes through them, they should be inserted into the editing path only when required, **Figure 19-7.**

Editing Picture and Track

With your equipment set up and cabled, you are ready to begin editing. The simplest method is called assembly editing. If you have a deck with flying erase heads, you can also do insert editing; if you have a second source deck and a switcher, you can perform A/B roll editing. We will look at each method, in turn.

Assembly Editing

Assembly editing means building a program by transferring one shot after another, in strict chronological order, from the first one to the last.

Assembly editing is sometimes called "crash cutting."

Every assemble edit requires the same five steps:

1. Position the ***assembly*** (record) ***tape***.
2. Find the new shot on the ***source*** (camera) ***tape***.
3. Rewind the source tape.
4. Roll the source tape.
5. Enable RECORD on the assembly deck.

In this discussion, VCR functions are printed in all-capital letters, like RECORD, and we use the generic term "enable" to mean activate them — cause them to start operating.

Here is each step in greater detail.

1. **Position assembly tape**. Using slow motion, if possible, find the last frame of the previously recorded shot that you wish to keep and PAUSE the assembly deck on the next frame after it. Then, enable RECORD to place the assembly deck in RECORD/PAUSE mode.
2. **Find new shot start frame**. Using the same slow motion technique, pause the source tape on the first frame of the new shot that you wish to copy to the assembly tape.
3. **Set up source tape preroll**. Note the numbers on the source deck time counter. Then rewind the source tape about five seconds or a bit more and pause it again.
4. **Roll source tape**. Enable PLAY on the source deck. When you reach the "runup point" on its time counter…

Figure 19-7.
Connecting hardware properly. A—*Correct:* Monitors are cabled separately; other processors are hooked up only when needed. B—*Incorrect:* Monitors and additional equipment are in the signal path.

Green path for straight cuts.

Red path only for titles and effects.

Monitors not in main signal path.

A   **B**

5. Enable RECORD on assembly tape. Copy the new shot until several seconds *past* the point where you think you want it to end (out-point), **Figure 19-8**.

Key terms are explained in the sidebar, Runup and Preroll. Some VCRs shift from RECORD/PAUSE to RECORD when you press PAUSE a second time. With others, you press the PLAY control instead.

In discussing source shots, the first frame transferred to the assembly tape is called the ***in-point*** and the last frame is the ***out-point,* Figure 19-9**.

In illustrations such as Figure 19-9, the individual pictures are not single frames, but merely indicators of the type used in computer editing timeline displays.

When you repeat this process with the next edit, you will back up the assembly deck to the desired out-point of this newly copied shot and go into RECORD/PAUSE. That way, the next shot copied will replace the unwanted tail end of this one. With practice, you will find that you can copy source material to your assembly tape with frame-accurate precision.

Assembly editing permits you to make professional edits with a minimum of equipment. But it does not allow you to fix mistakes or add new material to previously edited shots. For that, you need to perform *insert editing* instead.

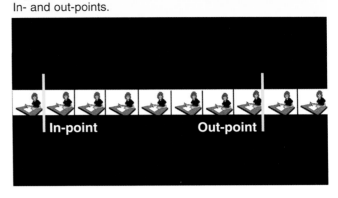

Figure 19-9.
In- and out-points.

Insert (and Dub) Editing

Insert editing means replacing a piece of picture, sound, or both with new material. (The terminology is confusing because the entire procedure is called "insert editing." However, replacing picture is called "inserting" but replacing audio track is called "dubbing.") As noted earlier, inserts and dubs require an assembly deck with flying erase heads.

Most editing VCR controls are labeled INSERT for picture and DUB (or AUDIO DUB) for sound.

Using video insert

A video insert allows you to replace previously transferred video while leaving the original sound under the new picture. For example, suppose you made a regular transfer of the woman's shot, **Figure 19-10**. Using the INSERT command, you can replace the middle of her shot with the man's shot, while her audio continues over it.

Figure 19-8.
Always record past your probable out-point.

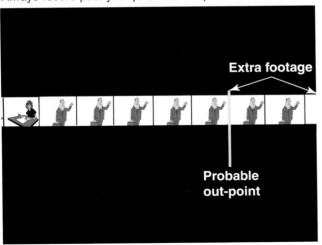

Figure 19-10.
A video insert.

Runup and Preroll

It is important to understand that your assembly (record) VCR will start recording exactly where you pause the tape, but it will *not* start transferring the instant you enable RECORD. It takes the deck between one and two seconds before it actually begins laying a signal down on tape.

Enabling RECORD at the in-point loses 1-2 seconds.

Previous shot on assembly tape

New shot on source tape

Preroll →

Starting record at edit point loses 1-2 seconds of incoming shot

This means that you cannot copy a shot accurately by starting the source and assembly decks together or by playing the assembly tape and enabling RECORD when you see the in-point go by on the source tape. Either method will produce edits that miss the first few seconds of the shot.

That is why you need to calculate runup and use *preroll.*

Runup

Runup is the exact amount of time between enabling RECORD and starting to actually copy a shot. If you know the runup time of your record deck, you can make frame-accurate copies by enabling RECORD just that much earlier.

For example, suppose you wish to begin a new shot at 01:20:10 on your source deck counter. (That means "1 hour, 20 minutes, and 10 seconds.") Suppose that your VCR takes exactly two seconds to start recording, which means that two seconds is its runup time.

To start copying at 01:20:10, then, you would need to enable RECORD two seconds early, when the source deck counter reads 01:20:08.

Preroll

Like RECORD on the assembly deck, PLAY on the source deck does not start as soon as you enable it. You must give the source deck time to get up to speed and begin sending a high-quality picture. This extra time is called **preroll.** You do not need to determine preroll time precisely; it is generally safe to allow it about five seconds. So if your in-point is

Enabling RECORD at the runup point captures the first frame of the incoming shot.

Runup time

Record start

Starting record early captures in point of new shot

01:20:10, then back up the source tape five seconds for preroll, to 01:20:05.

Counting down

In our example, the transfer sequence would resemble this (using the numbers on the source deck counter):

01:20:05: *enable source PLAY, to allow for preroll.*

01:20:06

01:20:07

01:20:08: *enable assembly RECORD, to allow for runup.*

01:20:09

01:20:10: *transfer begins at actual source shot in-point.*

Calculating runup

VCR runup times vary by brand and model, and even by individual machine. You can learn the runup time of your particular assembly deck by trial and error. But if you have a digital stopwatch (or stopwatch function on a wristwatch) you can determine it precisely. Here is the procedure:

- Begin videotaping a closeup of the stopwatch set to 00:00:00:00 (most stopwatches are accurate to one-one hundredth of a second), and then start it running. Stop taping after the watch has counted perhaps 20 seconds.

- Cue up the stopwatch footage in your source VCR at the head of the shot, before the watch is activated.

- Cue up a second tape in your assembly VCR and place the deck in RECORD/PAUSE.

- Play the stopwatch footage. At a selected point, such as 5 seconds exactly (00:00:05:00) enable RECORD on the assembly deck and copy the running stopwatch for a few seconds.

- Play back the shot on the assembly tape, noting the stopwatch time on the very first frame recorded (use slow motion or single frame advance, if possible). Suppose, for instance, that the reading is 00:00:06:50.

- Subtract the start reading from the first frame reading:

  6:50 (first frame actually recorded)
  −5:00 (frame at which RECORD was enabled)
  1:50 (runup time)

Due to lags in reaction time, your results will probably resemble those shown in the photos, where the nominal five-second mark is actually 00:05:12 and the first recorded frame is at 00:06:53. The runup time, then, is 1 and 41/100 seconds. For editing purposes, figuring 1.4 seconds is accurate enough.

For frame-accurate cutting, you would always enable RECORD 1.5 seconds *before* the in-point of the shot you wish to transfer. (Remember that this is only an example, and the runup time on your VCR will probably be different.)

Calculating runup time. A—Stopwatch reading when RECORD is enabled. B—First recorded frame of stopwatch.

A

B

Using Audio Dub

Audio dubbing replaces sound instead of picture. It is useful for adding narration, sound effects, or music.

You cannot use the dub function to combine (mix) audio tracks. The dub function completely replaces one sound track with another.

Suppose, for example, that you want to dramatize a car crash without wrecking an actual car. To do this, you let the car exit the frame and then use the AUDIO DUB command to replace the remaining production track with a car crash effect. Audio dub can also be used for dialogue replacement, Foley sound effect recording, and narration, but its most common application is probably for laying music under picture.

Procedures for insert and dub

Insert and dub use exactly the same steps, except for two very important differences. Instead of preparing your assembly deck by cuing the tape and entering RECORD/PAUSE, you enable INSERT/PAUSE or DUB/PAUSE. This difference is critical because if you mistakenly use RECORD/PAUSE, you will replace both picture and track and the fixed erase head will ruin the material following the transfer.

There is no way to fix this mistake. To recover, you will have to go back to the beginning of the original shot, re-transfer it, and continue editing from there.

And, instead of transferring past your intended out-point, stop the insert or dub *precisely* at the out-point or you will record over material that you wish to save.

Two notes about *insert* and *dub:* some assembly decks perform runup automatically when you use insert or dub. Experiment to see how your VCR works. Also, some decks allow you to use both insert and dub at the same time. This is useful for revising earlier work by laying in both the picture and sound of replacement footage.

For relatively simple dubs and inserts, these procedures work well in linear editing systems. If, however, you mix and match audio and video in more complex combinations, consider computerized nonlinear editing instead.

Where Did the Audio Dub Go?

VCRs record stereo audio by "multiplexing" (combining) the audio and video signals on the diagonal recording tracks.

When making audio dub edits, it is important to understand exactly what happens to the audio tracks on the tape:

● The original sound remains on the stereo tracks.

● The newly dubbed sound replaces the original audio on the linear, monaural track.

Most VCRs automatically default to stereo playback mode, so when you audition an audio dub, you may hear only the original track instead. To prevent this confusion, set your VCR to play back in mono mode.

The audio dub is audible only when played back in mono.

Mono version of original audio → | Audio dub replaces original → | Original audio resumes →

Stereo version of original audio ↑ | Stereo version remains with video ↑ | Stereo version continues ↑

A/B Roll Editing

A/B roll editing involves combining picture and/or track from two sources (called A and B) in real time. An A/B roll editing setup is illustrated in **Figure 19-11.**

Typically, both program sources are VCRs, but the B source can also be a CD player, a microphone, or any other video or audio input.

In a typical application such as a dissolve, Deck A plays the shot being copied to the assembly deck, while deck B plays the tape containing the next shot. At the transition point, the switcher cross-fades (dissolves) from Shot A to Shot B and continues the transfer.

This discussion makes all switches from the A deck to the B deck. In actual editing, you will often switch from B to A, too.

Figure 19-11.
A simple A/B roll setup.

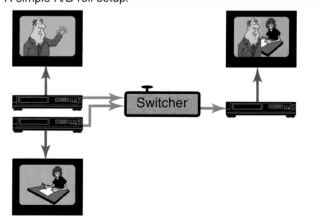

Essentially the same procedure is used to create other effects, to make composite shots, and to superimpose titles over video. A/B roll editing is also useful for combining the video of one source with the audio of another, without using the audio dub function.

A/X Roll Editing

Many camcorders have built-in digital effects, especially wipes and dissolves. If you are using one of these camcorders as your assembly deck, you can make so-called "A/X" transitions with your camera. (They are called A/X because a B roll is not involved.)

Basically, when you enable the camera's effect function, it captures the last frame of Shot A as a still and holds it in a memory called a frame buffer. Then, when you record Shot B, the camera automatically creates a transition between the still in its memory and the incoming signal.

Here is the general procedure for creating an A/X effect; in this example, a wipe (the specific steps depend on the design of the camcorder):

● Before transferring the outgoing (A) shot, enable the WIPE function on the camcorder.

● Transfer Shot A, ending it at the frame you want frozen.

● Transfer the incoming shot (B) in the usual way, **Figure 19-12.**

In planning an A/X transition, avoid cutting the A shot during obvious on-screen movement because the suddenly frozen frame will reveal the trick.

Figure 19-12.

Making an A/X transition: At the end of shot A...

stop recording after the subject has left the frame.

Transfer shot B in the normal way.

The camcorder will create the transition automatically

Transitions, Effects, and Titles

Transitions (like dissolves), visual effects (like superimpositions) and titles all involve two or more images on-screen at once. For this reason, most transitions and effects are achieved through the Digital Video Effects (DVE) functions of A/B switchers.

Stand-alone titling hardware can overlay titles on pictures without going through a switcher.

Working with these program enhancements requires care and planning because in linear editing, you must do everything simultaneously. You cannot return to previously edited shots and add titles or transitions. You cannot superimpose an image on visuals that you have already copied to the assembly tape.

Transitions

Transitions are visual effects that signal changes in program material. Traditional transitions like fades and dissolves indicate changes in time and place. Transitions that wipe, flip, fly in, tumble, turn like pages, or otherwise transform image A into image B are used to provide visual variety and excitement. Suggestions for selecting and using transitions appear elsewhere in this book.

Here, we are concerned with the techniques used to create them in a linear editing setup.

From here on, we will use the acronym for Digital Video Effects: DVE.

Programming transitions

You preset a transition (or any other effect) on your digital switcher. That way, at the transition point in your program, you need only enable the DVE, which creates the effect automatically. Programming presets include:

● *Speed*: You can make the effect last any-where from a fraction of a second to several seconds.

● *Background*: If you are not using A/B roll editing, the effect will bring the new shot in on top of a background, whose color you can select.

● *Edge*: Some transitions, especially wipes, include edges between the old and new images. Depending on the features of your switcher, you may be able to make the edge soft, hard, or highlighted with a colored line. As you can see from **Figure 19-13,** each type creates a somewhat different visual effect.

Figure 19-13.

Edge transitions. A—Soft edge wipe.   B— Hard edge wipe.   C—Colored edge wipe.

Graphic Effects

All switchers (and some camcorders, which can be used as assembly edit decks) include popular graphic effects such as:

- **Horizontal or vertical flop.** You can often correct an error in screen direction by reversing a shot left-to-right, **Figure 19-14,** or turning it upside down.

- **Mosaic.** Mosaic breaks the image up into small squares (you can program their exact size on the switcher).

- **Monochrome.** Monochrome lets you turn your image into black and white.

- **Paint.** This effect breaks the image into pieces and colors them with coarser hues.

- **Negative.** This effect can be useful for copying the negatives of still photographs as direct positives.

Motion Effects

Alterations of image movement can have many practical uses:

- **Strobe.** This effect creates jerky movement by repeating frames. Though exaggerated strobe effects have limited usefulness, a slight strobe can simulate the jerkiness of silent movies

- **Still.** Still is a useful DVE effect because, unlike the PAUSE control on a VCR, it produces a perfectly motionless and undistorted picture. However, both methods yield an inferior quality image because they display only one of the two fields that make up a full frame.

Figure 19-14.
Although flopping can be a useful effect, beware of image elements, like reversed words or letters, that can give away the flopped shot. (Western Recreational Vehicles)

- **Slow motion.** Slow motion is created not in a DVE but in the source deck. To achieve it, simply operate the VCR in slow motion as you copy the shot.

- **Fast motion.** Use exactly the same technique for fast motion.

Multiple Images

There are three types of screen display that contain more than a single video image.

Superimpositions

Superimpositions are pairs of images in which one picture is underneath the other and is partly visible through it. They are easily created by running one image on the A roll, the other on the B roll, and manually keying a partial dissolve between them.

Split screen

Create a split screen with a different image on each part by manually executing a partial wipe and then stopping part-way.

Picture-in-picture

This effect opens up a small second image within the main image, often in one corner of the screen. Picture-in-picture is useful when an on-screen person is required to comment on the main image — whether a teacher explaining a shot of a science experiment or a person signing for hearing-impaired viewers.

Compositing

Compositing means replacing one part of an image with part of another image. Compositing is used to insert someone or something into a scene, or to add an image or even a setting behind the subjects, **Figure 19-15.**

Perhaps the most widespread use of compositing is in TV news, where maps are composited behind the weather reporters.

Titles

In linear editing, titles must be inserted in chronological order; if superimposed over picture, they must be done as each shot is transferred to the assembly tape. There are three kinds of titlers: camera titlers, stand alone titlers, and computer software.

Camera titlers

Some consumer camcorders allow you to create titles in the camera and superimpose them over shots as you tape them. Normally,

Figure 19-15.
Compositing. A—The subject in front of a Chromakey screen.   B—The resulting composite.

A

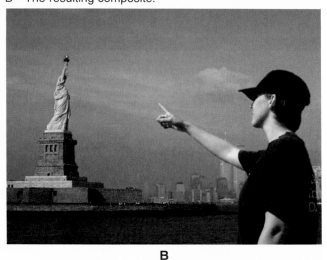

B

that would force you to make all titling decisions while shooting; but if you are using your camcorder as an assembly deck, you can add titles during postproduction, too. Unfortunately, most cameras produce crude-looking letters with very little choice of type, color, or size.

Stand-alone titlers

Video titlers are available as separate pieces of hardware, **Figure 19-16.** In addition to creating titles in a wide variety of colors, fonts, and sizes, they can also composite titles over live-action footage.

Computer-generated titles

With a computer presentation program like Corel Presentations or Microsoft

PowerPoint, you can create very sophisticated video titles.

You will also need a computer card or accessory box to translate computer video output into NTSC television signals.

Create your titles on a composite color background (usually blue or green). Because the computer-generated color is absolutely uniform, you can key titles beautifully over live action, through your DVE. For best results, always evaluate the titles on an NTSC monitor as you create them. A computer screen does not show them as they will appear on TV. For complex designs, record the titles on a work tape and key

Figure 19-16.
Titling. A—A stand-alone titler. (Videonics)

B—Titlers can create sophisticated composite effects. (Videonics)

A

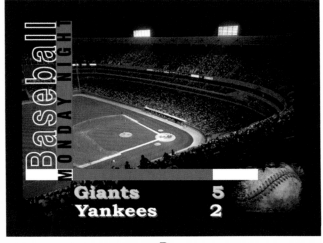

B

them from the B roll source deck, for more precise control.

From Linear to Nonlinear

Linear editing offers a simple, inexpensive entry into the world of video postproduction. Beyond this entry level, however, the traditional approach has been largely replaced by digital, nonlinear editing. Computer-based postproduction offers all the power and flexibility of film editing, but at a fraction of the cost. Nonlinear editing is the subject of the next chapter.

Technical Terms

Assembly editing: Constructing a video program by transferring shots in sequence to a master tape.

Assembly tape: The tape in the record VCR, on which the program is created.

Audio dubbing: Replacing a segment of previously recorded audio without disturbing the accompanying video.

Compositing: Combining foreground elements from one image with the background of another.

Fixed head: A record, play, or erase head that operates in a continuous line on the tape passing across it.

Flying head: A record, play, or erase head that operates on the tape in short discrete diagonal segments.

Generation: A level of tape copy. An original camera tape is first generation, a copy made from it is second-generation, a copy of the copy is third generation.

Generation loss: The decline in video and audio quality from one analog generation to the next.

Head: A tiny electromagnet that encodes signals by magnetizing particles on videotape (record), decodes previously recorded signals by reading their magnetic patterns (play), or destroys previously recorded signals by giving all tape particles an identical magnetic alignment (erase).

In-point: The first frame of a new piece of material.

Insert Editing: Replacing part of a previously edited video and/or audio segment with new material. The opposite of assembly editing.

Linear editing: Working with both source materials and finished program on videotape, rather than in a computer.

Out-point: The last frame of a new piece of material.

Preroll: Starting the source deck playback prior to the in-point of the shot being transferred.

Runup: The difference between the point in time when the RECORD function is enabled and the first frame of recorded material.

Source tape: The tape providing the raw material for editing; usually, but not always, an original camera tape.

The inputs of a linear DVE switcher (Videonics).

20 Nonlinear Editing

CONTENTS

About Nonlinear Editing

Configuring Nonlinear Projects

Basic Operations

Transformations

Nonlinear Audio

Objectives

After studying this chapter, you will be able to:

❏ Explain the key differences between linear and nonlinear editing.

❏ Configure a new project on your own editing software.

❏ Capture, edit, and archive digital programs.

❏ Work with multiple audio tracks.

(Casablanca/Macrosystems)

About Nonlinear Editing

The term *nonlinear* editing refers to postproduction using video and audio stored in **digital** form on a computer hard drive or other disk. Because you are working with files on disk you can jump almost instantly to any point in your material. And since those files are digital, you can copy, modify, move, or transform them with ease.

Linear editing is covered in Chapter 19.

Advantages of Nonlinear Editing

To realize the advantages of nonlinear postproduction, it helps to compare it to the traditional linear method.

- **Permanence:** Though digital recordings are not themselves permanent, they can be copied through many generations without appreciable quality loss. (Analog recordings suffer evident decay each time they are copied to a new generation.)
- **Flexibility:** Digital recordings are easy to modify, so that effects, composites, filters, titles, and other processes are simpler to work and revise. Digital audio is equally flexible. Although linear video can be processed externally by digital switchers, compositors, and titlers, the process is easier when all the material is stored in a computer.
- **Economy:** Because a single desktop computer can perform the operations of many different standalone editing components (switchers, titlers, audio mixers,

	Nonlinear Editing	**Linear Editing**
Data format	*Digital*	(Typically) *analog*
Storage medium	*Disk*	*Tape*
Access	*Random*: Because your material is stored on a disk, you can jump almost instantly to any point in it.	*Serial*: To reach any shot you must roll through all the footage between your start point and your destination.
Work order	*Random*: You can work on any section at any time, and you can return to previously edited material and revise it without disturbing the rest of the program.	*Sequential*: You must assemble your edited program in strict chronological order. Once you have edited a sequence, you cannot revise it without re-editing everything that follows it on the tape.
Multiple tasks	*Additive*: You can work on one element at a time. The final multi-layered program can be richer than anything you could achieve with tape-based postproduction.	*Concurrent*: You must perform all editing operations at the same time. This makes complex operations with multiple video and/or audio tracks difficult.

Nonlinear editing offers other advantages as well.

- **Speed:** Random access, additive editing, and easy revision let you work more quickly.

timebase correctors, etc.), a computer-based editing setup is often less expensive than a tape-based system of similar quality, **Figure 20-1**.

Figure 20-1.
Editing systems. A—Tape-based editing system.   B—Computer-based editing system.

A

B

- **Universality:** Broadcast video is recorded and displayed in several incompatible formats, including NTSC, PAL, and SECAM. In addition, high-definition video exists in a number of different standards. Finally, computer video display uses still other protocols. As a result, converting traditional video from one format to another has been a complex and imperfect process. In computer-based video, by contrast, you work in the digital format that your software prefers, and then output the result in whatever standard you need for storage and playback.

- **Timecode:** Digital video brings timecode (formerly reserved for expensive professional postproduction) to even the simplest setup. With this ability to give every single frame a unique and permanent address, you can maintain precise control of all your program components.

The underlying principles of editing (discussed in Chapter 18) are identical for both linear and nonlinear approaches, and the basic operations (covered in Chapter 17) are fundamentally the same, as well. However, nonlinear editing carries out those operations quite differently from the older linear approach. For this reason, much of this chapter shows how the procedures of editing operations are implemented in computerized postproduction.

Configuring Nonlinear Projects

The basics of nonlinear editing are much the same as linear basics. You select the raw materials (shots and audio clips), assemble them into an organized program, and store the finished product. There is, however, one big difference between the two approaches. Before you can begin nonlinear editing you must tell the computer the precise electronic characteristics of the program you will work on. That is, you must *configure* the project, **Figure 20-2.**

The following sections provide general descriptions and explanations of the many factors involved in configuring a project, starting with the program's basic format(s).

Video Formats

The format of a video is the set of electronic protocols used to record and play it. In analog video editing, you do not configure the program format because it is already "hard-wired" into all the equipment, as part of the TV standard in which you are working.

Figure 20-2.
A configuration screen from Adobe Premiere.

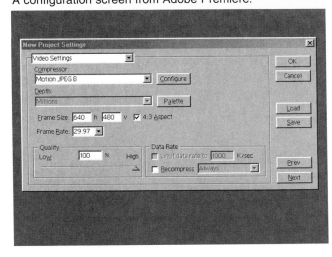

For example, if your hardware conforms to the NTSC standard, then NTSC is the configuration of every project you edit.

Computer-based video, however, is format-independent. That means you may start with source material in one format, process it in your computer in a second format, and export it for storage or viewing in yet a third format.

In many setups, the format is the same for both source and destination, **Figure 20-3.** For instance, you may import Mini-DV footage from your camcorder, work in QuickTime format on your computer, and export Mini-DV back to your camcorder to store your edited program on tape.

In other cases, you may be working with three different formats. For example, if you are editing NTSC original footage for streaming to the World Wide Web, your source will be analog NTSC, your editor will work in its native digital format, and your destination will require yet another digital format.

Figure 20-3.
Mini-DV tape is an excellent storage medium.

Varieties of Nonlinear Editing

The operations of traditional linear editing can be discussed in great detail because they are performed directly on hardware whose controls are nearly identical, regardless of make or model. Moreover, these controls and the functions they enable have remained the same for many years. Digital editing, however, is performed mainly on computers, and computers vary in several important ways:

● Different programs use different screens, commands, and procedures, even though they are performing essentially the same operations.

● Programs grow and change from one revision to the next, often so rapidly that a skilled user of, say, "Version 2.0" cannot even recognize "Version 5.5."

● Editors often customize their operations by using more than one software application, and/or by "plugging in" supplementary programs to their main software.

● Hardware components change quickly as computer systems continue to evolve.

For these reasons, it is impractical to discuss the fine details of nonlinear editing because your system will almost certainly differ from the setups covered here. To avoid these problems, we will focus instead on the essentials of nonlinear operations — essentials that stay the same regardless of differences in hardware and software.

Software applications. A—Work screen from Adobe Premiere. B—Storyboard work screen from Casablanca, by Macrosystems.

Even within basic formats there are choices to be made: full-screen image or partial? Smooth motion or economical 15 fps (frames per second) movement? The list goes on through many more such decisions. For this reason, you need to understand the major project parameters and set them systematically. The rest of this section discusses each one.

Video Standards

The NTSC, PAL, and Mini-DV formats are all examples of TV "standards." Video recording standards fall into two broad categories, digital and analog.

Analog standards

Historically, almost all broadcast and cable television has been recorded and displayed in one of three analog standards, PAL, SECAM, and the NTSC format used mainly in North America and Japan. These standards are completely incompatible. If you play a PAL videotape in an NTSC VCR, you will hear only garbled audio and see no picture at all.

Although you can probably select PAL output in your editing software, you cannot record it successfully on an NTSC VCR.

To edit *analog video* with a computer, you must import it through a video capture device that converts the signal to a digital format that is compatible with your editing software, **Figure 20-4.** When you have completed editing, you can choose to output the digital program through the same device, which will reconvert the signal to analog.

Figure 20-4.
A video capture card converts analog to digital and back again.

Some capture devices can process more than one analog format, but others will handle only one.

Digital formats

There are many different digital formats to suit the requirements of professional production, consumer video, satellite broadcast, and high definition TV. Since the camcorder records the signal digitally to begin with, it does not have to be converted as it is imported into your computer, **Figure 20-5,** though the importing device in your system (usually an I/O card) does need to be compatible with the digital format of the source material.

When exporting your finished program, however, you must use the format of your storage and display equipment. For example,

you may wish to output your program once to Mini-DV tape for permanence and quality, and again to a VHS VCR for simple TV playback. See **Figure 20-6.**

When you have selected your basic input, processing, and output standard(s), computer-based editing then requires you to set several parameters within the formats you have chosen. These include time and frame measurement, video scanning system, picture quality, and audio quality.

Time and Frame Measurement

Video (and film) systems do not record continuously. Instead, they divide each second of time into several equal parts and record a picture of each part. Displayed in real time, these separate pictures give the illusion of a continuous, moving image. There are several common ways to record video images, and in every one, the first recording parameter is frame rate.

Frame rate

The **frame rate** is the number of individual images (frames) recorded each and every second. It is important to know the frame rate of both your source material and your eventual storage medium, so that your software can process the source material and prepare a compatible final project.

Here are some of the principal frame rates:

● NTSC television (the North American standard): 30 fps. The actual frame rate of NTSC video is 29.97 fps, but it is informally referred to as "30 fps."

Figure 20-5.
A 1394 ("Firewire") I/O card does not have to digitize the signal.

Figure 20-6.
Most Mini-DV camcorders can export programs in analog form for NTSC playback or storage.

- PAL and SECAM television: 25 fps.
- Computer full motion: 30 fps.
- Computer limited motion: 15 fps (10 fps is a less-common alternative).
- Sound film: 24 fps.

Timebase

The word **timebase** refers to the way in which your system calculates time. In most formats, the timebase is identical to the frame rate; but the NTSC format used mainly in North America, is an exception. Though we speak of 30 fps for convenience, the true NTSC frame rate is actually 29.97 fps.

The change from a true 30 fps to 29.97 was made for technical reasons when color television broadcasting was developed.

If your computer uses a true 30 fps as the timebase, even the tiny difference of 0.03 frames per second will gradually make the frame count grow increasingly inaccurate. For this reason, it is preferable to set your editing software to a 29.97 fps timebase when you are editing projects intended for TV display.

Timecode

The way in which frames are labeled is called timecode. **Timecode** provides a unique address for every frame of video in your program. The most common timecode system is SMPTE, which labels each frame of picture and/or sound with a unique identifier. This address consists of the number of hours, minutes, seconds, and frames elapsed since the start of the timecode, **Figure 20-7.** So, the timecode

address 00:37:22:09 labels the frame that is 37 minutes, 22 seconds, and nine frames from zero. The leading "00" indicates that no hours have elapsed.

SMPTE stands for the Society of Motion Picture and Television Engineers and is pronounced "SIMP-tee."

Timecode is essential for accurate editing because it allows you to specify the exact frame on which you want each operation to start or end.

Keeping them straight

To understand the differences between frame rate, timebase, and timecode, remember that:
- *Frame rate* is the actual number of frames per second recorded by a camcorder or created in the editing process.
- *Timebase* is number of units per second with which editing software calculates all its operations. It may or may not be the same as frame rate.
- *Timecode* is the numbering system used to assign a unique address label to every frame. ("Drop-frame" timecode is used to prevent errors in applying 30 fps timecode to a 29.97 fps frame rate.)

Video Scanning System

Each video image (frame) is divided into several hundred horizontal lines, which are "painted" on the display, one at a time. This process is called scanning. There are two approaches to video scanning: interlaced and progressive.

Interlaced video

In this system, every frame of video is made up of two fields, one showing only the odd-numbered lines and the other only the even numbered lines. Since each of the two fields is scanned in 1/60 second, the complete frame is displayed for 1/30 second, in the NTSC standard, with the two fields interlaced (mixed together).

Interlaced video, **Figure 20-8,** was developed in the early days of television to work around technical limitations that have since been overcome, but it remains the standard for conventional TV.

When you place a VCR in PAUSE, the image quality degrades because the still consists of only one of the two fields.

Figure 20-7.
The parts of a timecode address.

Hours   Seconds
00:37:22:09
Minutes   Frames

Understanding Timecode
An unchangeable address?

The statement that each frame is assigned a permanent timecode address applies only to a single recording of that frame (and the other frames around it). This means that when you copy a shot you can sometimes copy its timecode address with it; but in other cases, your system may assign the material a new set of timecodes. In working with a project, you may be dealing with three separate sets of timecode:

● **Source timecode.** Each clip you import will have timecode addresses created in the camcorder.

● **Clip timecode.** In some editing systems, each separate piece of captured material has its own timecode.

● **Project timecode.** Your software will timecode your project with a single set of continuous addresses.

Though it is not the editor's responsibility to manage timecode on the original camera footage, pre-striping every camera tape with timecode before using it is highly desirable because it ensures that some sort of code is on every second of the tape.

When some camcorders sense the absence of timecode, they reset to zero and start over. If that happens, the editor may find multiple shots on one tape that have the same addresses. This can make locating and importing clips difficult.

Drop-frame and Nondrop-frame timecode

Timecode cannot label an interval shorter than a whole frame, so NTSC timecode counts frames as if they were displayed at 30 fps, rather than the actual rate of 29.97 fps. If timecode assigned an address to every frame, the count would very slowly

grow inaccurate. After ten minutes, the difference between the timecode readout and the actual elapsed time would be over one-half second, a huge difference where synchronizing picture and sound is concerned.

To solve the problem, so-called "drop-frame" timecode skips (drops) two frame numbers at the beginning of each new minute. (Since this method overcompensates just slightly, the two frame numbers are not dropped after every tenth minute.)

"Drop-frame" timecode does not really drop any frames, but only address numbers.

It is important to understand that drop frame timecode does not actually eliminate any frames. It simply drops numbers. In other words, between timecode addresses ending in "00:59" and "01:02" there are numbers missing, but not pictures.

To continue the address analogy, if two houses side-by side on Elm Street are 305 Elm and 309 Elm, it does not mean that a house between them has been removed, but only that the number 307 has been skipped in assigning house addresses.

Figure 20-8.
Interlaced (2-field) video.

Progressive scan video

In this system, every odd and even frame line is shown sequentially in one pass, **Figure 20-9.** There are no separate fields in progressive scan video.

Many digital video systems use progressive scanning. In digital post production, you may need to convert between interlaced and progressive scan video. An interlaced frame must be "deinterlaced" into a single scan in order to create a full-quality still image. A progressive scan frame must be broken down into two interlaced fields for export to a conventional video display standard such as NTSC.

Figure 20-9.
Progressive scan video.

Picture quality

The visual quality of a displayed image depends on three factors:

- *Resolution:* the perceived sharpness and amount of detail.
- *Color fidelity:* the accuracy and subtlety of the colors.
- *Integrity:* the freedom from **artifacts**, such as spots or areas with a blocky, mosaic appearance.

Of these factors, resolution is perhaps the most important.

Resolution

Resolution is the ability of a video system to resolve (distinguish) fine detail.

Many factors combine to determine resolution, as the sidebar, Resolution and Frame Size explains.

In digital editing, you set the resolution of each new project. If you are working with digital source material, it is often best to set the project resolution to match. So if you are using Mini-DV footage with a 640 × 480 resolution, the project resolution will also be 640 × 480. Analog video measures resolution differently, so you can only match the quality approximately. If your source is hi8 video, a 640 x 480 resolution is recommended; but if your source material is plain VHS, 320 × 240 will preserve the details in the original.

To compensate for small losses during the editing process, it may be advisable to set the digital project resolution one level higher than the minimum needed to capture detail in the analog originals.

Resolution and Frame Size

Analog television and digital video are different in the way they display images on screens. In conventional television, All monitors are set to match a single standard (such as NTSC) so images in that standard always fill the entire screen.

Digital displays such as computer screens, however, can be set to different resolutions, such as 1280 × 960, 800 × 600, 640 × 480, etc. Consequently, the apparent size of a displayed digital image depends on the relationship between the screen's resolution and its own. On a 640 × 480 (VGA) screen, for example,

- a 320 × 240 (VHS quality) picture will fill one quarter of the screen at its native resolution.
- a 640 × 480 (Mini-DV) picture will fill the screen exactly.
- a 1280 × 960 picture will fit only one fourth of its area on the screen.

Three different resolutions on a 640x480 screen.

Color fidelity

Color fidelity means the accuracy of the colors in the picture, and this quality depends heavily on bit depth. **Bit depth** refers to the length of the string of code numbers representing each picture pixel. The more bits recorded per pixel, the greater the amount of information about it. Typical color depths are 8 bit, 16 bit, and 24 bit. Consumer digital camcorders can record at least 16 bit color, and most editing software works in at least 24 bit.

Image integrity

Because of the tremendous amounts of data involved, digital video is often compressed. Digital compression can be complicated because there are at least three variables to consider:

- *Compression type:* Some systems, like **MJPEG**, reduce the data for each individual frame. Others, such as **MPEG**, record all the information for a "base frame;" but on the frames that follow it, they record only the pixels that have changed since the base frame.

- *Compression algorithm:* Each type of compression is available in more than one variety, with designations like "4-1-1" and "4-1-2."

- *Compression level:* Compression systems allow you to set the severity of the compression from slight to vigorous. The milder the compression, the better the picture quality and the bigger the file size as well.

Usually, the compression type and particular algorithm are determined by the codecs in your camcorder and computer. However, you can often set the level of compression for each project.

Codec is the name coined for the mechanism that codes the video digitally and decodes it for analog storage and playback. Some codecs have their programming built into hardware; others are software only.

Aspect Ratio

After frame rate, scanning system, and image quality, the last picture parameter to set is aspect ratio, the relationship of the frame's width to its height. The traditional aspect ratio of video is 4 to 3 — four units of width to three units of height (usually shown in the form 4:3), **Figure 20-10.**

The original 4:3 matches the ratio of all movies at the time broadcast TV was developed. Since then, films have been shot in many different aspect ratios, as wide as 2.2:1.

Nowadays, however, TV is also displayed in an aspect ratio of 16:9, **Figure 20-11.**

This proportion is close to the shape of most theatrical movies. Many digital camcorders can be set to shoot 16:9, and some editing software can modify traditional 4:3 video to the wider aspect ratio.

Audio Quality

In addition to setting project parameters for video, you can also select them for your sound tracks.

Figure 20-10.
A traditional 4:3 monitor (JVC).

Figure 20-11.
A 16:9 display (JVC).

Sample rate

All digital recording is created by sampling the signal and recording the result thousands of times per second. CD audio is sampled at a rate of 44.1kHz. Audio for the Internet or CD-ROM may use a 22kHz *sample rate,* and there are other rates between the two. (A rate lower than 22kHz is not generally recommended.)

Bit depth

As with video, this is the number of digits (bits) used to record each sample of the audio. Sixteen-bit audio is CD quality. Selecting a lower sample rate and bit depth will reduce the size of your audio files, but the results will be lower quality.

Matching video

If you set your video at 30 fps for editing, but then play it back at 29.97 frames for NTSC recording, your audio may grow slowly out of synchronization because it was captured to match the slightly faster 30 fps. For this reason, it is best to standardize all video operations at 29.97 fps throughout the capture/edit/export process. That way, your audio will remain in sync with the picture.

It is possible to re-sync 30 fps audio with 29.97 fps video by slowing the audio playback sample rate from 44.1kHz to 44.056kHz.

Working for NTSC storage and playback, you can, as a general rule, safely set a video frame rate of 29.97 and an audio sample rate of 44.1kHz at 16 bits.

Unlike video, which is recorded in separate frames, audio is recorded continuously. For convenience, however, timecode addresses are used for audio as well.

Though sizeable, audio files are smaller than video files, so you may not significantly reduce overall project size by skimping on audio quality.

Basic Operations

With the technical parameters of your project selected, you are ready to begin capturing files, creating your program, and storing the result for duplication and/or display. As you review these operations, keep in mind that most of them are considered at the generic level. Specific procedures will depend on the configuration of your hardware and the editing software you are using.

Capturing Raw Materials

The first step is to bring the raw materials of your program into the computer. This process is called capturing.

Generally, capture means to bring external materials into the computer. "Import" means to copy files already on a hard drive into an editing application.

Typically, the source files are recorded on videotape, although some systems record source material directly on disk or other media. As you capture your source files, you need to remember several things.

Analog or digital

The way in which your computer captures external sources depends on whether they are analog or digital: analog files must be digitized as they are brought into the computer. Digital files are captured and stored in their native form, without further conversion. The distinction is important because your ability to capture analog and/or digital originals depends on the capture cards installed on your system. So the first step in bringing in files is to determine their type and select the appropriate capturing system.

Some capture cards combine both analog and digital inputs and outputs.

Device control

Device control is the ability to operate your source VCR (deck or camcorder) from your computer, without touching the actual VCR controls, **Figure 20-12.**

Many editing applications include device control, and separate software may be included with the capture card you are using.

Device control is a great convenience for any kind of video capture.

Online or offline

In digital postproduction, you can work at two different levels of quality. Online editing creates the final program, so file capture and

Figure 20-12.
Device control lets you operate a VCR through your computer.

all editing operations are conducted at the highest quality level that your system can sustain. Offline editing creates a low-quality work print, plus a frame-accurate record (called an edit decision list or **EDL**) of every element in the program, for later use online in making a high-quality final version. Offline editing is useful in creating longer programs because the lower quality files permit you to store more material on your computer. Online editing, however, is often preferred for shorter programs.

Online and Offline Editing

The terms offline and online were originally coined to label editing at different types of facilities: online editing meant postproduction performed on high quality equipment, often at a specialized facility informally referred to as a **post house.** Offline editing meant assembling a work print of the program elsewhere, on inexpensive equipment.

The system of editing offline and then finishing online at a post house is still used when the quality of the source material and (especially) the final program is higher than a desktop editing system can conveniently handle. For example, footage shot in a professional digital format and intended for broadcast can be dubbed to a Mini-DV copy, edited offline, and then reassembled online and archived in the original professional format. Since postproduction houses rent their services at high hourly rates, producers try to do most of the editing offline, before bringing the program to a post house for completion online.

Offline editing

To do this, editors work with inexpensive copies of the source footage that include the original timecode. In traditional offline editing, the timecode is typically recorded twice: both electronically and also visually in a small rectangle "burnt in" at the bottom of every frame so it can be read right off a monitor screen. A work tape with visible timecode is often called a **window dub.** By means of a desktop computer, the timecode addresses of every element are recorded on an Edit Decision List (EDL) that will be used later to create the final program in online editing. In modern, nonlinear editing, a window dub is unnecessary because timecode is automatically displayed by the editing software.

Online editing

When offline editing is complete, the work print, the original source tapes, and the EDL are then taken to the postproduction house for online editing. There, a new, high-quality duplicate of the work tape is created by matching every shot on the work tape with the identical footage on the source tapes and copying the original to an edit master tape. The matching process is partially automated by loading the EDL into a computer at the post house. Titles, effects, transitions, and other processing are added during online editing. Sound tracks are mixed and "sweetened" to create a composite sound track.

Offline and online on your desktop

Online and offline editing can also be performed entirely on a desktop computer. If your software can do this, you:

1. Digitize source materials at lower quality (small size, high compression) to minimize file sizes.

2. Edit the program, including all transitions, effects and other processing.

3. Instruct the software to rebuild the program at full quality.

Then you re-insert the original tapes in the source deck as prompted by the computer. The system automatically locates and captures (at original quality) the clips used in the program, assembles them in order, and rebuilds all the titles, transitions, and other effects. In the same way, it recreates and mixes a full-quality audio track. Building a program offline and then batch-processing the final version online allows you to work faster and handle more footage in your computer. Today, however, as RAM size, chip speed, and storage capacity continue to grow, it is often practical to work at full "online" quality throughout the editing process.

A frame from a window dub. (Sue Stinson)

00:23:16:12

Individual or batch

Most editing software allows you to capture individual shots one at a time, or to identify shots you want captured and have them all done automatically after you have finished selecting them. Both methods have advantages:

- *Individual capture* allows you to examine each shot, select in- and out-points, capture the shot, and verify that the copy is free of dropped frames and artifacts.

The in-point is the first frame of program to be captured and the out-point is the last frame. A dropped frame is a frame that was not copied, usually because some components of your computer could not keep up with the speed of data transfer from the camcorder or VCR.

- *Batch capture* allows you to concentrate on picking the footage you want, without waiting for each one to be copied. This can make it easier to keep all the shots in your head as you make decisions about which ones to include.

Most editors employ both methods, often using batch capture for initial copying and individual capture for picking up other shots during the course of editing.

Saving captured material

Because of their large file sizes, shots are typically saved to disk as part of the capturing process. To conserve disk space, it is possible to bring them up, trim unwanted footage, and re-save them under the same file names. But it is faster (and often safer) to do most of the selecting and trimming before you capture, **Figure 20-13.**

Also, most editing software allows you to add descriptive comments about each shot and many programs let you organize your shots in a searchable database. It is a good idea to annotate your footage while it is still fresh in your mind. This will save time later, when you need to hunt for a particular shot.

Assembly Editing

Generally, the first task in creating a program (or section of a program) is to select the shots and assemble them in order. The next job, then, is to adjust each shot so it contains exactly the right content and runs exactly the desired time.

Figure 20-13.
A clip is captured, trimmed, and filed as a video-only shot.

For simplicity, assembly and insert editing are treated separately here. As you actually edit, you will generally use both approaches interchangeably.

Shots and clips

The term "shot" can be slightly misleading. Because a digital original can be copied and re-copied as often as necessary, it helps to think of the original shots as no more than the raw materials of your program. The working units of nonlinear editing are often called "clips." A **clip** is a piece of a shot (or shots) selected and used in editing a program. You can create clips that use or re-use all or parts of shots; you can make clips out of pieces of several shots together; you can modify clips to change color, speed, direction, length and other attributes.

Most editing software allows you to name subclips and otherwise identify material that is divided, duplicated, or modified.

Even after you have placed clips in your program, you can divide them into multiple clips and continue to manipulate them as long as you like.

Creating clips

Most editing programs allow you to work with a folder or "bin" containing the shots you will use in creating and placing clips. In effect, a shot becomes a clip when you select it from the folder and begin placing and shaping it for your program.

Trimming clips

Since you will rarely use all of an original shot, your first task is to trim it. Trimming means deciding exactly where the action in the clip will start and stop, and/or how long the clip will remain on screen.

One way to trim a clip is to display it in a window of its own, complete with timecode readout and movement controls (play/stop/single frame, etc.), **Figure 20-14.** By doing this, you can adjust length and content to your liking before placing the clip in the program. After trimming the clip, you drag it into position on the timeline.

Another way to trim a clip is by putting it on the timeline immediately and making adjustments in place. By trimming on the timeline, you can see the clip in relation to the clip ahead of it. This is useful for establishing cut points and matching action. In practice, many editors use both methods at once, establishing the basic length and content of the clip in its own window, placing it on the timeline, and adjusting the trimming there. It is important to understand that the trimming of a clip is not final. You can always change the in-/out-points to adjust the length or the content.

When you have every clip trimmed and placed on the timeline, you have assembled the program (or program sequence).

Insert Editing

Once you have selected, trimmed, and placed clips on your timeline, you will generally fine-tune the results, using various forms of insert editing.

In computer-based nonlinear editing, insert editing covers any and all procedures used to modify the original assembly of shots on the timeline.

Depending on your software, you may have many different ways to adjust clips, insert new material, change timing, etc. But all systems require an understanding of several different types of edits, including three-point, four-point, rolling, ripple, slip, and slide.

Three-point edits

As we have seen, every clip has an in-point, where it begins, and an out-point, where it ends. Think of these as points one and two. When you are inserting a clip into the middle of an existing program, you also have a *program* in-point, where the inserted clip will start and a *program* out-point, where it will end. Think of the program points as points three and four.

It often happens that you need to replace an exact range of material in the original program with a new clip. To specify that range, you indicate both the program in- and out-points. Then you indicate the in-point of the replacement clip. When you drop this clip into the original material, your software will start it at the clip in-point, run it until it comes to the program out-point, and then set the clip out-point automatically. This is called a ***three-point edit,* Figure 20-15.** Most frame-for-frame replacements are three-point edits.

Four-point edits

In rare cases, you may have to fit a new clip that is longer or shorter than the program

Figure 20-14.
The source window in Adobe Premiere.

Figure 20-15.
A three-point edit.

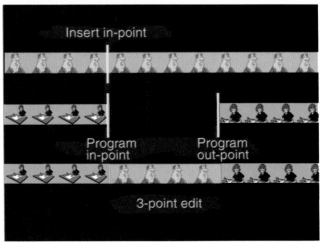

section that it replaces. In this situation, you specify a **four-point edit;** that is, you select the in- and out-points of both the source clip and the program, **Figure 20-16.** When you make a four-point insert edit, you may choose either of two ways to match the clip length to the program spot. You can change the speed of the source clip to fit. If the difference between source and destination is not great, the resulting slow or fast motion may be undetectable. But if you must squeeze, say, a six-second source to fill a three-second slot, the speed difference will be obvious.

Alternatively, you can change the length of the source clip to fit the target slot. When you do this, you essentially revert to a three-point edit, letting the software insert the source clip until it runs out of space and then set its out-point automatically.

Three- and four-point edits are useful when you cannot change the length of the program or the running time of other shots in it. However, it is more common to insert shots while allowing the rest of the program to adjust to them.

Rolling edits

One way to do this is with a **rolling edit, Figure 20-17.** When you make a rolling edit, you retain the original program length. However, the shot following the insert adjusts to compensate. If the replacement is shorter than the original, the in-point of the following clip moves up to fill the gap. But if the replacement shot is longer, the in-point of the following clip moves back, to open up the necessary space. To make a rolling edit with a shorter replacement clip, the next clip

must have previously trimmed material at its head. This is a good reason for digitizing and saving at least 5 extra seconds at the beginning and end of each clip you capture

Like four-point edits, rolling edits are useful when a program, such as a commercial, must retain a precise overall length. When length is not critical, however, it may be easier to perform a ripple edit instead.

Ripple edits

A **ripple edit** is a three-point edit in which all the material following the insert adjusts automatically to fit it, **Figure 20-18.** If the insert is shorter, all the following material closes the gap by pulling up to the end of the new shot. But if the insert is longer, all the following material makes room for it by moving over. In practice, you may find that ripple edits are the most common inserts that you make.

Figure 20-17.
A rolling edit.

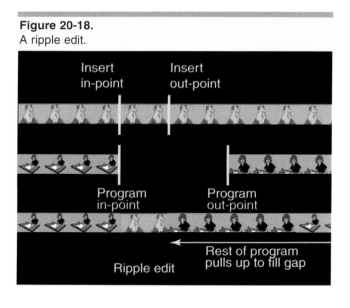

Figure 20-16.
A four-point edit.

Figure 20-18.
A ripple edit.

Slip and slide edits

If you wish to adjust the program on both sides of the new material, you can select either a slip edit or a slide edit. A **slip edit** preserves the in- and out-points of the preceding and following clips by shifting the in- and out-points of the source clip. This allows you to fine-tune the part of the new clip inserted into the program, **Figure 20-19**.

A **slide edit** preserves the in- and out-points of the new clip by shortening the clips on both sides. Generally, you can slide the new clip back and forth to decide how much of the previous and/or following shots to shorten. This allows you to change the length of the source clip without affecting the length of the program, **Figure 20-20**.

Figure 20-19.
A slip edit.

Figure 20-20.
A slide edit.

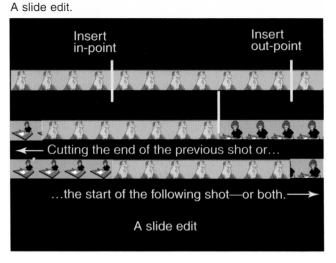

Editing tools and options

Three-point, four-point, rolling, rippling, slipping, sliding: these options can seem confusing at first, and professional editing software offers many more as well, including other forms of edits, different tools for making the actual edits, different windows in which to adjust clips, and a choice of keyboard or mouse-based commands for many editing functions. In practice, most editors gradually evolve personal working methods to suit their own needs, utilizing the features they prefer and ignoring the others. In other words, you need not master and use every option in a sophisticated postproduction application. Instead, use new features as you need them and then decide whether to continue with them or not.

Archiving the Results

Whenever you save a word processing or spreadsheet document, the file you store is a full version of the work you are creating. It is important to understand, however, that this is not always true of video programs. When you save your work as you edit, you are saving a project, not a program. A project is a record of everything you have done to create the program. A project is like a complete set of blueprints for a complex building, but it is not the building itself. A program is a video that can be played back at full quality, on some form of standard display. It is the building described in the blueprints.

Project files

Project files sometimes do not contain full quality versions of the shots themselves, but only references to those shots, **Figure 20-21**. It is a good idea to save your projects frequently, for protection.

If you plan a major revision of your program, you can save the project, then save it again under a different filename and revise this copy. That way, you have a complete backup copy of the original version. This procedure is practical because project files take up relatively little disk space.

Project files are not easily transported from one computer to another because all the shots and other materials for the finished program are in other files that remain behind.

Figure 20-21.
Adobe Premiere stores PC projects with a PPJ extension.

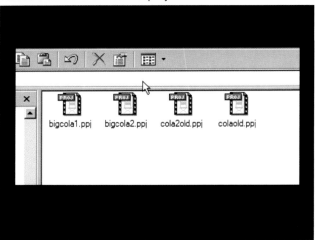

bigcola1.ppj   bigcola2.ppj   cola2old.ppj   colaold.ppj

Editing software uses project files to locate program materials on hard drives as it needs them.

Program files

Program files are finished videos (or sections of them). They consume large amounts of disk space because, unlike project files, they contain every frame of video and audio in full-quality versions.

Rendering program files

Your editing software creates a program file by automatically assembling it, following the frame-by-frame instructions in the project file. This assembly process is called *rendering*. Powerful editing programs running on high-speed computers may render in real time. That is, they create and recreate the program at full quality as you work on the project. This means that you can see full-quality results at any time, you can catch any defects in the rendering process and correct them on the spot, and you do not need to wait while the software builds your final program.

More modest setups may require you to render your program by batch processing when you have finished editing. With this approach, you instruct the system to assemble the final program, then wait (as long as several hours, with small systems) while it does the job.

Most editing software can render trial versions of transitions, effects, titles, etc. so that you can review them as you work.

Aside from the inconvenience of long rendering times, the other drawback of batch rendering is quality control. If the final program contains dropped frames, artifacts, or other imperfections, you may have to repeat the whole process.

Rendering versus archiving

Rendering (either real-time or batch-processed) gives you a final program file stored on a hard drive. But in most cases, you do not want to leave it there, tying up many gigabytes of drive space. Instead, you want to archive it by storing it permanently in a place where you can preserve it, make copies of it, or show it. Typically, you archive a program by exporting it to a disk recorder or to tape in a camcorder or VCR, **Figure 20-22.**

Formats for archiving

Whether disk or tape, a digital recording format is better for archiving because copies can be made without significant quality loss. However, most computer systems can output video and audio directly in an analog format such as NTSC. Using this format, you can make program copies on conventional videotapes from your computer. If possible, however, it is preferable to archive your program in digital form and then make analog versions for convenient viewing.

Archiving long programs

As noted elsewhere, you can save space by breaking programs down into sections and editing one at a time. When you have

Figure 20-22.
Rendering and archiving.

Archiving

Rendering

finished each one, archive it as a separate subprogram, clear out all the working files, and then start the next section as a new project. Remember: always end a section with a straight cut rather than a transition that must be rendered. If you need, say, a dissolve between sequences on adjacent sections, end the old sequence with a dissolve to the opening shot of the new sequence. Then, start the new sequence project with a straight cut to the second shot.

Transformations

Program material in digital form is easy to adjust, modify, or change into something quite different. There are hundreds, perhaps thousands, of ways to transform video originals. Each editing application comes with its own proprietary set of effects. So-called "plug-ins" can be added to the original package to extend its capabilities. You can export footage to completely separate software applications, work on it, and then import it back into your project.

With so many options available, it would be impractical to discuss every one. So this section covers the general types of image transformations that you are likely to encounter.

Transitions, composites, and titles are also covered in Chapter 19 and elsewhere in this book.

Transitions

The most common transformations are transitions from one sequence to another. Traditional transitions such as fades, dissolves, and wipes, are supplemented by scores of special effects.

Other DVEs

Fades and dissolves are digital video effects (DVEs) that signal a transition between sections, **Figure 20-23**. Other DVEs are used for punctuation, or just to impart extra energy and excitement.

Plug-in effects

Plug-ins are programs that become part of your editing software. They do not have to be opened separately because their commands and other features are automatically displayed in the menus of your application.

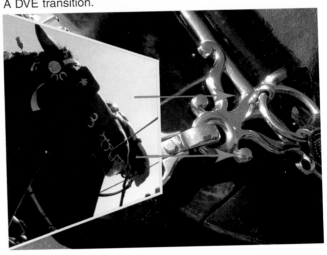

Figure 20-23.
A DVE transition.

Superimpositions

Superimpositions are combinations of two or more images displayed together, **Figure 20-24.** The most common superimposition is the double exposure, in which two full-screen images are visible at once. In digital postproduction, however, most superimposition involves replacing parts of one image with parts of another.

Compositing

Compositing is the process of placing part of one image (usually the subject or other foreground object) into a different background. This is commonly done by recording the foreground against a background of a very specific and very uniform solid color. Then the software replaces every pixel of this key

Figure 20-24.
A superimposition. (Sue Stinson)

color with the corresponding pixel from the background image.

Exporting to other programs

For more elaborate compositing, you can export a shot to a separate application, such as a painting and photo program. There, you work one frame at a time, adding and animating elements to your original shot. When you have finished, you import the result back into your project. Since full-motion video requires 30 frames per second, working frame-by-frame can be very time-consuming; however, many photo/paint applications can automate parts of the process, copying the changes made in one frame to the next frame, where they can be further modified as the sequence progresses.

Titles

Titles are usually transformations because they often replace parts of a live action scene.

In most titling software, it is possible to make the titles partially transparent, so that the live action is visible through them.

All editing software includes titling capability; and many plug-ins and separate programs are available for expanding your options in adding titles.

Image control

You can also change the basic nature of your visuals to suit the requirements of your project.

- **Speed.** You can create slow motion and fast motion shots.
- **Direction.** You can reverse the direction of the action by "flopping" shots left to right. If, for instance, a left-to-right shot violates a general right-to-left screen direction, you can correct it by flopping it digitally.

In computer graphics applications, the more common term is "flipping," rather than flopping.

- **Composition.** You can zoom in to fill the screen with just part of the original composition. This is useful to add emphasis, redesign shot compositions, or eliminate unwanted elements like microphones.
- **Photographic characteristics.** You can change the brightness, contrast, and color balance of your original footage, in order to correct errors in shooting, to match surrounding shots, or to create special effects like a sunset or a moonlit night. You can also turn color footage to black and white or give it an old-fashioned sepia tone, **Figure 20-25**.
- **Special effects.** Most applications include special effects. Though their number is almost limitless, an artificial lens flare is a representative example.

Figure 20-25.
Changing photographic characteristics. A—Original shot.

B—Shot converted to sepia monochrome, with added photographic "grain." (Sue Stinson)

A

B

Nonlinear Audio

Digital audio editing offers so much greater potential than the traditional analog approach that its major advantages are worth considering in detail.

Multiple tracks

To begin with, you can have as many audio tracks as you want — dozens of them, if necessary. These tracks can be mono, stereo, or a mixture, depending on the sound sources used. With nearly unlimited tracks to work with, you can create audio as complex as that of most Hollywood films, right on your desktop.

Timeline control

Working with a timeline, you can see all your audio elements in front of you, where you can select them, audition them, move them, and modify them with mouse or keyboard commands.

"Visible" sound

You can see each track as a waveform: a graphic representation of the sound's variations in loudness. With this tool, you can make extremely precise edits and time music passages exactly. See **Figure 20-26.**

Figure 20-26.
A waveform helps make precise edits.

Synchronization

You can unlock a sound track from its video and move it freely. You can synchronize two different video and audio tracks and then lock them together so that they become a single editing clip. In short, digital audio editing is so powerful that when you are working on a modest desktop computer, you have more creative control than you could find in even the most sophisticated analog sound studio. Editing software applications vary in their audio capabilities, but they all include the basic functions of sound capture, editing, and processing.

Capture

Digital sound editing can be so flexible because you work from audio files on your hard drive. So the first step is to get those files onto your drive in a form that your editing software can use.

External sources

Production sound tracks are recorded with video and transferred to your computer as part of the video capture process. If you want only the audio part, you can save it separately and discard the video half of the

---

A Simple Audio Production Design

Although editing software may offer close to 100 separate audio tracks, you can achieve very professional results with 12 tracks or less. To demonstrate, here is a simple audio design for a dramatic program. (For simplicity, this is a monophonic program. A stereo version would need twice as many tracks.)

Track	Content
1	Production dialog track A
2	Production dialog track B
3	Background A
4	Background B
5	Effects A
6	Effects B
7	Effects C
8	Effects D
9	Music A
10	Music B
11	Miscellaneous A
12	Miscellaneous B

As you study this layout, notice that all components have at least two tracks (A and B), so that sounds can be cross-faded between them. An extra pair of effects tracks allows the editor to layer up multiple sound effects. A pair of miscellaneous tracks can be used occasionally for dialogue, effects, or music, at places where the regular tracks already have sound in them.

capture. If the production originals are digital, the audio comes in through the Firewire (high speed data transfer) port. If the originals are analog, the audio may by captured by the video card, or by the computer's general-purpose sound card. Other external sources, such as microphones and music CD players, are generally captured by the main sound card.

Internal sources

Internal sound sources include files previously recorded or downloaded and music CD or DVD disks. Be aware that you usually must use sound card or operating system software to copy files and convert them to formats readable by your editing application.

Audio Editing

With your sound components on your hard drive, you are ready to build a sound track.

Production sound

The first step in sound editing is to assemble all the production audio. This happens automatically as you select, place, and trim video clips. With the basic production tracks in place you can modify every one to suit your needs: delete it, replace it with another take (usually for better sound quality), or substitute audio from other shots. If there is a separate production track of ambient (background) sounds, you can lay that under the scene, adjusting its volume to compensate for shot-to-shot differences created by different miking positions.

Sound effects

With the production tracks complete, the next step is to add sound effects. These may have been recorded as part of the production, copied from sound effects disks, or recorded in a Foley (sound effects recording) studio.

Music

Generally, music is the last set of tracks to be laid down. Blended together, the production, background, and effects tracks will sound like a single "live" sound track. Music, however, is perceived by the audience as a separate set of sounds. For this reason, it is often helpful to create the composite live sound track and then balance it with the music.

Transitions

To make transitions from one sequence to another, or simply from one sound to the next, you can blend audio elements together with fades, cross-fades, and split edits. Most editing software allows you to fade sound volume up or down by dragging a volume bar on the timeline, **Figure 20-27.**

Fade

A fade-in or fade-out makes a gradual transition. A fast fade-in will prevent a sound from seeming sudden and abrupt. A very long, slow fade-in can bring up a sound so unobtrusively that the audience is not aware of it. Fade-outs are especially useful for dispensing with music that does not have a clean ending. A three-second to eight-second fade-out will generally deliver a graceful exit.

Cross-fade

A cross-fade overlaps the fadeout of one sound with the fade-in of another sound. Cross-fades are often employed to match dissolves on the video track, but you can also use them to blend from one sound to another so that the audience does not notice it.

Split edit

A split edit is a transition in which picture and sound do not change at the same time. When video leads, the sound from the old shot continues over the video of the new

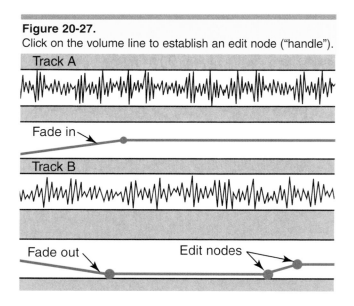

Figure 20-27.
Click on the volume line to establish an edit node ("handle").

shot. When audio leads, the audio from the new shot begins before the picture, giving the audience a brief foretaste of what is to come. Split edits are especially easy with timeline editing because you can see the overlaps exactly.

Sometimes, a split edit will include a cross-fade at the transition point. However, straight cut split edits can make powerfully dramatic punctuations.

Processing

Fading volume is only the simplest of many ways to manipulate the quality of individual audio tracks. Every editing application has its own set of tools, and plug-in products are available as well. In addition, you can process audio with the software tools provided with computer sound cards or sold separately as computer-based recording studios. Here are just a few of the many ways to process audio tracks.

- **Stereo imaging.** If you are working in stereo, you can place a sound anywhere on a line from left to right, or have it move from one side of the sound image to the other.

- **Sweetening.** You can clean up audio by adjusting treble and bass, suppressing some sounds, compressing or limiting range of loudness, and eliminating hiss or hum.

- **Distorting.** You can change the character of sound by adding reverberation, changing pitch, or applying one or more of the many sound filters supplied with your editor or available separately.

A Final Note

This brief survey of digital audio editing completes this chapter on computer-based postproduction. As noted, it has been impractical to cover this topic at a step-by-step level because different editing software uses different methods and approaches, and because computer systems continue to evolve so rapidly. Instead, we have focused on the principles behind the procedures— principles that are likely to remain constant, no matter how hardware and software evolve.

Technical Terms

Analog: A recording that imitates the original. The level of an analog video signal varies continuously to record the image or sound.

Artifact: A spot or other blemish on a digital image.

Bit depth: The number of digits (bits) used to encode each piece of digital data. Eight-bit, 16-bit, and 24-bit are common bit depths.

Capture: To bring program material into a computer from an external source.

Clip: A unit of program material in a digital editing project. A clip may contain anything from part of one shot to several shots together.

Codec: A program that encodes a signal in digital form and decodes it into analog form.

Device control: The ability of software to operate external hardware (camera or VCR) by remote control.

Digital: A recording that repeatedly samples the original continuous signal and records the numerical values of the samples, instead of the signal itself.

EDL (Edit Decision List): a computerized, frame-accurate record of every component in a program. Can be used to automatically recreate the program, using the original sources.

Four-point edit: An edit that specifies the in- and out-points of both the source clip and the place in the program at which the clip will be inserted.

Frame rate: The actual speed with which video frames are displayed. The frame rate of NTSC video is 29.97 frames per second.

MJPEG: A video compression system that reduces the data required to record each frame.

MPEG: A video compression system that records all the data of a "base frame." For subsequent frames, the system records only data that differs from that of the base frame.

Post house: Short for "postproduction house," a professional facility that rents editing setups and personnel for high-quality video editing.

Render: To execute any digital processing of an image. A dissolve between shots, for example, is rendered, frame-by-frame, by the computer.

Ripple edit: An insert edit in which all the material following the inserted clip is moved up or back to accommodate it.

Rolling edit: An insert edit in which the shot following the inserted material is shortened or lengthened to accommodate it.

Sample rate: The number of times per second at which an analog signal level is inspected and digitally recorded. Expressed in kilohertz (kHz). The sample rate of CD-quality audio is 44.1 kHz, meaning that the signal is sampled over 44,000 times per second.

Slide edit: An insert edit in which the out-point of the preceding shot and the in-point of the following shot are adjusted to accommodate the inserted material.

Slip edit: An insert edit in which the in- and out-points of the inserted material are adjusted so that the preceding and following shots remain unchanged.

Three-point edit: An insert edit in which both the in- and out-points of the program are specified, but only the in-point of the new material into which it is inserted

Timebase: The basis on which time-code is assigned to frames. The timebase of NTSC video is 30 frames per second.

Timecode: A unique identifier, expressed in hours, minutes, seconds, and frames, assigned to each frame of video.

Window dub: A copy of the original footage in which the timecode is visible in a small window at the bottom of the screen.

A nonlinear editing system for high-definition video. (Cinéwave/Pinnacle)

Glossary of Technical Terms

A

Act: A major division of a program, typically ten or more minutes long, and divided from other acts by fade-out/fade-in transitions.

Action line: An imaginary line separating camera and subject. Keeping the camera on its side of the line maintains screen direction.

Additive editing: Creating a program from raw footage by starting with nothing and adding selected components.

Analog: A recording that imitates the original. The level of an analog video signal varies continuously to record the image or sound.

Angle of view: The breadth of a lens's field of coverage, expressed as an arc of a circle, such as "10 degrees."

Aperture: The opening in the lens that admits light. The iris diaphragm can vary the aperture from fully open to almost or completely closed. Also, an opening of a particular size, as in "The aperture is f/8."

Artifact: A defect in a digital image, such as a spot or mosaic pattern.

Assembly editing: Constructing a video program by transferring shots in sequence to a master tape.

Assembly tape: In editing, the tape in the record VCR, on which the program is created.

Associative continuity: A sequence of shots related by similarity of content.

Audio: Collectively, the sound components of an audio-visual program.

Audio dubbing: Replacing a segment of previously recorded audio without disturbing the accompanying video.

Autoexposure: The camera system that delivers the correct amount of illumination to the recording mechanism, regardless of the light level of the shooting environment.

Autofocus: The camcorder system that automatically adjusts the lens to keep subjects sharp.

B

Balanced line: A three-wire microphone cable designed to minimize electrical interference.

Barn doors: Metal flaps, usually in sets of two or four, that are attached to the fronts of spotlights to control the edges of the beam.

Beat: A short unit of action in a program, often, though not always, corresponding to a scene.

Bit depth: The number of digits (bits) used to encode each piece of digital data. Eight-bit, 16-bit, and 24-bit are common bit depths.

Blacking the tape: Prerecording an entire tape with a pure-black picture, no sound, and time code (or in analog formats, a control track).

Blocking: A performer's movement within a shot. It is rehearsed and memorized so that the actor hits the correct spots with respect to camera and lighting, and so that the movements can be repeated exactly for other angles on the same action. Camera movement is also blocked.

Boom: A studio microphone support consisting of a rolling pedestal and a horizontal arm.

Booming: Moving the entire camera up or down through a vertical arc (also *craning*).

Brightness: The position of a pictorial element on a scale from black to white.

Budgeting: Predicting the costs of every aspect of a production and allocating funds to cover it.

Buffer shot: A shot placed between two others, often to conceal differences between them.

Business: Activities performed during a shot, such as writing a letter or filling a vase with flowers.

C

Camcorder: An appliance that both captures moving images (***cam***era) and stores them on tape (re***corder***).

Camera angle: The position from which a shot is taken, described by horizontal angle, vertical angle, and subject distance.

Camera dolly: A rolling camera support. A cart dolly resembles a wagon; a pedestal dolly mounts the camera on a central post.

Camera light: A small light mounted on the camera to provide foreground fill.

Capture: To bring program material into a computer from an external source.

Cardioid: A spatial pattern of microphone sensitivity, named for its resemblance to a Valentine heart.

CCD (Charge-Coupled Device): The camcorder imaging chip that converts optical images into electronic signals.

Century stand (C-stand): A telescoping floor stand fitted with a clamp and usually an adjustable arm, for supporting lights and accessories.

Cheat: To move a subject from its original place (to facilitate another shot) in a way that is undetectable to the viewer.

Clip: A unit of program material in a digital editing project. A clip may contain anything from part of one shot to several shots together.

Codec: A program that encodes a signal in digital form and decodes it into analog form.

Color temperature: The overall color cast of nominally "white" light, expressed in degrees on the Kelvin scale. Sunlight color temperature (5200K) is cooler (more bluish) than halogen light color temperature (3200K).

Color temperature meter: A light meter that measures the relative blueness or redness of nominally "white" light.

Compositing: A digital editing process in which elements of one image replace elements of another image to create a combination of both.

Composition: The purposeful arrangement of the parts of an image.

Concept: The organizing principle behind an effective program. Often called an angle, perspective, or slant.

Continuity: The organization of video material into a coherent presentation, giving the illusion that a program is a single continuous piece.

Contrast: The difference between the lightest and darkest parts of an image, expressed as a ratio (e.g. "four-to-one"). Also, the difference between one pictorial element and others.

Cookie: A sheet cut into a specific pattern and placed in the beam of a light to throw distinctive shadows such as leaves or blinds.

Correcting: Making small continuous framing adjustments to maintain a good composition.

Crew: Production staff members who work behind the camera. In larger professional productions, the producer, director, and management staff are not considered "crew."

Cross cutting: Showing two actions at once by alternating back and forth between them, presenting part of one, then part of the other, then back to the first, and so-on. It can also be used to show three or even more parallel actions.

Cut together: A term with two meanings: 1) to follow one shot with another; 2) to select edit points on outgoing and incoming shots so that an edit is not apparent.

Cutaway: A shot other than, but related to, the main action.

D

Decoding: Identifying and understanding the elements in a composition.

Default: A setting that is selected automatically unless the user changes it manually.

Delivery system: The method (such as website, TV monitor, or kiosk) by which a program will be presented, and the situation (alone at a desk, in a training room, in a crowded store) in which it will be watched.

Depth of field: The distance range, near-to-far, within which subjects appear sharp in the image.

Device control: The ability of software to operate external hardware (camera or VCR) by remote control.

Dialogue: Speech by performers on-screen.

Digital: A recording method that repeatedly samples the original continuous signal and records the numerical values of the samples, instead of the signal itself.

Digital video effect (DVE): Informally, any digitally-created transitional device other than a fade or dissolve. (Technically, fades and dissolves are usually digital, too).

Digital zoom: Increasing the subject size by filling the frame with only the central part of the image.

Digitize: To record images and sounds as numerical data, either directly in a camcorder or in the process of importing them to a computer.

Dissolve: A fade-in that coincides with a fade-out, so that the incoming shot gradually replaces the outgoing shot. Typically used as a transition between sequences that are fairly closely related.

Dollying: Moving the entire camera horizontally (also *trucking* and *tracking*).

Dress: To add decorative items to a set or location. Such items are called "set dressing."

Dutch: Referring to an off-level composition. The "put dutch on a shot" is to purposely tilt the camera.

E

Editing: Creating a video program from production footage and other raw materials.

EDL (Edit Decision List): A computerized, frame-accurate record of every component in a program. Can be used to automatically recreate the program using the original sources.

Emphasis: The process of calling attention to a program element.

Equalization: The adjustment of the volume levels of various sound frequencies to balance the overall mixture of sounds.

Equalizer: A device for adjusting the relative strengths of different audio frequencies.

F

Fade-in: A transition in which the image begins as pure black and gradually lightens to full brightness. Used to signal the start of a major section such as an act or an entire program.

Fade-out: A transition in which the image begins at full brightness and gradually darkens to pure black. Used to signal the end of a major section such as an act or an entire program.

Filename: The identification of an editing element as it is stored in a computer.

Fill light: The light that lightens shadows created by the main (key) light.

Film: An audiovisual medium that records images on transparent plastic strips by means of photosensitive chemicals.

Fishpole: A microphone support consisting of a hand-held telescoping arm.

Fixed head: A record or erase head that operates in a continuous line on the tape passing across it.

Flag: A flat piece of opaque metal, wood, or foam-core placed to mask off part of a light beam.

Flashback: A sequence that takes place earlier in the story than the sequence that precedes it.

Floodlight: A large-source instrument that typically lacks a lens, for lighting wide areas.

Flying head: A record or erase head that operates on the tape in short discrete diagonal segments.

Focal length: Technically, one design parameter of a lens, expressed in millimeters (4mm, 40mm). Informally, the name of any particular lens.

Focus: Photographically, that part of the image (measured from near to far) that appears sharp and clear; also, generally, the object of a viewer's attention.

Foley studio: An area set up for recording real-time sound effects synchronously with video playback.

Four-point edit: An edit that specifies the in- and out-points of both the source clip and the place in the program at which the clip will be inserted.

Frame: A single still picture, 30 of which make a second of NTSC video. Also, the four edges that make up the border of the screen. In production terms, "to frame" is to feature a subject in a composition.

Frame off: To exclude an object completely from the screen.

Frame rate: The actual speed with which video frames are displayed. The frame rate of NTSC video is 29.97 frames per second.

f-stop: A particular aperture. Most lenses are designed with preset f-stops of f/1.4, f/2, f/2.8, f/4, f/5.6, f/8, f/11, f/16, and f/22.

G

Gaffer: The chief lighting technician on a production crew.

Gag: Any effect, trick, or stunt in a movie.

Gain: The electronic amplification of the signal made from an image, in order to increase its brightness.

Generation: A level of tape copy. An original camera tape is first generation, a copy made from it is second generation, and a copy of the copy is third generation.

Generation loss: The decline in video and audio quality from one analog generation to the next.

H

Head: A tiny electromagnet that encodes signals by magnetizing particles on videotape (record), decodes previously recorded signals by reading their magnetic patterns (play), or destroys previously recorded signals by giving all tape particles an identical magnetic alignment (erase).

Head room: The distance between the top of a subject's head and the upper edge of the frame.

I

Image: A single unit of visual information. An image may last for many frames, until the subject, the camera, or both, create a new image by moving. Most shots contain several identifiable images.

Image stabilization: Compensation to minimize the effects of camera shake. Electronic stabilization shifts the image on the chip to counter movement; optical stabilization shifts parts of the lens instead.

Incident light: Light emitted by a lighting instrument.

Incident meter: A light meter that measures the illumination as it comes from the light sources.

In-point: The first frame of a new piece of material.

Insert: A closeup detail of the action.

Insert editing: Replacing part of a previously edited video and/or audio segment with new material. The opposite of assembly editing.

Instrument: A unit of lighting hardware such as a spotlight or floodlight.

Intercutting: See *Cross cutting.*

Iris diaphragm (iris): A mechanism inside a lens (usually a ring of overlapping blades) that varies the size of the lens opening (aperture).

J

Jump cut: An edit in which the incoming shot is too similar, visually, to the outgoing shot.

K

Key light: The main illumination of a subject.

L

Lamp: The actual bulb in a lighting instrument.

Large-source: Describing a lighting instrument, such as a scoop or other floodlight, with a big frontal area from which light is emitted. Light from large-source instruments is relatively soft and diffused.

Lavaliere: A very small microphone clipped to the subject's clothing, close to the mouth.

Lead room: The distance between the subject and the edge of the frame toward which it is moving.

Leading lines: Lines on the picture plane that emphasize an element by pointing to it.

Leading the eye: Using compositional techniques to direct the viewer's attention.

Line reading: A vocal interpretation of a line that includes its speed, emphases, and intonations. In simple terms, "You came back!" is one reading of a line, and "You came *back*?" is a different reading.

Linear continuity: A sequence of shots organized chronologically and/or logically.

Linear editing: Working with both source materials and finished program on videotape, rather than in a computer.

Lines: Scripted speech to be spoken by performers.

Live: Recorded and (usually) transmitted for display continuously and in real time.

Look room: The distance between the subject and the edge of the frame toward which it is looking.

Looping: Replacing dialogue in real time by recording it synchronously with video playback.

M

Magnification: The apparent increase or decrease in subject size of an image, compared to the same subject as seen by the human eye. Telephoto lenses magnify subjects; wide angle lenses reduce them.

Marks: Places within the shot where the performer is to pause, stop, turn, etc. These spots are typically identified by marks made of tape or chalk lines.

Match point: The places, in two shots, where they can be cut together to make the action appear continuous.

Microphone (mike): A device that converts sound waves into electrical modulations, for recording.

Mixer: A device that balances the input strengths of signals from two or more sources, especially microphones.

Mixing: The blending together of separate audio tracks, either in a computer or through a sound mixing board.

MJPEG: A video compression system that reduces the data required to record each frame.

Montage: A brief, multilayer passage of video and audio elements designed to present a large amount of information in highly condensed form.

MPEG: A video compression system that records all the data of a "base frame." For subsequent frames, the system records only information that differs from that of the base frame.

N

Neutral density filter: A gray lens filter used to reduce incoming light.

O

Objective insert: A detail of the action presented from a neutral point of view.

Optical zoom: Changing a lens' angle of view (wide angle to telephoto) continuously by moving internal parts of the lens.

Out-point: The last frame of a new piece of material.

P

Pan: To pivot the camcorder horizontally on its support.

Parallel cutting: Presenting two or more sequences at once by showing parts of one, then another, then the first again (or a third), and so-on.

Pedestaling: Moving the camera up or down in place, on its central support.

Perspective: The representation of the third dimension (depth) in a two-dimensional medium such as video. Common forms of perspective include size, overlap, vertical position, converging lines, resolution, and color saturation.

Pickup pattern: The directions (in three dimensions) in which a microphone is most sensitive to sounds.

Playback: Previously recorded video and/or audio reproduced so that actors or technicians can add to or replace parts of it synchronously, in real time.

Point of view (POV): A vantage point from which the camera records a shot. Unlike a camera *angle*, a point of view is not described by subject distance ("closeup," etc.) and unlike a *setup*, a point of view is not concerned with production equipment.

Polarizer: A filter that can be rotated in front of the lens to reduce reflections and darken blue skies.

Post house: Short for "postproduction house," a professional facility that rents editing setups and personnel for high-quality video editing.

Practical: A light that is included in shots and may be operated by the actors. Also, an actual subject to be videotaped and then combined with digital elements created in postproduction.

Preroll: Starting the source deck playback prior to the in-point of the shot being transferred.

Production track: The "live" sound recorded with the video.

Program: Any complete video presentation, from a five-second commercial to a movie two or more hours long.

Protection shot: A shot made to help fix potential problems with other shots.

Pulling focus (following focus, racking focus): Changing the lens focus during a shot to keep a moving subject sharp.

R

Reflected light: Light bouncing off a subject.

Reflective meter: A light meter that measures illumination as it bounces off the subjects and into the camera lens.

Reflector: A large silver, white, or colored surface used to bounce light onto a subject or scene.

Render: To execute any digital processing of an image. A dissolve between shots, for example, is rendered, frame-by-frame, by the computer.

Rendering: Creating a full-quality version of material previously edited in a lower-quality form.

Rim light: A light placed high and behind a subject to create a rim of light on head and shoulders, to help separate subject and background.

Ripple edit: An insert edit in which all the material following the inserted clip is moved up or back to accommodate it.

Roll to raw stock: To advance a videotape through previously recorded sections to blank tape, in preparation for additional recording.

Rolling edit: An insert edit in which the shot following the inserted material is shortened or lengthened to accommodate it.

Rule of thirds: An aid to composition in the form of an imaginary tic-tac-toe grid superimposed on the image. Important picture components are aligned with the lines and intersections of the grid.

Runup: The difference between the point in time when the RECORD function is enabled and the first frame of recorded material.

S

Sample rate: The number of times per second at which an analog signal level is inspected and digitally recorded. Expressed in kilohertz (kHz). The sample rate of CD-quality audio is 44.1 kHz, meaning that the signal is sampled over 44,000 times per second.

Scene: A short segment of program content, usually made up of several closely related shots.

Screen: A mesh material that reduces light intensity without markedly changing its character.

Screen direction: The subject's orientation (usually left or right) with respect to the borders of the screen.

Screen time: The length of real-world time during which a sequence is displayed on the screen (in contrast to the length of video world time that apparently passes during that sequence).

Script: A full written documentation of a program that is formatted like a play. It includes scenes, dialogue, narration, stage directions, and effects.

Sell: To add details to increase the believability of a screen illusion.

Sequence: A segment of program content, usually consisting of several related scenes.

Setting focus: Adjusting the lens to make the subject appear sharp.

Setup: An arrangement of production equipment (typically camera, microphone, and lighting) placed to record shots from a certain point of view.

Shoot: To record film or video; also, "a shoot" is an informal term for the production phase of a film or video project.

Shot: A single continuous recording. In editing, shot A may be interrupted by shot B before resuming. When this happens, the second part of the original shot A may be considered a new shot.

Shutter: The electronic circuitry that determines how long each frame of picture will accumulate on the imaging chip, before processing. The standard shutter speed is 1/60 per second for NTSC format video.

Silk: A fabric material that reduces both light intensity and directionality, producing a soft, directionless illumination.

Slate: A written video or spoken audio identification of a component such as a shot, a line of narration, or a sound effect.

Slide edit: An insert edit in which the out-point of the preceding shot and the in-point of the following shot are adjusted to accommodate the inserted material.

Slip edit: An insert edit in which the in- and out-points of the inserted material are adjusted so that the preceding and following shots remain unchanged.

Small-source: Describing a lighting instrument such as a spotlight, with a small frontal area from which light is emitted. Light from small-source instruments is generally hard-edged and tightly focused.

Soft light: An extremely large-source lighting instrument (as big as four feet square) that emits extremely soft, diffuse light that imitates natural light.

Sound: The noises recorded as audio.

Sound effects: Specific noises added to a sound track.

Source tape: The tape providing the raw material for editing; usually, but not always, an original camera tape.

Specular reflections: Hard, bright reflections from surfaces such as water, glass, and automobile paint that create points of light on the image. Often controllable by a polarizer.

Speed: The light-gathering ability of a lens, expressed as its maximum aperture. Thus, an f/1.4 lens is "two stops faster" (more light sensitive) than an f/2.8 lens.

Split edit: An edit in which the audio and video of the new shot do not begin simultaneously. When "video leads," the sound from the preceding shot continues over the visual of the new shot. When "audio leads," the sound from the new shot begins over the end of the preceding visual.

Spotlight: A small-source instrument, usually but not always fitted with a lens to concentrate the light, that emits a narrow, hard-edged beam.

Storyboard: Program documentation in graphic panels, like a comic book, with or without dialogue, narration, stage directions, and effects.

Straight cut: An edit in which audio and video change simultaneously; also, an edit that does not include an effect such as a fade or dissolve.

Subjective continuity: A sequence organized according to the feelings of the director/editor, rather than by chronological or other objective criteria.

Subjective insert: A detail of the action presented from a character's point of view.

Subtractive editing: Creating a program by removing redundant or poor-quality material from the original footage and leaving the remainder essentially as it was shot.

T

Tabletop: Videography of small subjects and activities on a table or counter.

Talent: Every production member who performs for the camera.

Tally light: A small light on a camera that glows to show that the unit is recording.

Telephoto: A lens or a setting on a zoom lens that magnifies subjects and minimizes apparent depth by filling the frame with a narrow angle of view.

Teleprompter: A machine that displays text progressively as a performer reads it on-camera.

Television: Studio-based, multicamera video that is often produced and transmitted "live."

Tent: A white fabric draped all around a subject to diffuse lighting completely for a totally shadowless effect.

Three-point edit: An insert edit in which both the in- and out-points of the new material are specified, but only the in-point of the program into which it is inserted.

Tilting: Pivoting the camera vertically in place.

Timebase: The basis on which timecode is assigned to frames. The timebase of NTSC video is 30 frames per second.

Timecode address: The unique identifying code number assigned to each frame of video. Timecode is expressed in hours, minutes, seconds, and frames, counted from the point at which timecode recording is started.

Timeline: The graphic representation of a program as a matrix of video, audio, and computer-generated elements.

Transducer: The component of a microphone that converts changing air pressure ("sound") into an electrical signal ("audio").

Treatment: A written summary of a program, formatted as narrative prose, that may be as short as one paragraph or as long as a scene-by-scene description.

Tripod: A three-legged camera support that permits leveling and turning the camera.

U

Unbalanced line: A two-wire microphone cable subject to electrical interference, but less bulky and expensive, for use in amateur applications.

V

Video: An audiovisual medium that records on magnetic tape or disk by electronic means; also, single-camera taped program creation in the manner of film production rather than studio television.

Visual literacy: The ability to evaluate the content of visual media through an understanding of the way in which it is recorded and presented.

Voiceover: Narration or dialogue that is recorded independently and then paired with related video.

W

White balance: The camera setting selected to match the color temperature of the light source illuminating the subject.

Wide-angle: A lens or a setting on a zoom lens that minimizes subjects and magnifies apparent depth by filling the frame with a wide angle of view.

Window dub: A copy of the original footage in which the timecode is visible in a small window at the bottom of the screen

Wipe: A transition between sequences in which a line moves across the screen, progressively covering the outgoing shot before it with the incoming shot behind it.

Z

Zoom: To magnify or reduce the size of a subject by changing the focal length of the lens while recording.

Zooming: Changing the lens' angle of view to fill the frame with a smaller area (zooming in) or a larger area (zooming out). The effect is to apparently reduce or expand the size of subjects in the frame.

Index

A

A/B roll editing, 324
A/X roll editing, 324
act, 82, 294
action
    continuity of, 247
    coverage, 244–246
    matching, 81
    omitting, 46
    overlapping, 46, 245
    speeding or slowing, 282
action line, 256
actors
    and lines, 238
    expressing emotion, 240
    hitting marks, 239–240
    insecurity, 236–237
    looking at the camera, 240
    matching action, 81, 240
    performance, 235–236
    self-consciousness, 237
additive editing, 272–273
ambient track, 208–209
analog standards, 332–333
analog video, 333
analog vs digital, 316–317
    capturing raw materials, 338
angle of view, 145
anti-style, 175
aperture, 139, 159
    and exposure, 165
    and f-stop, 148
    automatic, 159–160
    exposure control, 159–160
    manual, 160
    maximum, 147
    programmed, 160
aperture range, 148
archiving, 283–284, 343–345
    vs rendering, 344
artifact, 336
aspect ratio, 337
assembling video footage, 276–279
assembly deck, 314
assembly editing, 320–322, 340–341
associative continuity, 286–287, 291–292

associative sequence, 292
asymmetrical balance, 63
atmospheric perspective, 61
audience, 101–102
audio, 88. *See also* sound.
    and emphasis, 232
    capture, 347–348
    continuity, 295–296
    dubbing, 321, 323–324
    editing, 348
    enhancing, 280–281
    functions, 94
    layering, 282–283
    nonlinear, 347–349
    problems, 117–118, 206–207
    processing, 349
    quality, 337–338
    recording tips, 25
    synchronization, 347
    transitions, 348
audio lead, 52
audio production design, 347
audio recorder, 218
audio recording, 205–226
    background sounds, 208
    camcorder, 217–218
    music, 210
    production sound, 207
    sound effects, 209
    techniques, 220–225
    types of, 207–210
    voice recording, 209–210
audiovisual media, 10
auditioning, 112–114
autoexposure control, 19
autofocus, 155–157
    control, 19
    lock, 157–158
automatic aperture, 159–160
automatic level control, 218
automobiles, scenes in, 255

B

back-cross lighting, 191
background
    light, 197–198

noise, 222
   sound, 94, 208
   track, 222
backlight, 160
balance, 56, 63
barn doors, 182
batch capture, 340
batteries, 20–21, 132–133
big closeup, 69
bird's eye angle, 73
bit depth, 336–337
blacking the tape, 119
blocking, 166, 236
booming, 262
booms, 214
budgeting, 123–124
buffer shot, 299
business, 236

C

cabled mikes, 211
cables, 184
   microphone, 215–216
cabling, 319
camcorder, 10
   controls, 18–19
   operation, 21–23
camcorder setup, 132–137
   lens, 137–140
   monitor, 134–135
   power supply, 132–133
   videotape, 135
   viewfinder, 133–134
   white balance, 135–137
camera
   avoiding problems, 23
   checking settings, 22
   dolly, 132
   functions, 126
   height, 72–75
   lights, 180
   operation, 143–168
   systems, 126–142
camera angles, 26, 68–78
   and effect, 233–234
   and emphasis, 231
   camera height, 72–75
   enhancing a subject's authority, 240
   horizontal angle, 71
   lens perspective, 75
   name variations, 72
   shot purpose, 75–76
   subject distance, 69
camera movement, 166–168, 261–267
   reasons for, 263, 265–266
   techniques, 267
   types of, 262–263

camera titlers, 326–327
capturing raw materials, 338–340
cardioid microphones, 213
careers, 12
casting, 112–114
Century stand, 178, 184
charge-coupled device (CCD), 126–127
cheat, 39
classical coverage, 248
clip, 340–341
closeup, 69
codec, 337
color
   and lighting instruments, 183
   recording, 127
color fidelity, 336
color shot, 246
color temperature, 137
color temperature meter, 185
commercials, 11
communication, directing for, 228–235
compensation, 164, 166
composing on the picture plane, 65
composite movement, 263–264
composites, 282
compositing, 326, 345–346
composition, 56
   and camera movement, 267
   and focal length, 151
   and frame, 35, 57
   balance, 56, 63
   depth in, 60–62
   emphasis in, 56, 58–60, 233
   organization in, 56–60
   perspective in, 62
   positioning an element, 58
   relationship between elements, 58
   rule of thirds, 64–65
   significance of an element, 58
   techniques, 62–66
compression, 336–337
computer-generated titles, 327–328
concept, 103–104
   samples, 105
condenser transducer, 211
configuring nonlinear projects, 331–338
connectors, 216
contemporary coverage, 248–249
content, pace of delivery, 308–309
contingency fund, 123–124
continuity, 78–81, 286–296
   and sound, 295–296
   associative, 286–287, 291–292
   editing principles, 286–296
   maintaining, 246–247, 250
   methods of organization, 286–288
   of direction, 250
   program, 293–295

sequence, 292–293
    shot-to-shot, 288–298
    subjective, 287–288
contrast, 58–60, 171
    estimating, 172
cookie, 183, 196
costumes, 120
coverage, 244–246
    styles, 248–249
crew members, 110–112
cross cutting, 49–50, 294
cross-fade, 348
cue cards, 238
cut together, 78
cutaway, 76, 245–246, 291
    as a buffer shot, 257, 299
cutting, 270. *See also* editing.

D

database, 276
decoding, 56
default settings, 19
delivery system, 102–103
depth, 38–39, 60–63
    enhancing, 260
    suppressing, 260–261
depth of field, 147, 156
detailed treatment, 106
device control, 338
dialog, 88–89
dialog replacement, 94, 210
    recording techniques, 224
diffusion, 183
digital
    camcorders, 128
    compression, 336–337
    formats, 333
    video effect (DVE), 83–84, 295,
        325–326, 345
    zoom, 153–154
digitizing, 11
dimmer, 184
diopter correction, 134
directing
    for communication, 228–235
        effect, 231–234
        emphasis, 229–231
        information, 229
    for content, 227–242
    for form, 243–268
    for performance, 235–241
    the shoot, 27–28
direction, continuity of, 250
disjointed time flow, 50
dissolve, 83
distortion, 151
dollies, 132, 266
dollying, 167, 262

drag, 130
drop-frame timecode, 335
dubbing, 321, 323–324
dutch, 233
dynamic transducer, 210–211

E

editing
    additive, 272–273
    altering speed, 46
    operations, 269–284
        archiving, 283–284
        assembling, 276–279
        enhancing, 279–281
        organizing, 274–276
        phases, 272–284
        synthesizing, 281–283
    principles, 285–312
        continuity, 286–296
        emphasis, 303, 306–308
        pace, 308–311
        performance, 296–303
    subtractive, 272–273
editing monitor, 315
editing system, setting up, 317–320
editing VCR, 314–315
electrical accessories, 184
electronic news gathering (ENG), 199–200
emphasis
    audio, 232
    brightness and color, 232
    camera angle, 231
    composition, 56, 58, 229–231
    contrast, 58–60
    editing principles, 303, 306–308
    image size, 231
    movement, 232
    shot duration, 231
enhancing raw editing materials, 279–281
equalization, 94
equalizer, 217
equipment, 118–119
    basics, 18–21
    security, 28–29
establishing shot, 75–76, 248
exporting to other programs, 346
exposure, 159–164
    factors affecting, 165
expressionism, 174–175
extension cables, 184
extreme closeup, 69
extreme long shot, 69

F

fade, 348
fade-in, 83
fade-out, 83

fast motion, 45–46, 326
filename, 276
fill light, 193–196
film, 10–11
film lighting, 188
film vs video, 11
filter, 138, 155, 177–178
    for aperture control, 163–164
    for bright conditions, 163
fishpoles, 214–215
fixed heads, 318
flags, 176, 178, 182
flashback, 51–52
flip, 83
flipping, 291, 346
floating frame, 164
flopping, 291, 326
fluorescent lamp, 182
fly-in, 83
flying heads, 318
foam-core board, 177
focal length, 144–145, 156–157
    and composition, 151
focus, 59–60, 139
    setting, 155–159
Foley effects,
    recording techniques, 222–223
    sound, 94
    studio, 209
footage, 144
four-point edit, 341–342
frame, 32–36, 68, 82, 259–260
    and composition, 57
    and screen direction, 251–252
    using to control content, 33–35
    using to determine composition and
        movement, 35–36
frame rate, 333–334
framing moving shots, 166
framing off, 33
framing the shot, 164, 166
front angle, 71
f-stop, 148
full shot, 69
furniture pads, 219

G

gaffer, 188
gaffer tape, 184
gag, 38
gain, 163
generation, 316
generation loss, 317
glance-object shot, 76
gloves, 184
graphic effects, 326

H

halogen lamp, 181–182
halogen work light, 181
hand-holding the camera, 22–23
    crane shots, 266
    moving shots, 167–168
hardware, 318–319
headphones, 218
head room, 23
high angle, 73
high-definition video, 11
high key lighting, 194
high light levels, 162
horizontal angle, 71

I

illusion of depth, 38–39
image, 68, 82
    control, 346
    integrity, 336–337
    stabilization, 139–140
impedance, 212
incandescent lamp, 181
incandescent light, 191
incident meter, 185
independent microphones, 211
individual capture, 340
information, continuity of, 247
in-point, 321
insert, 245, 299
    editing, 321, 323, 341–343
    shot, 76
interlaced scanning, 128, 334
    and shutter speed, 161
interviews, 200–201
iris diaphragm, 148

J

jump cut, 78

K

key light, 193, 195

L

large source lights, 180, 197
lavalieres, 214
laws of video space, 32–42
layering, 282–283
lead room, 23, 166
leading lines, 58
length of program, 103
lens
    characteristics, 145, 147
    cleaning, 138, 141

focal length, 144–145, 156–157
focus and aperture, 139
hood, 138
mount, 137–138
perspective, 75, 234
pictorial qualities, 147–151, 153
   distortion, 151
   magnification, 148–149
   movement, 150–151
   perspective, 149
setup, 137–140
level, 212
library sound, 94
light,
   accessories, 182–183
   character, controlling, 193
   color, 172
      controlling, 177–178, 192
   contrast, 171
   diffusion, 183
   direction, controlling, 176–177, 193
light masking, 182
light meter, 185
light quantity, 170–171
   controlling, 176, 191–192
   reduction, 182–183
light stands, 183–184
lighting
   adding effects during postproduction, 190
   character, 173–175
   design, 169–186
   evaluation tools, 184–185
   instruments, 178–181
   outdoor locations, 198–199
   principles, 189–190
   quality, 170–172
   styles, 173–175
   techniques, 187–203
   tools, 175–185
lighting applications, 198–202
   electronic news gathering (ENG), 199–200
   interviews, 200–201
   small location interiors, 201–202
   tabletop videography, 202
lighting designs, 191–198
   controlling existing light, 191–193
   enhancing existing light, 193–194
   replacing existing light, 194–195, 197–198
line balance, 216
line reading, 236
linear continuity, 292
linear editing, 273, 276, 279, 283, 313–328
   editing picture and track, 320–324
   equipment setup, 314–320
   titles, 326–328

transitions, 325
   visual effects, 326
linear sequence, 292
linear vs nonlinear, 316–317
long shot, 69
look room, 23, 166
low angle, 73
low key lighting, 194
low light levels, 162

M

M.O.S., 208
magic hour, 199
magic realism, 174
magnification, 148–149
makeup, 120–121
manual
   aperture, 160
   focus, 159
   shutter, 162–163
masking accessories, 182
master shot, 75, 248
match point, 81
matching action, 81, 288
maximum aperture, 147
medium closeup, 69
medium long shot, 69
medium shot, 69
microphone, 210–216
   cables, 215–216
   cardioid, 213
   condenser transducer, 211
   dynamic transducer, 210–211
   lavaliers, 214
   shotgun, 213
   stands, 215
   supports, 214–215
mismatch, intentional, 291–292
mixer, 217
mixing, 92
monitor, 184
   editing, 315
   inexpensive, 319
   setup, 134–135
monochrome, 326
montage, 304–305, 311
mosaic, 326
motion effects, 326
movement
   and emphasis, 232
   and screen direction, 253–255
   in relation to the frame, 35–36
moving shot, 267
   framing, 166
   hand-holding the camera, 167–168
moving the camera. *See* camera movement.
multiple images, 282, 326

music, 94
    editing, 348
    recording, 210, 224–225
    using to evoke emotion, 97

N

narration, 89
naturalism, 173
negative, 326
neutral angle, 73
neutral density filter, 155, 163–164
night scenes, shooting during the day,
        190–191
nondrop-frame timecode, 335
nonlinear audio, 347–349
nonlinear editing, 272, 276, 329–350
    advantages, 330–331
    archiving, 283, 343–345
    aspect ratio, 337
    assembly editing, 340–341
    audio quality, 337–338
    basic operations, 338–340
    capturing raw materials, 338–340
    configuring projects, 331–338
    image control, 346
    insert editing, 341–343
    picture quality, 336–337
    time and frame measurement, 333–334
    tools and options, 343
    transferring, 279
    transformations, 345–346
    varieties of, 332
    video formats, 331–332
    video scanning system, 334–335
    video standards, 332–333
normal-angle lens, 75

O

objective insert, 231
objectives, identifying, 100–101
offline editing, 339
omitting action, 46
online editing, 338–339
optical zoom, 153
order, 56
organizing picture and sound material,
        274–276
outdoor locations, lighting, 198–199
out-point, 321
overlapping action, 46, 245
over-the-shoulder shot, 76, 248

P

pace, 308–311
paint, 326
panning, 22, 167
parallel

cutting, 294
sequences, 294
time flow, 48–50
pedestaling, 262
performance
    actors, 235–236
    controlling pace, 289–290
    directing for, 235–241
    editing principles, 296–303
    enhancing or adding meanings,
        300–301
    increasing performer's prominence,
        302–303
    selecting the best, 297–299
personal coverage, 249
perspective, 60–62, 149
pickup patterns, 212–214
pictorial realism, 174
picture-in-picture, 326
picture quality, 336–337
playback, 210
plug and cable adapters, 219
plug-ins, 345
polarizing filter, 155
portrait, 161
post house, 339
postproduction, introduction to, 15
POV shot, 76
power checklist, 133
power supply, 132–133
practicals, 180–181
preproduction, introduction to, 14–15
preroll, 322
presence, 94
preshoot checklist, 21
production, introduction to, 15
production lamps, 181–183
production planning, 109–124
    audio problems, 117–118
    budgets, 123–124
    crew and cast, 110–115
    equipment and supplies, 118–120
    location, 114, 116–118
    logistics, 120–123
    video problems, 116–117
production sound, 94, 207
    editing, 348
production track, 94
    recording techniques, 220–221
profile angle, 71
program, 82
program continuity, 293–295
program development, 99–108
    creating a storyboard, 106
    defining the program, 100–104
        audience, 101–102
        concept, 103–104
        delivery system, 102–103
        length, 103

objectives, 100–101
subject matter, 100
preparing a treatment, 104–106
script writing, 106, 108
program files, 344
programmed aperture, 160
programmed shutter, 161–162
progressive scan video, 335
project files, 343
props, 119–120
protection shot, 245
pulling focus, 159

R

reaction shot, 245
realism, 174
real-world time, 44
rear angle, 71
receivers, 216–217
record switch, 18
recorder functions, 128
recorders, 217–218
reflective meter, 185
reflectors, 171, 178, 198–199
controlling direction of light, 176–177, 193
rehearsal, fixing problems in, 236
reinforcement, 308
releases and permissions, 120, 122
rendering, 284, 344
repetition, 244
resolution, 336
reverse-motion, 51
reverse shot, 76
rhythm, editing for, 310–311
rhythmic cutting to music, 311
rim light, 197
ripple edit, 342
rolling down to raw stock, 20, 135
rolling edit, 342
room tone, 208–209, 222
rotation, 83, 262
rule of thirds, 24, 64–65
runup, 322–323

S

sample rate, 337
scaling for video screen, 261
scanning systems
interlaced, 128, 161, 334
progressive scan, 335
scene, 68, 78, 82
scenes and sequences, 290
scheduling, 120–123
screen dimensions, 37
screen direction, 250–257
and frame, 251–252

changing, 256–257
consistency, 251
controlling, 256
convention, 255
look, 252–253
maintaining, 291
movement, 253–255
screen time, 45, 302
screens, 176, 178–179, 199
script writing, 106, 108
selling an illusion, 38
sequence, 68, 82, 290, 296
associative, 292
continuity, 292–293
linear, 292
parallel, 294
subjective, 292–293
serial time flow, 48
set dressing, 119
setup, 40, 79
sheet filters, 177–178, 192
shooting session, 27–29
directing, 27–28
managing, 28–29
security, 28–29
shot, 68, 82
duration, 231
editing order, 307
length, 234, 309–310
names, 77–78, 85
population, 76–77
purpose, 75–76
shotgun microphones, 213
shutter, 160–163
and exposure, 165
manual, 162–163
programmed, 161–162
silks, 176, 178–179, 199
simplicity, 56
single, 76
skeletal treatment, 105
slate, 219–220, 224, 274
slide edit, 343
slip edit, 343
slow motion, 45–46, 326
small location interiors, lighting, 201–202
small source lights, 179–180
soft lights, 202
sound, 87–98. *See also* audio.
and continuity, 295–296
card, 218
communicating with, 97–98
conveying implications, 90–91, 93
delivering information, 88–90
dialog, 88–89
distortion, 206
editing, 11
effects, 89–90, 94, 209, 348

recording, 209, 222
evoking feelings, 96–97
in montages, 304
layers of, 94
narration, 89
perception of, 92
strengthening continuity, 95–96
source deck, 314
spatial relations, 39–42
direction of movement, 41
relationships among objects, 39–40
size, position, and distance, 39
specialty lights, 180–181
specular reflections, 155
speed, 309–310
split edit, 52, 95–96, 348–349
split screen, 326
sports, 162
spotlight, 160, 179–180
stabilizers, 130–132
stage performances, 221
staging for the screen, 257–261
creating a screen geography, 258–259
working within the frame, 259–260
stand-alone titlers, 327
standard production budget, 123
Steadicam, 268
still, 326
stop-motion commands, 46
storing, 284
storyboard, 106
straight cut, 95
strobe, 326
subject distance, 69
subject matter, 100
subjective
continuity, 287–288
insert, 231
sequence, 292–293
subtractive editing, 272–273
summary treatment, 106
superimpositions, 282, 326, 345–346
support services, 123
sweetened sound, 94, 349
switcher/DVE generator, 317
synthesized sound, 94
synthesizing, 281–283

T

tabletop videography, 202
talent, 110, 235
talent release form, 120, 122
target audience, 101–102
telephoto lens, 75, 145–146
teleprompter, 238–239
television, 10–11
television lighting, 188

tent lighting, 202
three-chip cameras, 127
three-point edit, 341
three-quarter angle, 71
three-quarter rear angle, 71
three-quarter shot, 69
three-shot, 77
tilting, 167
time and frame measurement, 333–334
timebase, 334
timecode, 275, 331, 334–335
timecode address, 275–276
timeline, 281–282, 347
titles, 282, 326–328, 346
transducer, 210–211
transformations, 345–346
transitions, 81, 83–84, 282, 295, 345
audio, 348
linear editing, 325
treatment, 104–106
tripod, 21–22, 129–130
two-shot, 76
two-way split edit, 95–96

U

user-worn microphones, 211

V

variety, 310
varying shots, 78–80
VCR, 218, 314
editing, 314–315
video
dimensions, 36–39
expression, 13–14
formats, 331–332
insert, 321, 323
language, 13–14, 67–68
lead, 52
production, 12, 14–15
program components, 82
program construction, 14
space, 31–42
frame, 32–36
playing tricks with, 38
spatial relations, 39–42
summary of laws, 32
video dimensions, 36–39
standards, 332–333
time, 43–54
coherence, 52–53
direction, 50–52
flow, 48–50
speed, 45–47
vs film, 11
video communication, introduction, 12–14
video composition. *See also* composition.

videotape, 19–20
    preparation, 20, 119
    labeling, 136
    setting up and testing, 135
viewfinder
    information displayed, 21–22
    setup, 133–134
visual hybrids, 11
visual literacy, 13
voice recording, 209–210
    techniques, 223–224
voiceover, 89
voiceover narration, 52
volunteer helpers, 115

W

weights, 179
white balance, 135–137, 191
    conforming, 281
    during magic hour, 199

switch, 18–19
wide angle lens, 75, 145–146
window dub, 339
window gel, 177
windscreen, 219
wipe, 83
wireless microphones, 212, 215
worm's eye angle, 73

X

XLR plugs, 212, 216

Z

zebra, 161
zoom, 139, 144–145
    and autofocus, 157–158
    digital, 153–154
    operating, 152
zoom control, 18
zoom lens, 147
zooming, 262–263